Hands-On
Systematic
Innovation

CREAX Press

This text is printed on acid-free paper.

This publication is deigned to provide accurate and authoritative
information in regard to the subject matter covered. It is sold with
the understanding that the publisher is not engaged in rendering
legal, accounting or other professional services. If legal advice
or other expert assistance is required, the services of a competent
professional person should be sought.

Library of Congress Cataloging-in-Publication Data
Mann, Darrell L
      Hands-On Systematic Innovation
   Darrell L Mann

ISBN 90-77071-02-4

Printed in Belgium.

F

Foreword

Benefits not features, lad, benefits not features.
My old boss.

In keeping with the rising interest in TRIZ in all corners of the world, the number of books on the subject is rapidly heading skyward. So why write another one? This is a debate I've been having with myself for some time. At the same time, I've been busy buying and reading (even translating from Russian) all of the currently available books, and finding myself getting increasingly frustrated that none of them is something that I could wholeheartedly recommend to the various people that I either train to use TRIZ or approach me with a request for a recommendation. Sure, some of the books contain some very good parts – parts that I will make sure to mention and reference in this book – but overall, for me they all somehow fail to convey what TRIZ is about, and, more importantly, how to use it. I mean really use it.

I think the roots of my frustration with the currently available TRIZ books goes back to one of my formative experiences, way back when I had just left school and started an apprenticeship at a big UK engineering company. One of the first apprentice jobs I was given was to visit a partner company in France in order to observe how they managed the flow of components through their various manufacture processes. I think the general idea was that I observed their good practices in order that my boss might 'borrow' and apply them in our manufacture facilities. When I got to the company, I was straight away taken with their computerised system and the special control terminals dotted everywhere around the shop-floor. These special terminals had special slots for punch cards (that's my age given away then), so that operators were able to punch a card every time they finished a job. Actually they punched two cards – one to identify themselves, another to identify the operation they had just finished. It all looked very space-age at the time. Consequently, I came back to base with a glowing report describing the terminals and the punch cards, the specification of the mainframe that drove it all, the programming language, the supplier of the cards, you name it, I brought it back. My report made a substantial sounding thud when I dropped it on my boss's desk.

Two days later, my boss approached me – no doubt I imagined to hand me the keys to the executive bathroom for my beyond-the-call-of-duty diligence. Imagine my surprise then when instead of the congratulatory handshake, I received nothing more than a grunt and the sight of my suspiciously unread looking tome flying past my head. 'Benefits, lad,' he said, 'I want to know what they're doing; what the purpose of the thing is, not a bunch of features. Benefits not features, lad, benefits not features'.

The point of this lesson? Actually, I think it's somewhat paradoxical. If I think about the importance TRIZ places on the function of things – their purpose, what they do – why are all the books on the subject all intent on describing a bunch of features?

So the simple, but I hope effective shift in underlying theme between this book and all the others is that this one is about delivering benefits not features. Sure, it will have to describe some features in order to enable the benefit to be delivered, but the main focus throughout will be that the reason you've picked the book up is because you have a problem (in its broadest sense) to solve, you think TRIZ might be able to help, and you want to go about actually using TRIZ to help deliver the benefit you're seeking.

Alongside this shift is the knowledge that TRIZ is a very big thing. So big in fact that, realistically speaking, it is going to take months if not years to appreciate its depth and richness. Here lies an interesting contradiction between wanting to achieve tangible benefit now and potentially being at the lower end of a substantial learning curve. TRIZ recognises that we are all different – different in the way we work, different in what we want different in how we learn, different in every aspect. In this regard, the ideal book would be one that tailors itself to suit everyone's different preferences; those at the top of the learning curve, those at the bottom, those with a problem to solve by tomorrow morning, and those that simply want to explore this strange beast called TRIZ. I can't claim that this book has completely solved all of these problems, but what we have done is provided a structure that will enable you to use it as a start-to-finish problem definition and solving recipe, or to just dip into the parts that fit into your way of doing things, or to just get a helicopter view of how TRIZ fits into the bigger scheme of things.

One final thought before allowing you to head towards that helicopter, given the 'benefits not features' theme of the book, it is important to note that (deep breath) TRIZ contains some holes. In the ten or so years I have been using TRIZ across a variety of problems from jet-engines to cream-cakes to computer programs to insurance sales to human relations to chemical process engineering, I have encountered several situations where TRIZ hasn't solved the problem – or rather that other routes have provided stronger solutions. This causes a problem in writing a 'TRIZ book'. Do I describe the holes? Discretely pretend they're not there? Or do I remember the fact that I want you to be able to use the book to correctly define (usually the most difficult bit!) and solve your problem? 'Benefits not features' means I am forced to go down the latter route. The consequence of this is that the book contains elements of things – some of them at quite a high philosophical level – that I can't claim are TRIZ or even have their roots in TRIZ. In other words, if you're looking for a book on 'classical TRIZ' you're probably going to be happier going somewhere else. On the other hand, if you're looking for tangible benefit, I hope that this book is the one you will take down from the shelf.

Darrell Mann
Buckland Brewer,
January 2002.

Contents

Appendices

1.
Introduction

"People will agree with you only if they already agree with you, you do not change peoples' minds."
Frank Zappa

Or

"For every complex problem there are solutions that are simple, easy and wrong."
H.L.Mencken

In putting together the specification for this book, we set ourselves some interesting challenges. We wanted a book that focused on benefits (i.e. that it enabled the reader to successfully tackle any problem or opportunity situation they were working on), rather than being just another collection of features. Given the possible number and type of different things that different readers might be expecting to tackle, this seemed like no small ambition. If that wasn't enough, we also decided we wanted a book that would be useful to both experienced TRIZ users and complete novices; we wanted a book that could be read from start to finish, or could use as a quick-dip reference; and we wanted it to be both academically rigorous and at the same time not the stultifyingly dull experience most academic books tend to be. In other words, we identified a number of contradictory requirements and decided we wanted to avoid compromising on any of them. How successful we have been remains to be seen.

In keeping with all of the above aims, the book has been structured and sequenced in such a way that anyone working on a problem (in the most general terms that word implies) could begin at the beginning of the book and be taken on a journey through only those chapters necessary to solve the problem.

The main means of achieving this feat of navigation is the small figure appearing at the top right hand corner of each page of the book. A larger version of that figure is shown in Figure 1.1 below.

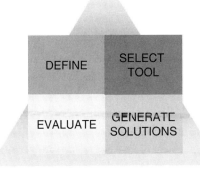

Figure 1.1 Hands-On Systematic Innovation Navigation Aid

Three of the four steps contained in the box at the center of the figure are like any generic problem definition and solving process; it being necessary to define what the problem is, to generate some solutions and to then evaluate those solutions. We add in a fourth step – 'select tool' because of the richness and breadth of the problem solving tools available to us through TRIZ and the other things we have found it necessary to include. We examine this four step process in more detail in the next chapter, and follow this by a chapter on each of the elements of each box in turn. As you will see, some of the boxes – most notably the problem definition and generate solutions boxes, contain a host of other boxes.

The aim of this chapter is both to set the scene for the book and also to discuss the triangle drawn behind the four boxes (hence the reason the top right hand corner of this page emphasizes the triangle to indicate that this is what we're talking about at this point in the book). The triangle is there to define the existence of an underlying philosophy behind the process being discussed in future chapters.

If you're already familiar with TRIZ, you may wish to delve straight into the next Chapter. If you're not, we recommend that you read this chapter and the following two – 'process overview' and 'psychology' in order to obtain the maximum benefit from subsequent chapters.

The rest of this chapter, then, is split into two main sections. The first section describing a little of the underlying philosophy of TRIZ and how you might try and fit it (or parts of it) into the way you think about solving problems, and the second provides a general introduction to TRIZ and those philosophical concepts that, in any event, you should aim to keep in mind all the time you are using any part of TRIZ or its related cousins.

1) TRIZ For Everyone
(Even Those Who Don't Want To Spend A Year Learning It)

Different people will use TRIZ in different ways. This section is about trying to find a common ground and understanding between the people describing themselves as having the 'TRIZ virus', and those who don't have the time, will or desire to invest a lot of time learning the tremendous amount of available richness.

We explore the possibilities of structuring a hands-on systematic creativity and innovation process so that it can accommodate a full spectrum of user types and capabilities, and also some of the consequent implications for TRIZ educators.

Another Way of Looking at TRIZ

Is TRIZ a set of tools? A method? A way of thinking? A philosophy? Answer; all of the above. Figure 1.2 illustrates a hierarchical perspective of what this thing called TRIZ is. It is this figure that offers the triangular shape underlying the figure at the top of each page of the book.

The figure suggests that, at its very highest level, TRIZ may be seen as the systematic study of excellence. This study was initially focused on patents (a very good source of excellence for the most part), and then evolved to look at excellence in the sciences, and latterly, the arts, business, social sciences and politics.

Five key philosophical elements have emerged from this study. In no particular order, these are Ideality – and the concept of systems evolving to increasing good, decreasing bad – Resources – and the concept of maximizing the effectiveness of things inside and around a system (even the bad things) – Space/Time/Interface – and the importance of viewing systems in terms of their space, time and interface contexts – Functionality – and the over-riding importance of the functions being delivered when thinking about systems – and Contradictions – and the concept of contradiction elimination as a primary evolution driver. Some of these are unique to TRIZ; some have parallel precedent within other similar studies of creativity. We will discuss each in turn in the second section of this chapter.

At the bottom of the TRIZ hierarchy, then, are a wide-ranging and comprehensive series of tools and techniques. The tools contain a great deal – some might say overwhelming – level of richness, and to all intents and purposes, it may be said that there is a tool for practically any problem or opportunity situation that may be encountered.

In between the philosophy and this collection of tools is something we might loosely describe as 'method'. In actual fact, several methods – with just about every TRIZ provider presenting their own version of a method to string the tools together in whatever fashion they think most appropriate. It is at this level that many of the problems of TRIZ occur. Quite literally the choice and quantity of available advice is overwhelming for the large majority of people encountering TRIZ.

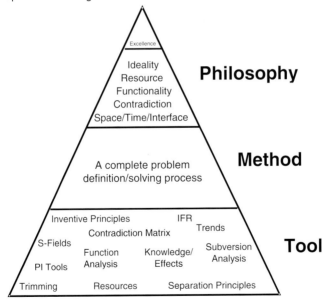

Figure 1.2: Hierarchical View of TRIZ

The essence of philosophy is distillation of large quantities of knowledge and experience into a small entity. It might take users a considerable amount of time to appreciate the significance of the five philosophical strands of TRIZ, but they can at least be remembered in a few minutes.

At the other end of the hierarchy pyramid, the TRIZ toolkit contains a series of tools that, to varying degrees can be learned and applied also in a relatively short space of time. There is a deal of variation, but as an average, a half-day of learning and doing is usually enough to give a newcomer the will, confidence and ability to use a given tool.

In between toolkit and philosophy, the learning curve for any of the TRIZ methods and processes (with or without software 'support') is probably measurable in weeks.

'Weeks' unfortunately is then at the heart of a big problem for the large majority of newcomers to TRIZ. A week is a serious investment of time for anyone in these busy times; there is simply too much else needing to be done, and not enough time to do it.

Does this mean we should give up? Or does it mean that it might be better to think about alternative ways of presenting and delivering TRIZ?

This author and this book believe it is the latter.

Different User Profiles

Figure 1.3 illustrates a graph compiled from the experiences of watching several hundred students, engineers, scientists, strategists and managers go through at least two-days worth of TRIZ 'training'. (Admittedly two days is not a lot in a TRIZ learning context – but it is a fair approximation of the sort of course it is currently possible to sell in the West.)

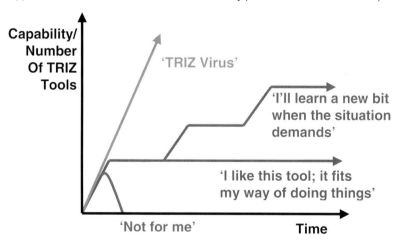

Figure 1.3: Typical TRIZ User Profiles

The first category of user types is the 'not for me' variety. This is the individual who, for whatever reason (with bad teaching and instinctive aversion because people have been instructed to attend by their boss being probably the top two reasons), decides they do not like TRIZ or do not want to commit the time necessary to learn it.

The second category involves those who discover a part of TRIZ that they like and chose to adopt it into their way of doing things. This 'part' might be a tool like the Contradiction Matrix or the Trends of Evolution, or it might simply be one or two of the Inventive Principles. At the end of their initial exposure to TRIZ, this category of user has achieved some success using the particular tool or element of, is 'satisfied' by that success, and shows no desire to expand their TRIZ knowledge. In some small way, however, this category of user has been changed by their TRIZ experience.

The third category of user might be seen as the pragmatist. They usually start as users of the second category, but find that there are certain types of problem – or more usually a specific problem – that the TRIZ tool they know has failed to solve. They therefore look at other elements of TRIZ (or beyond) until they find something that does solve the problem. The success with the new tool then prompts the incorporation of that tool into that persons 'way of doing things'. (The importance of 'success' in determining whether someone picks up a part of TRIZ or not cannot be under-estimated.)

The fourth category of user profile is what is commonly described amongst long-time TRIZ users as 'having the virus' or 'being infected'. This type of user typically reads all of the books, papers and articles they can find on TRIZ, and sees TRIZ change a large part of their life.

Statistics can be used to show anything, and this author's data set is not as large as others, but approximations can nevertheless be very telling. A breakdown of how people are presently distributed between the four different categories is suggested in Figure 1.4. These figures are based on the author's own personal experience and might have an accuracy of ±10 or more percent. Even with that level of inaccuracy, we think they contain some very important messages for user and provider alike. We will discuss four.

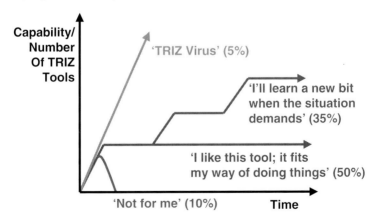

Figure 1.4: Typical TRIZ User Profiles With Approximate Percentages

The Folly of 'I Am Right; You Are Wrong'

Everyone has their own way of doing things. Some of these ways are demonstrably more effective than others, but nevertheless those embedded ways are present and they are constraints that will dictate how much and which parts of TRIZ people will be attracted to and which they will reject. There have been several questions in TRIZ discussion forums along the lines 'which are the most important parts of TRIZ?' The simple answer to the question is that it depends. It depends on the circumstances of the problem or opportunity under consideration, it depends on the user, and it depends on how TRIZ is delivered to them.

Given this belief, it is perhaps surprising that so many in the TRIZ community insist that their way of doing things is the right way. In simple terms, in each case, while it might be 'right' for them personally, it might be the complete opposite of right to someone else. So, to take a particular example, certain versions of ARIZ place the Psychological Inertia tools before Physical Contradiction separation methods, while others reverse the sequence. Which is right? Answer; both and neither. It depends.

To take a cooking analogy; there are definitely right and wrong ways of using the various tools contained in the kitchen. There is a right and a wrong way of holding a whisk, in the same way that once we have picked the whisk up by the handle instead of the blades, there is then a considerable degree of flexibility in how we can use the tool to achieve the desired function; we can stir clockwise or anti-clockwise, with or without a vertical component of motion, we can stop and start, we can change speed, we can change direction, we can do pretty much anything so long as the whisk is in the product and moving it.

At a higher level, we can then use a recipe to help us sequence ingredients and the things we do to them in order to eventually get me to a finished product. If we are trying to make soup, we could probably find several hundred recipes to help us do it. Some will say put the stock in first, and some will say don't. Assuming that the different authors are all trying to help me make soup that is edible, we can probably safely assume that each of them has created a recipe that will work. Some recipes will produce better (to me!) soup than others, but they will all provide me an output that looks and functions like soup.

The point? For users – find something that fits your way of doing things (whether it be one Inventive Principle or a complete problem solving method/recipe). For providers – think carefully before you tell people that your way of doing things is 'the right way'. You can probably guarantee that it is not. As far as this book is concerned, one of the major underlying aims has been to present things in a way that enables this pick-and-choose flexibility to happen.

Self-Adapting Systems

The folly of 'I am right; you are wrong' (see Reference 1.1 if you want more information on the subject) is somewhat paradoxical given the importance of identifying and eliminating contradictions within TRIZ. So is it psychological inertia tools before or after contradictions in ARIZ? Or would the smart solution be either? Or neither? Perhaps it would be useful to see it as a physical contradiction separable on condition. Psychological inertia tools before contradictions IF that's what we prefer; contradictions before psychological inertia tools IF we don't.

A large proportion of users will only ever know and use one or two tools of TRIZ. Chapter 18 later in the book suggests the importance of 'self' in the drive towards increased ideality; self-adjusting, self-organising, etc, and any system that works out 'for itself' what is right are all good solution directions. If TRIZ is about encouraging people to think, perhaps a useful goal would be to offer them a structure that allows them to – as much as is feasibly practical – mix and match tools (both within and beyond TRIZ) to suit their particular individual circumstances. In other words, that they are able to adapt what tools and methods they use, how and when they use them to suit themSELVEs.

If I choose to ignore a recipe that is my decision. If I'm making soup it doesn't matter-I may get a thin soup or a thick one or even a stew, but it will be edible. If I'm making bread, and stray too far from the recipe, I will end up with something that isn't bread, and might not even be edible, or I might end up with something exciting and new. The former is usually more likely than the latter however, so in future, I might be well advised to follow some form of structure. I also know that I have my own tastes and that if I take a bit of this recipe and add a bit of that and then add this bit of my own, then I will end up with my ideal bread. 'My' being the important word.

If we ask ourselves the question is it better for us to adapt to TRIZ or for TRIZ to adapt to us, for the most part, many of us (especially those working in a time-constrained environment) would choose the latter. This again represents an important underlying theme of the book and its layout.

Mastery

The profiles illustrated in Figure 1.2 bear some striking similarities to the profiles described in G Leonard's book 'Mastery' (Reference 1.2). The book describes the four broad categories as 'dabblers', 'hackers', 'masters' and 'obsessives' respectively. The book makes two points that have particular relevance to the latter two categories:

The first is that the third profile in the figure – the 'I'll learn a new bit when I need it' category – is the most effective route to 'mastery' of a subject. The book makes the point that the time gap between picking up successive new capabilities (i.e. the flat parts on the graph) is an important part of the knowledge acquisition process. The gap is useful because it provides an opportunity for consolidation; it allows the brain to fully embrace the new capability. In many senses it emphasizes the importance of a learning-doing cycle as a fundamental necessity in 'mastering' anything new.

The second interesting point made by the book involves the 'TRIZ virus' or 'obsessive' profile. The book actually draws a different characteristic profile of the 'obsessive' character. It looks something like the picture illustrated in Figure 1.4.

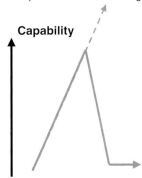

Figure 1.4: Propensity to 'Burn-Out' In Obsessives

In other words, there is a very strong correlation between obsessive drive towards a goal and burn-out. The characteristic is reported to be particularly common in situations where individuals pursue singular or non-diverse pursuit of a particular tool or method.

Overlap

Some (many?) people complain or are concerned that TRIZ appears to contain a considerable amount of overlap. This overlap exists between different tools, but it also exists within the same tool – note for example how much overlap exists in amongst just the Inventive Principles.

The response of some people to this overlap – particularly among TRIZ providers – is to eliminate it. This is perhaps understandable given that the overlap can become frustrating after a few years of using TRIZ.

On the other hand, what about the 50% of people that will only ever learn one part of TRIZ? Or the next 35% who will expand their knowledge only after what might be a considerable period of time? Is the overlap useful to them or not? Two answers; firstly as they are not aware of the bigger picture they are unlikely to be aware of any overlap and so it cannot harm or frustrate them. Secondly, if they are using TRIZ to try and solve a problem – or, in other words, 'achieve a benefit', the existence of overlap means that they are more likely to reach a solution. The point is made again in Figure 1.5.

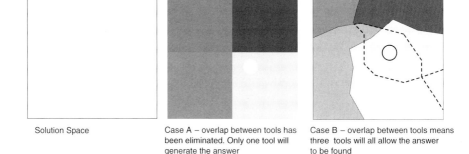

Solution Space

Case A – overlap between tools has been eliminated. Only one tool will generate the answer

Case B – overlap between tools means three tools will all allow the answer to be found

Figure 1.5: The Overlap Advantage – in Case A, if the user doesn't know the relevant tool they will not solve the problem. In case B, they have several opportunities to reach a successful solution.

If you are one of the readers who expect to read the whole of this book, you may like to note points in the book where you notice this overlap occurring.

Final Thought

There are generally believed to be two basic ways of achieving a goal. The first involves having a clear vision of what the goal is and an absolute determination to achieve it no matter what the obstacles are. The second involves having a clear vision of what the goal is, and an absolute determination to maximize the use of available resources to help reach the goal. The first might be called 'brute force'; the second 'harnessing natural forces'. Both can succeed. One route is harder work than the other.

The same choice exists when thinking about the use and spread of TRIZ. We can bludgeon people until they submit, or we can recognize that everyone is different, learns in different ways and wants different things. We can force them to do it our way, or allow them sufficient slack to adapt TRIZ (and indeed other tools, methods, and philosophies) to suit their particular differences. One is more likely to succeed than the other. One is harder work than the other.

2) A General Overview of TRIZ

TRIZ (Teoriya Resheniya Izobreatatelskikh Zadatch) is the Soviet initiated Theory of Inventive Problem Solving. As illustrated in Figure 1.1, TRIZ is a philosophy, a process and a series of tools. The whole has developed through what best estimates suggest to be over 1500 person years of research and the study of over a significant proportion of the world's most successful solutions whether they be from the sciences, mathematics, engineering (and the systematic analysis of successful patents from around the world), as well as the study of the internal, psychological aspects of human creativity (see Chapter 3).

The key findings of TRIZ research are:-
- that all innovations emerge from the application of a very small number of inventive principles and strategies
- that technology evolution trends are highly predictable
- that the strongest solutions transform the unwanted or harmful elements of a system into useful resources.
- that the strongest solutions also actively seek out and destroy the conflicts and trade-offs most design practices assume to be fundamental.

TRIZ offers users access to the knowledge and experiences of the world's finest inventive minds. It is intended to complement and add structure to our natural creativity rather than replace it.

TRIZ can be used in a number of different ways. An overall process enables users to systematically define and then solve any given problem or opportunity situation. Some users will rigorously apply this process. Others are happier extracting individual elements from the overall structure and using those. This book has been configured in such a way as to allow users significant flexibility in how to use TRIZ, offering both an over-riding structure and access to individual problem definition and solving tools. Although TRIZ is easily the most exhaustive creativity aid ever assembled, it does contain some gaps and holes. In keeping with TRIZ philosophy, we have looked outside TRIZ at the best of creativity practice from all disciplines and integrated them together into what we believe is a seamless whole. The overall aim of the book has been to construct a problem definition and solving process that works for any situation users may care to throw at it – whether that be technical or non-technical, simple or complex, highly constrained or clean-sheet, step change innovation or incremental improvement, or focused on products, processes or services. TRIZ effectively strips away all boundaries between different scientific, engineering and creative discipline and its effectiveness has been proved across a broad spectrum of fields and problem types.

TRIZ is both simple and complex. To learn and gather a working knowledge of the whole structure will probably take six months. Some people are prepared to make this investment, and others are not. Those that are not usually take great comfort from the fact that they will be able to learn and realise significant benefit from just a short exposure to individual elements of the overall structure. In many instances these benefits are enough. We've tried to design the book to suit every individual requirement.

TRIZ is different to most other creativity aids, and may appear a little unnatural at first. Here are some of the things that may help how you think about TRIZ and the way you will use it to best effect in the context of this book:

TRIZ BASICS

TRIZ is about providing means for problem solvers to access the good solutions obtained by the world's finest inventive minds. The basic process by which this occurs is illustrated below. Essentially, TRIZ researchers have encapsulated the principles of good inventive practice and set them into a generic problem-solving framework – Figure 1.6. The task of problem definers and problem solvers using the large majority of the TRIZ tools thus becomes one in which they have to map their specific problems and solutions to and from this generic framework.

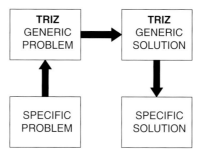

Figure 1.6: General TRIZ Process

THE FOUR Plus One PILLARS OF TRIZ

1500 person years of TRIZ research have produced a significant number of innovation tools and methods. This section offers a brief summary of the four main elements that make the method distinct from other innovation and problem solving strategies.

Contradictions
TRIZ researchers have identified the fact that the world's strongest inventions have emerged from situations in which the inventor has successfully sought to avoid the conventional trade-offs that most designers take for granted. More importantly they have offered systematic tools through which problem solvers can tap into and use the strategies employed by such inventors. The most commonly applied tool in this regard is the Contradiction Matrix – a 39x39 matrix containing the three or four most likely strategies for solving design problems involving the 1482 most common contradiction types. Probably the most important philosophical aspect of the contradiction part of TRIZ is that, given there are ways of 'eliminating' contradictions', designers should actively look for them during the design process.

Ideality

While studying the patent database, TRIZ founder Genrich Altshuller identified a trend in which systems always evolve towards increasing 'ideality' and that this evolution process takes place through a series of evolutionary S-curve characteristics. A key finding of TRIZ is that the steps denoting a shift from one S-curve to the next are predictable. A number of underlying technology evolution trends consistent with the ideality concept have been identified during the course of research on the global patent database. Used as a problem definition tool, the ideality part of TRIZ encourages problem solvers to break out of the traditional 'start from the current situation' type of thinking, and start instead from what is described as the Ideal Final Result (IFR). The simple definition of IFR is that the solution contains all of the benefits and none of the costs or 'harms' (environmental impact, adverse side-effects, etc). Although there are many instances where systems have been seen to evolve all the way to their Ideal Final Result, many have not. The method gets users to think about these situations by working back from the IFR to something which is practicably realisable. Generally speaking these solutions incorporate the concept of systems solving problems 'by themselves'. The key word is 'self'; things that achieve functions by themselves – self-cleaning, self-balancing, self-heating, self-aerating, etc – all represent, when incorporated in a true TRIZ fashion, very powerful and resource-efficient solutions.

Functionality

Although the functionality aspects of TRIZ owe a significant debt to the pioneering work on Value Engineering, the method of defining and using functionality data is markedly different; sufficient at the very least to merit discussion as a distinct paradigm shift in thinking relative to traditional occidental thought processes. Three aspects are worthy of particular note:-

1) The idea that a system possesses a Main Useful Function (MUF) and that any system component which does not contribute towards the achievement of this function is ultimately harmful. In a heat exchanger, for example, the MUF is to transfer heat to the working medium; everything else in the system is there solely because we don't yet know how to achieve the MUF without the support of the ancillary components. (Systems may of course perform several additional useful functions according to the requirements of the customer.)

2) In traditional function mapping, the emphasis is very much on the establishment of positive functional relationships between components. TRIZ places considerable emphasis on plotting both the positive and the negative relationships contained in a system, and, more importantly, on using the function analysis as a means of identifying the contradictions, in-effective, excessive and harmful relationships in and around a system. Function and attribute analysis thus becomes a very powerful problem definition tool.

3) Functionality is the common thread by which it becomes possible to share knowledge between widely differing industries. A motor car is a specific solution to the generic function 'move people', just as a washing powder is a specific solution to the generic function 'remove solid object'. By classifying and arranging knowledge by function, it becomes possible for manufacturers of washing powder to examine how other industries have achieved the same basic 'remove solid object' function. 'Solutions change, functions stay the same' is a message forming a central thread in the TRIZ methodology: People want a hole not a drill; benefits not features.

Use Of Resources

The Resources part of TRIZ relates to the unprecedented emphasis placed on the maximisation of use of everything contained within a system. In TRIZ terms, a resource is *anything in the system which is not being used to its maximum potential.* TRIZ demands an aggressive and seemingly relentless pursuit of things in (and around) a system which are not being used to their absolute maximum potential. Discovery of such resources then reveals opportunities through which the design of a system may be improved. In addition to this relentless pursuit of resources, TRIZ demands that the search for resources also take due account of negative as well as the traditionally positive resources in a system. Thus the pressures and forces we typically attempt to fight when we are designing systems, are actually resources. By way of an example of this 'turning lemons into lemonade' concept, TRIZ users often think of resonance as a resource. This is in direct contradiction to most Western practice, where resonance is commonly viewed as something to be avoided at all costs. TRIZ says that somewhere, somehow, resonance in a system can be used to beneficial effect. In effect, resonance is a potent force lever capable of amplifying small inputs into large outputs. Resonance is currently being used to generate beneficial effects in a number of new product developments from vacuum cleaners, paint stripping systems on ships (firing a pulsed jet of water – existing resource! – at the local resonant frequency of the hull), and in helping to empty trucks carrying powder-based substances more quickly.

Thinking in SPACE, TIME and INTERFACE

While not strictly speaking a TRIZ development, TRIZ researchers have also recognized the enormous importance of thinking about situations from all angles. Experienced TRIZ users are continuously changing their perspective on problems – zooming in to look at the fine details, zooming out to see the bigger picture, thinking about how the situation is affected by changing time – whether that be nano-seconds or decades – in both the past and future, and also thinking about how different parts of systems connect and relate to one another. This is not a natural process for most people – our brains aren't wired that way – and so we introduce and discuss tools to help in the process of thinking in TIME, SPACE and INTERFACE as we work our way through the book.

What Do I Do?

The book has been designed as something that can be read from start to finish, and also be dipped into as a working reference. The general hope is that you will find a way if using the book to fit whatever style of working you personally prefer; there is a complete process we have called 'systematic creativity' for those that want it, or you may prefer to just concentrate on one or two individual tools.

If you are new to TRIZ, we recommend you read the next two chapters to get a broader feel for what the bigger picture looks like and how it matches to the ways in which our brains function.

Whatever happens, you should keep in mind the four plus one pillars – CONTRADICTIONS, IDEALITY, FUNCTIOANLITY, RESOURCES and SPACE/TIME/INTERFACE. – in everything you do with TRIZ.

References

1) De Bono, E., 'I Am Right; You Are Wrong', Penguin Books, 1991.
2) Leonard, G., 'Mastery: The Keys To Success and Long-Term Fullfillment', Plume Books, 1992.

2.
Process Overview

'Be sure you know the structure of all you wish to depict.'
Leonardo Da Vinci

A COMPLETE PROCESS

If it's what we want, TRIZ offers us a complete start to finish process through which – as shown in Figure 2.1 – will take us from whatever vague start point we might be at through a series of steps that will first help us to define what the right problem is, through to identifying the best solution to that problem. While it might be said (often with good cause) that 99% of the problem comes in the implementation, we hope that the 1% we are covering is of value. In any event, the other 99% will be full of other issues and problems to solve – all of which will benefit from the use of this process.

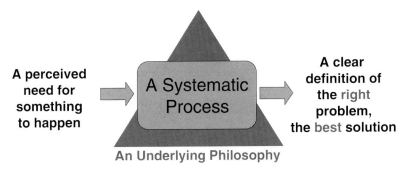

Figure 2.1: TRIZ/Systematic Creativity Process Overview

The start point for the process has been that we should literally be able to begin from any place. We have included inside that wide ranging ambition the desire to look at business, political, social science, architecture and even what might be loosely termed 'the arts' in this start point. While the focus throughout this book will be the application of TRIZ in engineering/technology centred situations (check out the other books in the series for examples of other application areas), it is worth noting that it is more or less exactly the same process that we can apply to any of these other problem types.

Any start points we could possibly imagine have to be amenable to treatment if the process is to be of generic use. We have tried to validate the process on as many situations as possible, and always present the challenge to problem solvers to try and come up with a scenario the process cannot handle. The sorts of start points we see emerging on a regular basis, and which the process has been validated against include the following sorts of 'perceived need for something to happen' start point:

- How do I improve process output rate by x%?
- How do I improve sales?

- How do I improve the reliability of system Y?
- What is the best strategy for exploiting solution Z?
- How do I reduce noise by AdB?
- How do I improve efficiency by B%?
- How do I cut down on scrap?
- How do I reduce the environmental impact of C?

And so on ad infinitum. Note in particular that the process has been designed to cope with the things we normally view as 'problems' (challenges, or whatever politically correct terminology happens to be fashionable at the moment), but also the other side of the coin, the 'opportunities' – those situations where we think we have a solution, but we don't know hat to do with it, or how to exploit it. In this latter case, we need to re-cast our thinking a little (we will do this at the end of the chapter), but for now all we need to know is that the same generic process will apply to both scenarios.

Some, of course, will argue against both the need for a truly generic process, and whether, even if such a thing is possible, whether it is ethically or morally right to 'inflict' a rigorous structure to something (creativity) that is often fundamentally about doing things differently. We have some sympathy with this view – and TRIZ itself, as discussed in the last chapter, makes great play on the need for 'self-organizing'/'self-adapting' systems. On the other hand, there are two reasons which have prompted us to include and detail a generic process:-
1) some people like the structure it provides, and
2) whether we like a structure or not, the framework provided by a systematic process makes it far easier to communicate our problem or opportunity situation to others in a recognizable and reproducible form.

Like many other problem/opportunity definition/solution (from now on, we'll stick to the abbreviation 'problem solving') processes, the one used in this book contains three basic steps; things start with a part of the process called 'define', then there is a step called 'generate solutions', and finally, a step called 'evaluate solutions'. One of the most interesting aspects of TRIZ is that it is far richer than any other process we've ever seen in terms of the options available during the 'generate solutions' part of the process. We usually describe this part of the process when it appears in other methods as the 'insert miracle here' part; because if you check out these processes (we don't need to name them), they all rely very heavily on brainstorming as the means of generating solutions. This is not to denegrate brainstorming (we will use many of the underlying principles in the systematic creativity process), merely to say that, TRIZ provides a substantially higher level of generative richness. So much so in fact that the process we describe includes a fourth step into the three basic 'define', 'solve', 'evaluate' ones you will find everywhere. That fourth step sits between 'define' and 'solve' and is called 'select'. The basic idea behind the 'select' part of the process is that, having defined a problem situation, and seeing the broad array of possible TRIZ and other solution tools, how do we know which ones are the ones we should use to tackle the problem? This is an area that seems to confound many newcomers to TRIZ. We hope that Chapter 9 describes a tool selection process that will lift the fog.

To continue describing the overall process then, we now have a four step process – 'define', 'select', 'solve' and 'evaluate' as illustrated in Figure 2.2.

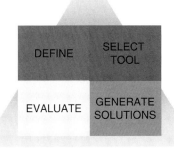

Figure 2.2: Four Basic Steps of the Systematic Creativity Process

Let us now zoom in a little to examine each of these steps in a little more detail:

DEFINE
It is often said that 90% of a problem is defining what the problem is. TRIZ concurs with this view. It also goes further. It recognises that the average human brain is much happier in 'solve' mode than it is in 'define' mode. A very typical scenario seems to involve the obligatory 10 minutes thinking about the problem, followed by an hour or so of the enjoyable creative 'solving' part, followed by a race to implement the solution to see how good we were at solving it. The usual outcome of this race is we discover that if we'd just spent a few more minutes thinking about exactly what problem it was that we should have been looking at, we would have saved ourselves an awful lot of time and energy racing to the right answer to the wrong problem. TRIZ tries to encourage us to stay in 'define' mode for as long as possible. It does this in ways that are both explicit and subtle. Taken as a whole, the 'define' part of the overall four step systematic creativity process itself involves four groups of activities. Three of these four – the 'problem explorer', some kind of function and attribute analysis, and some kind of s-curve analysis - are as close to 'fundamental' to defining a problem situation adequately as makes any difference. The recommended 'define' process will **always** encourage problem solvers to go through these three activities. We would also highly recommend that a fourth 'define' activity – involving the consideration of ideality – is also carried out. We don't include this fourth step in the 'fundamental' category, because, frankly, the social and business constraints present in a given situation may dis-allow this activity. We will discuss the potential implications of this in Chapter 8, but as far as this overview is concerned, the overall process of defining a problem situation should involve three compulsory plus one highly recommended activity. Figure 2.3 reflects how these four groups of activities will be displayed in the context of this book.

Each of the four groups is discussed in its own chapter. For ease of reference, the navigator icon at the top right hand corner of each page in the book lets you flick through to view the chapter relevant to the part of the process you are involved in at any point in time.

Staying in overview mode for the moment, however, it is worth recording a few comments here about how these four groups of 'define' activities should be approached:

First, it is worth noting that although there are three compulsory define activities, it doesn't matter what order we tackle them. The chapter sequence

5 – Problem/Opportunity Explorer
6 – Function and Attribute Analysis
7 – S-Curve Analysis, and
8 – Ideality/Ideal Final Result

tells you what sequence we recommend, but if you prefer a different way of doing things, then great.

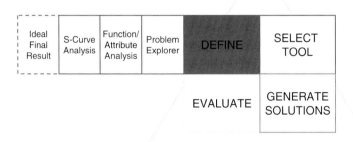

Figure 2.3: Four Basic Steps of the DEFINE part of the Systematic Creativity Process

Second on the list of important things to note is that it is highly possible that when we exit any of the four activities, we leave with nothing. This is particularly common, for example, if we are in that very fortunate position of having a blank sheet of paper start to a problem – 'think of a new product idea that will make lots of money' to take an extreme example. It is not possible to conduct a function analysis of a system that doesn't exist yet. The main point in each of the four groups, though, is that although the answer we come out with might be a blank, it is vitally important that we at least enter and ask the question.

Each of the four groups of define activities has a distinct purpose:

- The **Problem Explorer** – is the foundation of the problem definition. It is the part of the process that gets us to record things like where we are now, where we are trying to get to, how will we know when we've got there, what resources have we got available to us, and, perhaps most significant for any 'real' problem, what constraints have we got to work within. This is the part of the process where we define the boundaries of the problem/opportunity setting.
- **Function & Attribute Analysis** (FAA) – is where we will gain our appreciation of the functionality of an existing system. It is where we will delve into the details of a system in order to examine and record what is supposed to be happening within and around it, and also what is happening that we don't want to happen. FAA is the place where we will usually find ourselves doing the majority of the problem definition detail. If we do this task correctly, we will often find that the problem suddenly becomes 'obvious'. If TRIZ and systematic creativity are about 'managing complexity', function analysis is where an awful lot of that management happens.

- **S-Curve Analysis** – the preceding two activities are, conceptually at least, common to most TRIZ-based problem definition processes. The need to conduct some kind of assessment of the relative maturity of the different parts of an existing system – which is the task we are performing during this s-curve analysis – is not commonly found. This part of the define process is vital as it forces us to obtain a better understanding of the evolutionary mechanics that dictate so much of the how, why, when and where's of problem solving. It will also play a significant role in helping us to determine how we should proceed after the define stage is completed. This part of the define process is often the most qualitative in nature. Fortunately, we will see in Chapter 8, such qualitative output is in most cases sufficient to allow us to proceed to subsequent stages with confidence.
- **Ideal Final Result** – the fourth activity in the 'define' process involves an analysis of where we are, and where we're trying to get to in the context of 'where could we be ultimately'. It is an extremely powerful tool for helping us to think 'out of the box'. As stated above, the process will always recommend that this activity be carried out – you can be pretty sure your current and future competitors are going to be doing it even if you're not – if only to obtain a gauge of how far along the line of evolution you and your problem currently are. On a more profound level, the thinking provoked by this activity can often lead to the definition of a much better problem than the one you started with.

Appendix 1 at the back of the book provides a series of blank sheets to help structure your thinking as you progress through these four problem definition steps. Please feel free to photo-copy and use them on any problem or opportunity situation you are involved in.

SELECT
Having completed the 'define' part of the systematic creativity process, we progress to the second major stage 'select'. This is where the method guides us through a series of steps aimed at helping us to identify what sort of problem situation we have, and what the most appropriate tools to help us solve it are. The 'select' process is described in detail in Chapter 9. While we are still sitting in our helicopter looking down at an overview of the whole process, it is worth recording here that this part of the process has been designed in such a way that we recognise that not everyone reading the book will be equally skilled in all aspects of TRIZ. As discussed in the previous overview chapter, TRIZ contains, and we have configured, an amount of overlap between the different tools in the kit. This means that except for very specialised cases, the select process will give us more than one recommendation on possible routes to solve a given problem. In actual fact, for the majority of cases, we will be able to access a menu of three or four possible routes. This menu is ranked, to reflect the fact that some tools will take you to 'good' answers more directly than others. The general idea is that as your working armoury of tools expands (assuming you want that to happen!), you will increasingly find yourself heading straight to the tool recommended at the top of the menu. We believe also that this 'select' navigation tool is a useful addition to what can look like an overwhelming level of complexity when trying to transition from defined problem to best solve tool.

SOLVE
Given the richness of the TRIZ and systematic creativity solve tool-kit, the number of possibilities once a problem enters the third 'solve' or 'generate solutions' stage is

extensive. For the purposes of this book, we have provided eleven basic clusters of solve tools. These are shown in the navigation icon reproduced in Figure 2.4 below.

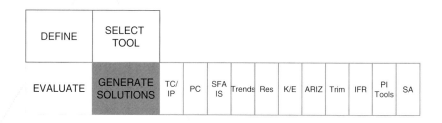

DEFINE	SELECT TOOL											
EVALUATE	GENERATE SOLUTIONS	TC/ IP	PC	SFA IS	Trends	Res	K/E	ARIZ	Trim	IFR	PI Tools	SA

Figure 2.4: Eleven Basic Steps of the DEFINE part of the Systematic Creativity Process

The general idea is that the 'select' process tells us exactly which of the chapters – one for each of the eleven tool clusters – we should be heading towards for any given problem. Thus Chapters 10 to 20 inclusive describe the different tools as follows:

Chapter 10 – Technical Contradictions/Inventive Principles
Chapter 11 – Physical Contradictions
Chapter 12 – S-Field Analysis/Inventive Standards
Chapter 13 – Trends of Technological Evolution
Chapter 14 – Resources
Chapter 15 – Knowledge/Effects
Chapter 16 – ARIZ
Chapter 17 – Trimming
Chapter 18 – Ideal Final Result
Chapter 19 – Psychological Inertia Tools
Chapter 20 – Subversion Analysis

Generally speaking, the 'select' tool will manage the process of navigating between and around the different tools, while the above chapters concentrate on the detailed mechanics of the specific tool in question. A couple of general points about navigation are worth making here from this overview perspective, however:

1) Readers already familiar with TRIZ will recognise that ARIZ – the Algorithm for Inventive Problem Solving – has been included as a 'solve' tool, when in actual fact it (or any of the multitudinous versions of 'it') was designed as a complete problem definition and solving process in it's own right. We include it as a solve tool in light of Altshuller's stated view (Reference 2.1) that it was something that was only necessary for the 5% most difficult problem settings. In the terms of this book, we will primarily use ARIZ as a safety back-up; as the thing the 'select' tool will point us towards only if we have emerged from the earlier problem definition part of the systematic creativity process still unable to determine what sort of problem we are facing. We hope this will be a very rare event.

2) It is of course possible, that we emerge from the 'define' part of the process with what turns out to be a wrong or fundamental unsolvable problem definition. In this regard it is worth noting that while many experience TRIZ users will tell you there is no such thing as an 'unsolvable' problem, they will also tell you that there are very

definitely constraints that can make the problem unsolvable. We believe this is a useful output from the solve part of the process – 'knowing' that your problem plus your constraints means you will fundamentally not be able to generate a viable solution offers good justification to go around and re-challenge the constraints. We also believe that – and have tried to structure the solve tools in such a way that – they become self-correcting. In other words, if your constraints have taken you into a cul-de-sac, or if it turns out you have defined a problem situation incorrectly, the tools will first try and tell you, and then second, try and tell you which directions to travel in order to rectify the situation. You will experience this most commonly in solution triggers that suggest you try and solve a problem at a higher or lower hierarchical level (the most common kind of required re-direction), or that you should re-challenge a given constraint. This 'self-correcting' nature will initially require a little faith on your part – the tendency is often to fight the direction being suggested – but experience tells us that the benefits of following the re-directions being offered are there to be taken.

3) By way of offering a final back-stop, it is worth noting as a final point that, on the rare occasions when we have been through all of the tools recommended as relevant to a problem and not generated any solutions, there is a specific set of tools (the psychological inertia tools – Chapter 19) that can help us to work out why we aren't generating solutions, and what to do about it. (They feature amongst the eleven solve tool clusters because they are also commonly used in precisely the 'solve' role.)

EVALUATE

The last of the four major parts of the overall systematic creativity process is 'evaluate'. This is the part of the process where we identify the 'best' solution from the ones generated during the preceding 'solve' part. The 'evaluate' process is described in detail in Chapter 21. The real essence of it involves the mechanics of transforming the uncertainties commonly involved in making 'apples versus oranges' comparisons between different solutions. TRIZ is generally quite weak in this area, and so we introduce established and new techniques from outside the TRIZ canon.

And so there is the overall process. Except not quite. At several points in the book you will see the four-stage process being drawn as a repeating loop – Figure 2.5.

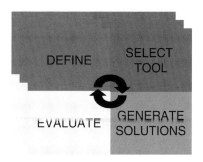

Figure 2.5: The Cyclic Nature of the Systematic Creativity Process

This is an extremely important point in the context of ensuring we *really* achieve the 'best' solution to a given problem. Again the point stems from one of the cruel tricks our brains often play on us. The trick in this case is similar to the one where our brain is over-eager to jump from problem definition mode to problem solution mode, except in this case, having generated a solution we like, our brain is over-eager to jump into what we might call 'satisfied' mode. In other words, we come up with a solution we like and our brain switches out of creative mode, out of critical mode and into a mode that says ' look what a great job we did'. We will see several examples of this in action in case studies throughout the book – solutions where the inventors came up with a good idea, which they sought to exploit without stepping back to wonder whether they could make it better.

We include the looping process image as a way of reminding ourselves of the dangers of this 'satisfied mode' thinking. The general message we should draw from it is that we should always look to go around the loop at least once more after we have derived a good solution.

Innovation Chains
The 'going around the loop again' idea should provide us with a very useful image of what TRIZ is trying to do in terms of helping us to evolve a system in the direction of increasing ideality.

In Chapter 10 we will discuss this 'chain' idea further in the context of how the contradiction elimination process in particular will produce the chaining effect.

Problems and Opportunities

Questions along the lines of 'I can see that TRIZ is useful for solving problems, but can it do anything to help me identify opportunities for exploiting my existing solutions' seem to appear increasingly frequently in the TRIZ context. The question of identifying opportunities is, of course, not a new one – Edward DeBono's important book on the subject, for example, dates back to 1978 (Reference 2.2). The book offers much advice that remains relevant (and highly TRIZ-like in its approach) and is highly recommended.

The simple answer to the question, though is 'yes, TRIZ can help you to identify opportunities for exploiting existing solutions'.

Here we overview some of the most common 'opportunity identification' and 'opportunity exploitation' strategies available from within the armoury of TRIZ tools. Never wishing to pass up the chance of a rant about problems versus opportunities, however, we begin with a short section on possible ways of thinking about and articulating the differences and similarities between the two definitions:

Problems And Opportunities

One of the most useful things an academic ever said to us was that in management, everything has to be distilled down to a maximum of 4-boxes – plan-do-study-act, strengths-weakneses-opportunities-threats, important/not-important versus urgent/not-urgent, being just three examples that spring immediately to mind from the days we were forced to attend these kinds of 'training' event. The 4-box limit obviously presents some serious problems when trying to establish TRIZ as a standard part of the manager's toolkit (see the new 31x31 contradiction matrix in the CreaTRIZ for managers software for example), but should not, however, stop us presenting a new 2x2 matrix to help structuring our thinking for problems and opportunities.

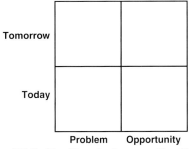

Tomorrow

Today

Problem　　Opportunity

Figure 2.6: Problem/Opportunity versus Time Matrix

Even in this crude form, we think the picture offers a useful image, in that if we see the 4 boxes together as a way of plotting the 'whole world', we can quickly see that the large majority of organizations spend the large majority of their efforts working in just one of the four. Surprise, surprise, this turns out to be the near-term, problem box, we probably all know as 'fire-fighting'. The other three boxes give us some useful additional generalizations – as illustrated in Figure 2.7.

	Problem	Opportunity
Tomorrow	FMEA/ Subversion Analysis	Major Paradigm Shift Opportunities
Today	**Fire-Fighting**	'Low-Hanging Fruit'/ 'Rembrandts In The Attic'

Problem　　Opportunity

Figure 2.7: Useful Interpretations of the Matrix Segments

Both axes, of course, actually represent a continuum rather than a segmented 2x2 box. This is probably more obvious for the time axis than the problem/opportunity axis, but a very useful image to hold – one that will help considerably in guiding how we think about problems and opportunities – is that the problem-opportunity axis extends from sub-system to system to super-system. In other words, the problem/opportunity axis can usefully be seen as a SPACE axis. Figure 2.8 illustrates the idea.

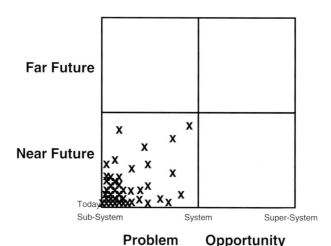

Problem Opportunity

Figure 2.8: Space-Time Version of Problem/Opportunity Matrix

Thinking of the problem/opportunity axis as space like this, we think, provides a very useful image and a good way of discriminating between 'problems' and 'opportunities'. Thus, in our picture, a 'problem' becomes defined as something focused on the internal issues – we are looking at the system level and smaller. An 'opportunity' on the other hand becomes those situations where we lift our heads to look at the outside world; the times when we start thinking about how our system and its sub-systems and how they might be applied in other situations. Thus, if we have a situation where the fasteners (i.e. a component deep into the detail of the sub-system) holding our system together corrode, then we have a problem. If we have a situation where we have a fastener design which doesn't corrode, we might lift our heads to the super-system and ask the question 'who else might want a fastener that doesn't corrode?' In this situation, we have identified an opportunity.

Coming back to the figure for a final moment, and seeing the two axes as continuous variables, we should be able to imagine plotting an X for each 'thing' a hypothetical organization might be working on at any one time, and where/when it is focused, we gain another image of how the business is being managed. Again in our hypothetically drawn figure, we see a strong clustering towards the very near-term, fine detail fire-fighting work.

We make no judgement on whether this is right or not – priority one in business is to stay in business – merely that the figure usefully defines a way of seeing the bigger picture as well as allowing us to offer a useful way of seeing problems and opportunities.

So now let us now overview the opportunity side of the picture and how we can deploy TRIZ to help take maximum advantage of opportunities. We can split this story into two parts; the first looking at opportunity identification (i.e. the equivalent of 'problem definition'), the second looking at opportunity exploitation (i.e. the equivalent of 'problem solving'). As with 'problem definition', 'opportunity identification' is probably 90% of the solution, and so we will concentrate our discussion on that focus.

TRIZ and Opportunity Identification

Opportunity identification is essentially about two things. The first is about working out which of the things an organisation knows how to do, that they do better than other people (maybe some, maybe all) outside the organisation. These things might be 'core competencies' or, more interestingly, things that are merely taken for granted in the way the company does business. The second is about what happens when we find things that outsiders are better able to do than the current inside capability and wish to import those ideas.

The key to identifying possible opportunities in both cases, is understanding FUNCTION: What functions do we deliver, what functions would we like to deliver, and how do others deliver the same functions represent the core questions.

An important concept to introduce at this stage is that of 'functional benchmarking'. Everyone is aware of the term 'benchmarking', but few have thus far made the connection with the TRIZ idea of classifying knowledge in terms of function. By way of example of functional benchmarking we examine a hypothetical graph drawn for the functional classification 'join solid objects' (we will come back to this idea in more detail in chapter 15). Several sources have begun the process of classifying functional capabilities into categories like this one. None have as yet found a way of making it easy for users to see which of the solutions contained in the database are most relevant to a specific application, however. A start along the road to this aim is to recognize the main attributes of the function. In the case of the 'join solid objects' function, the main useful attributes (MUA) might be seen as the strength or strength/weight ratio of the join and the adaptability of the join (as an aside, we might note the similarities here between MUA and the parameters of the Contradiction Matrix). A hypothetical functional benchmarking graph for the 'join solid objects' function might then look something like that drawn in Figure 2.9; in which the axes of the graph are made from two of the MUAs identified.

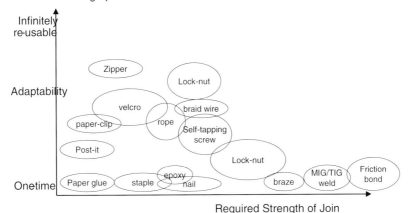

Figure 2.9: 'Join Solid Object' – Functional Benchmarking Graph

Pictures like this one provide an excellent framework within which organizations are able to quickly compare their functional capabilities with the outside world. The graphs can be used to identify both 'good' solutions from outside that might be imported to solve a problem inside the company, but also provide visibility of outside opportunities. This latter capability is perhaps not so obvious. Careful observers of the graph (and others like it) will observe a characteristic hyperbolic shape (actually a cluster of several hyperbolic curves). Such curves are representative of technical contradictions, and, those aware of the contradictions part of TRIZ will recognize that the aim of 'eliminating' contradictions is to shift the curves (as drawn here) in an upward and rightward direction – Figure 2.10. In other words, systems will evolve to the top right of the picture.

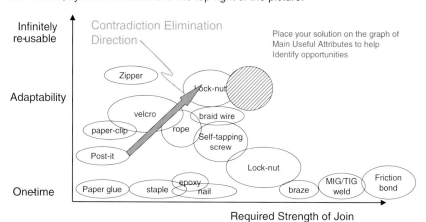

Figure 2.10: Functional Benchmarking Graph And Contradiction Elimination

In simple terms, then, any solution lower or more leftwardly positioned than your capability is likely to be inferior to your capability and may therefore be an area of opportunity. This is of course a somewhat simplified outlook, but the concept of MUA (and more specifically, identifying the right ones to plot) means that functional benchmarking graphs like this one offer a potent start point for opportunity identification.

TRIZ Trends and Opportunity Identification

The trends of evolution contained within TRIZ provide another means of identifying opportunities. The most important connection here comes with the concept of evolutionary potential (something discussed in much more detail in Chapter 13). The concept is based on the idea that all systems and system components have the potential to evolve through all of the stages identified in each of the generic TRIZ technology evolution trends. A component that has evolved all the way along all of the trends may be said to have used up all of its evolutionary potential; a component that has not, has some remaining untapped potential still left to exploit. We introduce here the image of an evolutionary radar plot as illustrated in Figure 2.11 below.

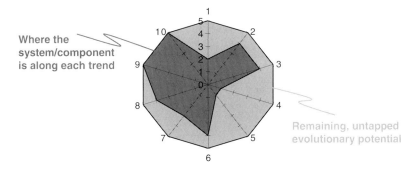

Figure 2.11: Evolutionary Potential Radar Plot

The plot is drawn by comparing the component or system under evaluation with each of the known TRIZ trends in order to establish first whether the trend is relevant, and second, assuming it is, to establish how far along the trend the component has evolved. Thus in the above example 10 relevant trends have been identified – these make up the spokes of the radar plot – and in the case of the first trend, the component has used two of the possible 5 evolution stages.

Again in simple terms, this type of plot enables users to begin to identify opportunities. This works in both inward and outward directions; in the above example, it may be speculated that the component has hit the limits of its evolutionary potential for trends 9 and 10. In both of these cases, the component may be presenting opportunities for outside exploitation if equivalent components elsewhere have not evolved so far. Conversely, the example radar plot suggests that trends 4 and 5 have hardly been exploited at all, and as such may be amenable to the introduction of a more evolved design from outside.

By way of a simple example of how this works in practice, take the example of the design of a casting for some form of simple casing and the 'space segmentation' technology evolution trend (illustrated in Chapter 13) that says that solid things tend to evolve to hollow things, which in turn evolve to multi-hollow and then capillary hollow things. The casing is likely to be designed as a monolithic solid and as such is very much at the immature end of the space segmentation trend. The trend suggests that the casing contains significant space segmentation evolutionary potential. We might then choose to look for anyone that has successfully achieved hollow castings (evolution step 2). No doubt others have solved this problem, and we may now have identified an opportunity to use them. We might also, however, look further along the trend and ask the question whether anyone has achieved a capillary casting capability (as the trends have been compiled based on historical data, it must be that *someone* has done something similar somewhere). In this case we might then discover foam metals and thus have tapped into a much bigger opportunity.

We examine this whole subject in more detail in Chapter 13 – including the critical parallel issue of opportunity timing – and how we can use systematic creativity tools to help us get both right.

In summary, then, opportunities exist outside the current system. There are several different means of identifying opportunities. In the most random sense, opportunity finding depends on the connection-making capabilities of the human brain, and the chance connections made by individuals as they experience life outside the system and capabilities within the system. Some organizations maximize such opportunity finding chances by encouraging and empowering everyone within the organization to look for and exploit such connections rather than just specifically tasked individuals (Reference 2.3). TRIZ provides a much more systematic way of identifying opportunities. In the first instance, it recognizes and classifies knowledge in terms of function delivery. In the simplest sense, then, we might view 'opportunity finding' as the successful connection of either a function someone else is capable of delivering that might be imported into an organization, or that a function currently delivered by the organization is more effective than other known ways of delivering the same function outside the organization. At a more detailed level, the TRIZ trends of evolution tools and the concept of evolutionary potential, and the resources part of the method offer even more structured ways of identifying opportunities.

Finally, we re-emphasise the point that whether we are looking at a problem or an opportunity situation, the same basic four stage process overviewed in this chapter has been designed to cater for both. We will find that the main differences between problem and opportunity strategies will emerge during the 'solve' parts of the overall systematic creativity process. We will also find that Chapter 9, which describes the 'select' part of the process, will take on the management of those differences should we so desire.

What Do I Do?

As we've stated previously, TRIZ is a very big and rich thing. We readily accept that some people will use the full process being espoused here, while others will just want to delve into the parts that they are interested. Still others will wish to mix and match parts of the process to suit the way they do things. As we will discuss later in the chapter on ARIZ, this is absolutely fine. There are several versions of ARIZ precisely because different TRIZ masters propose doing things in different ways. Ultimately, any process you might use has to belong to you.

That being said, if you are looking for 'a process' this is the one we recommend. We recommend it not because we defined it, but because we defined it to be flexible enough to accommodate a wide range of personal tastes. Thus, to take a specific example, the process suggests that there are four distinct activities that should be carried out if we are to be confident that we have defined the 'right' problem, but it doesn't dictate what order you do them in. The limitations of a hard-bound book have meant that we have had to present a certain order, but our suggestion to you is that if you'd rather conduct things in a different order, by all means do so.

If you decide to try the whole process, we suggest you first read all of the first four chapters, then let this chapter be your guide through the ones in the rest of the book relevant to defining and solving your problem or opportunity.

Because the possible variety of problem types and application routes is so large, and the space in this book so limited, we have not included any complete start-to-finish case studies – although you will find many examples of parts of the process in action. It is planned to publish a book of complete case studies in the not too distant future.

References

1) Altshuller, G., 'Creativity As An Exact Science', Gordon & Breach, New York, 1984.
2) DeBono, E., 'Opportunities', Penguin Books, 1978.
3) Fradette, M., Michaud, S., 'The Power of Corporate Kinetics', Simon & Schuster, New York, 1998.

3.
Psychology

"It's not the size of the ship, it's the size of the waves."
Little Richard

At first glance, it might appear that TRIZ has got very little to do with psychology at all; being seen by many as a distillation of other peoples' good solutions to technical problems. This, of course, is one of the aspects that distinguishes TRIZ from the mass of other creativity tools, methods and strategies. To generalize further (and hence even more unfairly simplistically), the main differences between TRIZ and 'other' creativity tools may be summarized as shown in Figure 3.1.

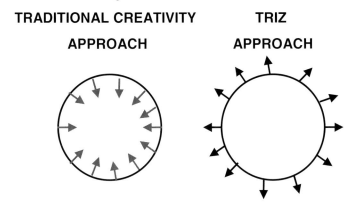

Figure 3.1: Difference Between TRIZ and 'Other' Creativity Tools

The large majority of other creativity tools are built on the belief that our brains are highly inefficient and that most of us use a very small proportion of its capacity (every time we read a text in this area, the proportion of our brain capacity that gets used seems to be reported as an ever smaller percentage – 5%, then 1%, now about 0.1%, and so on). Hence the main task of 'creativity tools' is to help us to think more effectively, to 'unblock' us, to help us get all the great ideas trapped inside us out into the world.

One of the key findings of TRIZ research on the other hand is that 'someone, somewhere has already solved a problem something like mine'. In other words, it takes as its start point the belief that we should be looking outside for solutions to our problems.

The contrast between these two internal and external approaches can be clearly elicited with a knowledge problem like asking a group of people to think of ways of getting water out of a glass. The best creativity tools will enable the group to 'unblock' and be able to suggest many ways of achieving a solution, but none will be able to elicit ideas which do not exist in any of the heads present. Access to a TRIZ knowledge base (Chapter 15), on the other hand, will allow the group to access all of the good solutions of everyone in the world. Clearly, no amount of 'unblocking' is going to allow us to develop ideas which do not exist inside our heads. This global knowledge outlook is a definite advantage that TRIZ has over other creativity tools.

The purpose of this short chapter, on the other hand, is not to suggest that the external perspective is 'better' or that there is a need to make any kind of choice between internal or external creativity strategies, but that – in line with the philosophical importance of eliminating contradictions – we should be looking to combine the strengths of both approaches. Thus, the view taken throughout this book is the one illustrated in Figure 3.2 – if a particular tool, method or strategy has something to offer in helping us to define and solve problems more effectively, we will use it.

Systematic Creativity

APPROACH

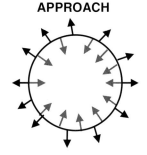

Figure 3.2: Combined 'Internal' and 'External' Systematic Creativity Strategy

It is our clear and distinct belief that in order to create effectively it is absolutely essential to combine the internal and the external. It also appears clear that we need to do this in as coherent and jargon-free manner as possible. Consequently, this chapter aside, we will not make any distinction between 'internal' or 'external' approaches. More specifically, when we are describing or demonstrating the use of a particular tool or part of the systematic creativity process, we will attempt to integrate 'internal' and external invisibly in a way that allows us to focus on benefits rather than features.

That being said, there are a number of points that are worth making here in order to set a scene for the 'internal' elements of the creative process, in order that we can see what is expected or desirable when we come to the job of defining and solving actual problems.

We will make five points; the first relates to the mechanisms by which our brains interpret and use the solution 'triggers' that TRIZ and other tools provide; the second relates to the higher level physiology that dictates the manner in which our brains operate during 'problem solving' in its most general context; the third discusses the meaning of the important TRIZ term 'psychological inertia, why it is a bad thing, and how we can overcome the problems it causes; the fourth looks at mechanisms to help us to better sequence and structure our creative thinking, and the fifth briefly outlines the importance of psychology during group problem solving sessions. It is not our intention to be comprehensive – the list of references at the end of the chapter should provide a number of useful links for anyone wanting to find out more.

1) The Space Between 'Generic' and 'Specific' Design Solutions

TRIZ offers a systematic creativity process built primarily on the concept of abstraction – in which a problem owner maps from a specific problem to a generic framework, out of which comes a generic solution requiring translation back to the specific. As detailed in the previous chapter, the process is illustrated in Figure 3.3.

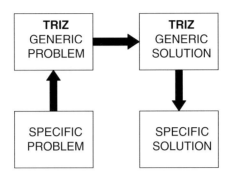

Figure 3.3: The General Model For TRIZ Problem Solving

Unfortunately, the systemisation process effectively ends at the delivery of the Generic Solutions. These 'generic solutions' include the 40 Inventive Principles, the 78 Inventive Standards, the 35 Trends of Evolution, and the databases containing several thousand scientific effects that we will be covered in later chapters of the book. Although highly valuable, many problem solvers still find there is a considerable gap between these generic solution triggers and the desired specific solution. This gap is illustrated in Figure 3.4.

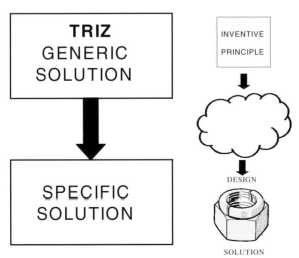

Figure 3.4: The Space Between Inventive Principle and Design Solution

TRIZ is being used successfully in a wide and widening variety of fields. The space – this 'gap' – between Principles and design solutions is obviously therefore not a vacuum. Whatever it is, however, is at present obscured by clouds. The question is what is behind those clouds, and whatever it is, is it in any way mappable?

The Irreversible Nature of Good Ideas

The best if not only way of usefully looking beyond the clouds is through examination of case study examples. Every successful patent and every successful innovation offers potential data. There is thus an awful lot of case study material from which to choose. Unfortunately there is a problem, and it is a fairly fundamental problem associated with each and every case. It is a problem of irreversibility: Moving forwards from problem to solution – in effect the process hidden behind the cloud – is a highly nebulous, highly intractable path. Before that moment when the light-bulb finally lights, the engineer is often literally as well as metaphorically in the dark.

The other way around – looking back at the problem after the solution has been discovered – however, is a completely different matter. Now the solution is viewed as 'obvious', often to the point of being almost facile. It's the 'why didn't I think of that' experience. In fact the very 'obviousness' of a solution is very often used as a test of how 'right' the solution is. The more 'obvious' the answer, the better the solution.

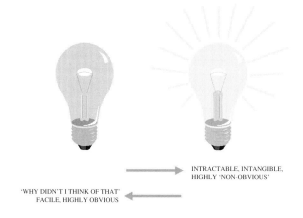

INTRACTABLE, INTANGIBLE, HIGHLY 'NON-OBVIOUS'

'WHY DIDN'T I THINK OF THAT' FACILE, HIGHLY OBVIOUS

Figure 3.5: The Irreversible Nature Of Creative Ideas

Think, for example, of how obvious a solution the wheel is. Then think how non-obvious it was for the first 95% of human existence. Or think how it is now taken for granted that a Benzene molecule takes the form of a ring.

This 'obviousness' irreversibility and the speed with which the light gets turned on once the switch is found makes it extremely difficult to establish what the turning on process actually was. Most famously with Kekule and his solution of the Benzene ring problem, the solution process took the form of a dream about a snake chewing on its tail. It is difficult to see how this might be a mappable process. Without direct access to the problem solver – as was the case with TRIZ researchers looking at the patent database – likely as not the problem will be even greater.

In trying to get 'behind the cloud', the irreversibility problem can be expected to be a fairly major one.

First, however, let us have a look at a number of case studies in order to gain a more specific feel for the size of the unknown behind the cloud:-

Case Study 1: Flanged Joint

A solution to the 'halving the number of bolts on a flange joint' is a case study described in Chpater 10. The solution to the problem was patented in the US as patent number 5,230,540. It is reproduced here in Figure 3.6.

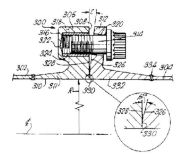

Figure 3.6: Fluid-Tight Joint With Inclined Flange Face, US Patent 5,230,540

The Inventive Principle used to derive this highly elegant and simple solution was Inventive Principle 17, 'Another Dimension'. Case Study 1 then leaves us with 'Another Dimension' and patent number 5,230,540 as the entry and exit points respectively of any process that may exist behind the cloud.

Case Study 2: Bicycle Seat

Another case study from Chapter 10 derived the bifurcated bicycle seat illustrated in Figure 3.7. It is, conceptually at least, a means of achieving both comfortable sitting position and freedom to pedal.

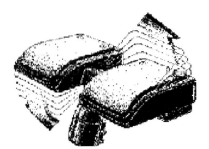

Figure 3.7: ABS Sports Bifurcated Saddle

Case Study 2 sees the bifurcated bicycle seat as the specific design solution emerging from simultaneous application of Inventive Principle 15, 'Dynamic Parts'.

Case Study 3: Particle Separator

Another, more complex problem concerning a novel design solution to the problem of particle separator systems for helicopter engines is described below.

There are a number of separator types available. Engine mounted forms are probably the most common. All current engine mounted separators look like the device illustrated in Figure 3.8; essentially an axi-symmetric, bifurcated duct taking clean air around a sharp bend into the engine, and using the inertia of contaminants to expel them through a scavenge duct.

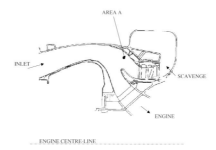

Figure 3.8: Typical Engine Mounted Particle Separator

Much effort has been expended trying to improve the performance of these designs. Reference 3.1 describes the background to the realisation of the novel solution shown in Figure 3.9. This new design offers the potential to not only double contaminant separation efficiency, but also to offer significant reductions in volume, weight, aerodynamic losses, and power requirement.

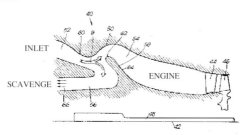

Figure 3.9: US Patent 5,139,545 Particle Separator

While the improved design may be seen to be relatively simple – the innovation comes about by simply transposing the position of the engine and scavenge ducts - the process of deriving it was rather more complex. The Inventive Principle used was Number 13 'The Other Way Around'.

Mechanisms of Mind: Pattern Recognition

To solve the mystery of what lies behind the cloud in the gap between generic and specific, would be to solve a problem that has confounded many hundreds of man-years of effort. To suggest that a solution exists here, therefore, would be an action of extreme folly. That being said, it is apparent that TRIZ has already done much to de-mystify the creative process. Wonder, for example, whether Kekule might have discovered the ring structure of Benzene any quicker if he had been aware that there were Inventive Principles called 'Merging', or 'Self-Service', or 'Curvature Increase'? The Inventive Principles of TRIZ provide 40 very good start points from which to search for problem solutions.

TRIZ provides a powerful foundation point. A pointer to how the steps between Inventive Principle and design solution might then be plotted perhaps comes from some of the research on how the human brain functions and, particularly, on its pattern recognition capabilities.

By way of demonstration, and adapting the 'Connect-Up' idea first written about by Edward de Bono (Reference 3.2), if any two words are picked at random, the brain will almost without fail manage to come up with another word which connects them. The process is often expressed in a manner like that shown in Figure 3.10. Here the two chosen random words are BANANA and PENCIL – at first glance neither word has anything at all to do with the other, but the brain will almost inevitably make some kind of connection. Indeed, given a couple of minutes, most people will be able to make associations with ten or more connecting words.

Figure 3.10: Connecting Words

Figure 3.11 illustrates the connections made by this author when using the word 'banana' to help generate ideas for a better design of pencil.

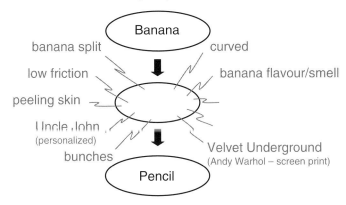

Figure 3.11: Example Connections Between Apparently Un-Connected Words

This pattern making capability is an undoubtedly powerful one. Perhaps not so powerful, however, that some kind of mammoth artificial intelligence computer-code might be constructed to mimic the process? Even with only ten words connecting any pair and a typical individual's word vocabulary, though, mammoth would certainly be the word.

Unfortunately, the situation becomes even more complicated if a number of people are asked to perform the same exercise. Research in this field (Reference 3.3) suggests that if ten people are asked to write down ten connecting words each, the level of duplication of words between individuals would be very small. On average, the number of duplicated words would be around 5%. In other words, ten people writing down ten connecting words each would tend to produce a total of over 90 different connecting words. (Try it as an exercise sometime and watch it happen.)

Knowing there to be a finite number of words, maybe some people can still imagine this being a situation amenable to a software implementation – albeit one in which we might hope the software itself does the large majority of the 'learning'/programming.

Unfortunately, even this scenario is a very long way away from the full story. A very long way because given a series of pictorial images to connect, one brain is usually capable of making even more connections. Take a population of brains and the number of connections may well be as close to infinite as makes any difference to even the biggest imaginable computer code.

Figure 3.12: Case Study 3 Connections

So what does this mean from the perspective of TRIZ and the need to solve problems?

On the positive side, it means that given a problem and an Inventive Principle – for example the Case Study 3 scenario as re-drawn in Connect-Up form (Figure 3.12) – the brain **will** make interesting connections.

Knowing the eventual solution to Case Study 3 and seeing this picture, it is already extremely easy to see how the solution came about. Recognising the Irreversibility phenomenon described in Section 2.0, perhaps it is too easy to be believable? (The historical facts, however, show that the gas-turbine industry collectively spent several tens of millions of dollars **not** finding the solution.)

The same may be seen to apply to the other two Case Study examples.

So what about another case study? One where the 'answer' may not previously been seen? Your turn to have a go!

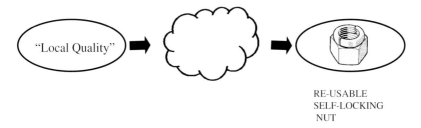

Figure 3.13: Connecting Inventive Principle and Desired Design Outcome

The (an?) answer to this one can be found in Reference 3.4.

Of course, even this example is over-simplistic. Over-simplistic in two important ways:-

1) There are 40 Inventive Principles. 'Local Quality' happened to be one that gave an excellent answer to this problem, but that was not known a priori. In reality, there will have been at least three – and quite possibly all 39 – other Inventive Principles to also try to connect.

2) More significantly, who is to say that the picture and its corresponding problem definition ('re-usable self-locking nut') is either the 'right' picture or the 'right' definition?

In other words, although it is possible to demonstrate that the brain is able to make the right connections, the 'Connect-Up' idea is still some considerable distance from being a systematic procedure.

Use of System Operator

Reference 3.3 discussed the connections between TRIZ and mind-mapping in an idea generating context. Discussed then was the concept of combined use of the generic solution triggers (in the case here, the Inventive Principle 'Local Quality') and the need to think in TIME and SPACE. The System Operator is seen to provide an excellent framework for focusing our thinking when trying to make the connections we require between generic and specific solution.

Thus, in the case of the self-locking nut, in order to make best use of the solution trigger 'Local Quality' we need to apply it not just to the nut – the thing our brain's would tell us to do! – but to the nut in its bigger (super-system) and smaller (sub-system) contexts, and in terms of how the nut's behaviour and function changes with time. The thinking in space context – and the idea of our viewing perspective continuously zooming in and out – is particularly important with the Local Quality Principle.

In order to make most effective use of the Principle, we need to be looking to apply it at each viewing perspective (Figure 3.14). In essence we are looking for any element of the system where there is homogeneity. The presence of homogeneity means the current solution has not used the 'local quality' Principle. In actual fact, therefore, anywhere we see homogeneity, Local Quality is telling us we have a potential resource:

- The nut has parallel, unbroken threaded surfaces – homogeneity and therefore a resource.
- Each thread is the same as the one next to it – more homogeneity
- The external sides of the nut are parallel and continuous – ditto
- And so on

The perspective shifting capabilities offered by the System Operator offer potent ways of structuring brainstorm sessions filling the gap between believing 'Local Quality' is a good solution direction, and actually applying it to good effect on the problem.

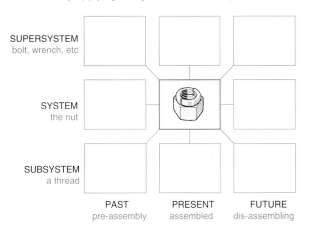

SUPERSYSTEM
bolt, wrench, etc

SYSTEM
the nut

SUBSYSTEM
a thread

PAST   PRESENT   FUTURE
pre-assembly   assembled   dis-assembling

Figure 3.14: 9-Windows/System Operator Helps Focus Use Of Inventive Principles

The system operator tool is important throughout the systematic creativity process. We will return to it in more detail in Chapter 4.

Conclusions

1) The space between Inventive Principle and problem solution is not a vacuum. If a formal route between the two exists, it is very unlikely to be mappable (software implementable) in a generic sense.
2) For specific problem types – such as mechanism design – a formalised, mappable systematic innovation tool based on TRIZ principles may well be constructable.
3) Meanwhile, the 40 Inventive Principles of TRIZ provide a very powerful tool for breaking out of existing design paradigms and into new and exciting ones.
4) The de Bono based 'Connect-Up' idea – getting engineers to find connections between Inventive Principles and the problem at hand through the viewing perspectives offered by the System Operator offer very powerful means of deriving inventive problem solutions.

2) TRIZ THINKING HATS

Edward De Bono's 'Six Thinking Hats'™ concept (Reference 3.5) is one area where a great deal of synergy exists with TRIZ. This section describes how the Six Thinking Hats™

concept has been integrated into the generic TRIZ-based problem definition and solving process described in this book.

The Thinking Hats concept is built on the fact that the human brain works in physically different modes depending on the sort of task it is being asked to perform. Thus, to take two extremes, the mechanisms used by the brain when generating new ideas is significantly different to those present when we are calculating the pros and cons of an existing idea. In all, De Bono has identified six different important modes of thought which are relevant across the range of actions taking place during the problem solving process (Figure 3.15). Each mode has been identified by a different coloured hat, such that:-

A WHITE hat – denotes a mode of thinking during which an objective look at data and information is required.

A RED hat – denotes the mode of thinking associated with feelings, hunches, and intuition.

A BLACK hat – denotes the mode of thinking associated with caution, judgement, and looking logically at the negative aspects of a problem – often described as the 'devil's advocate' mode of thinking.

A   hat - denotes the mode of thinking associated with examining the feasibility and benefits of a given situation, and looking logically at the positive aspects.

A GREEN hat – denotes the mode of thinking associated with the generation of new ideas, creative and 'lateral' thinking.

A BLUE hat – denotes the mode of thinking associated with the overall control and organisation of the thinking processes.

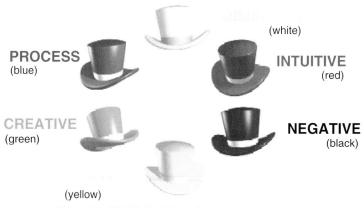

Figure 3.15: Six Thinking Hats – Schematic Representation

We describe here how the Hats concept can be integrated into a TRIZ problem solving scheme covering the complete spectrum of activities – from initial situation assessment, to problem definition, to problem solution – present in a facilitated inventive problem solving session. Thus, for example we see the conducting of a function analysis conducted in two parts – the first, looking at the positive functional relationships in a system, operating in 'White Hat' mode, followed by a second 'Black Hat' mode in which the negative relationships in the system are systematically analysed. Similarly the value of switching between White and Green Hat modes when using the Contradictions parts of the TRIZ tool-kit is detailed.

We begin, however, with an examination of the different Hat modes, and the times we might chose to wear them when using different elements of the TRIZ toolkit:

White Hat

We wear the white hat when we are seeking to take a non-emotional, objective look at data and information. We are most likely to require use of White Hat thinking strategies at the following points during use of the TRIZ problem definition and problem solving process:

- During the initial problem assessment and definition phase. Specifically, when conducting the first stages of a function analysis – in which we are seeking to describe the actual functioning of the existing system – but also when examining statements describing the desired end point for the problem, and understanding the present level of maturity of the system in terms of it (and its sub-systems') position on their respective evolutionary S-curves.
- During the phase in which, having completed an initial problem definition, the problem owner is looking to select the most appropriate of the TRIZ problem solving tools.
- Defining the Ideal Final Result, and using the Ideality problem solving tool concept of working back from this IFR to a physically realisable solution.
- When defining contradictions, and when using the Contradiction Matrix or the Physical Contradiction solution method tools.
- When using a functional knowledge-base.
- When recording generated solutions.
- When assessing and ranking the quality of solutions during the down-select part of the overall process.
- In conjunction with the 9 Windows tool, throughout the overall problem definition and solving process in order to ensure that space and time dimensions are given appropriate attention.

As TRIZ has been configured as a 'systematic' creativity tool, it should not come as a great surprise to learn that the White Hat is worn most during a TRIZ session. The other 5 Hats, however, are still vital at certain points during the process:

Red Hat

The red hat is worn when we are using our intuition and relying on our feelings and emotions. The red hat mode of thinking may at first sight appear to be the complete antithesis of a systematic creativity process, but it has its uses, and – most importantly – we need to recognise that the way our brains operate means that many of us spend a large proportion of our time naturally thinking in a Red Hat mode. At the very least, therefore, we need to be aware of Red Hat thinking modes, if only to recognise that we need to step out of it for much of the time. We are most likely to wish to use Red Hat thinking strategies positively, though, at the following points during the TRIZ problem definition and problem solving process:

- Almost inevitably given the way our brains are wired and the way we have been thought to problem solve traditionally, when given a problem we shift immediately into Red Hat 'problem solving' mode. We should recognise this phenomenon and try to use it to positive effect. It is common, therefore, to include a five or ten minute period either right at the beginning of a session, or immediately after the initial problem definition phase, of brainstorming. The output from such a brainstorming session is commonly recorded and placed in a 'car-park' where all participants can see that their input has been registered and will be returned to at the appropriate time during subsequent parts of the process.
- Red Hat thinking mode can also be useful as a psychological inertia-breaking tool if use of the TRIZ problem solving tools has not produced any viable solutions.
- Red Hat thinking mode can also be used to good effect at times during a problem solving session to break out of the rut that can sometimes occur if participants have been kept in other thinking modes – but particularly White Hat – for extended periods. Provocations like 'spend five minutes thinking about the worst possible means of solving the problem' have not uncommonly generated some interesting and subsequently viable solution options.

Nevertheless, these points aside, Red Hat thinking mode should be deployed only sparingly when using TRIZ methods.

Black Hat
We wear the black hat when we employing caution and judgement, and looking logically at the negative aspects of a given situation. We are most likely to require use of Black Hat thinking modes at the following points during the TRIZ problem definition and problem solving process:

- During the initial problem definition phase, where we are attempting to identify all of the constraints that exist in and around our problem.
- During the conducting of a function/attribute analysis of the problem situation, when we are looking to identify the harmful, insufficient and excessive functions that exist in the current system. (NB it is very important to recognise that Black Hat thinking and White Hat thinking are two significantly different modes, and that a proper function analysis requires both. The most effective function analysis sessions occur when the White Hat and the Black Hat modes are conducted sequentially, with White Hat first, and Black Hat being allowed to commence only after a specific instruction from a problem facilitator that modes should now be shifted.)
- During a 'how can I destroy this system?' subversion analysis
- During assessment of solution options when trying to gauge the relative weaknesses of the solutions under consideration.
- When answering the question 'is the chosen solution good enough?' at the end of a session. Another common human trait is that we are highly inclined towards accepting and settling on a solution that we think is novel. This is particularly evident when we have successfully broken a contradiction. An excellent example of the need to put on a Black Hat at the 'end' of a problem solving

session comes from the bifurcated bicycle seat design to be described later in Chpater 10 – here the idea of bifurcation successfully eliminated the 'I want the saddle to be wide AND narrow' contradiction, and the company decided that this alone was a good enough solution. If they had put on their Black Hats at this stage, they might have forced themselves to recognise that the bifurcated seat had generated a number of new problems which, in retrospect, if they had solved before trying to launch the new product, they might have had a runaway success as opposed to the largely failed design they currently try to sell.

Yellow Hat

We wear the yellow hat when we are examining the feasibility and benefits of a potential solution, or are seeking to logically assess the positive aspects of a given situation. We are most likely to require use of Yellow Hat thinking strategies at the following points during use of the TRIZ problem definition and problem solving process:

- During the initial definition stage of a problem when we are examining the resources that exist in and around the current system.
- During assessment of solution options when trying to gauge the relative strengths of the solutions under consideration.
- When seeking to challenge the validity of the initially defined problem constraints.
- When using the Trimming part of the TRIZ toolkit – particularly when asking the questions 'do I need this function?' or 'can an existing part of the system perform the function for me?' or 'can a resource perform the function?' (NB some users find that Trimming works more successfully in White Hat mode; the author has generally had more success getting groups to wear a Yellow Hat.)
- When using the Standard Inventive Solutions, and trying to relate them to the problem situation. Solution triggers like 'add a substance' can be a little too obtuse for some people; this is less of a problem if such people are specifically asked to be in Yellow Hat mode.

Green Hat

We wear the green hat when we are looking to generate new ideas or are seeking to 'be creative'. We are most likely to require use of Green Hat thinking strategies at the following points during use of the TRIZ problem definition and problem solving process:

- During the initial definition stage, a short period of Green Hat thinking immediately after the Yellow Hat search for resources often sees the realisation of a considerable number of additional ideas that did not arise previously. (NB the preceding Yellow Hat mode is important and should not be replaced by Green.)
- During any point when using the TRIZ problem solving tools when we are seeking to translate generic solution triggers e.g. Inventive Principles, Trends of evolution, translation of conceptual solutions from the Ideality tool, use of Smart Little People, Size-Time-Cost, etc – into specific solutions. The importance of Green Hat thinking here cannot be over-estimated.

Blue Hat

We wear the blue hat when looking to provide a controlling function, or when organising the overall thinking process. The Blue Hat is the hat that we wear when judging when and where to put on the other Hats. The Blue Hat is the overall process organising Hat. It is the one worn almost continuously by the facilitator of a problem solving session rather than specifically by all members of a problem solving team. That being said, there are times when the team may benefit through collective donning of the Blue Hat:

- During post-session recording of events.
- Periodically during subversion analysis when trying to ensure that all failure modes are being adequately traced and recorded.
- When a problem solving team is getting bogged down in the detail of a particular part of a process, it is often useful for the facilitator to get the rest of the team to shift into Blue Hat thinking mode in order to zoom out of the details and to re-datum or re-orient themselves to see where they are in the overall process.

Putting It All Together

There is no one definitive version of a 'TRIZ process'. In many senses, such a thing can only exist in the mind of an individual. With this in mind, this book does not in any way seek to propose an all-encompassing 'TRIZ process'. On the other hand, in order to examine how a 'typical' problem definition and solving session might require us to shift from one Hat to another, a number of generic steps are present in the vast majority of situations. These generic steps will be described below alongside a description of how we might shift from one Hat to another as we progress through the steps.

At the very broadest level, as we described in the previous chapter, we might see the systematic creativity process as consisting of four major steps – starting with Problem **Definition**, then **Select**ing the most appropriate solution routes, then generating **Solution**s, and finally **Evaluat**ing and down-selecting. We might see these steps as a looping process which repeats until we obtain a solution with which we are happy – Figure 3.16.

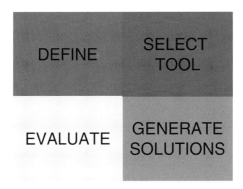

Figure 3.16: Four Major 'Systematic Creativity' Steps

Looking at each of these in turn:

DEFINE
- What benefits are we looking to achieve, how will we know when we've got there? (White Hat)

- What are the constraints? (**Black** Hat, possibly followed by)
- What resources are available? (Hat, possibly followed by Green)
- Where is the 'sore point'? (White Hat)
- What are the functions and attributes contained in the current system? (White Hat to define intended functions, then specifically followed by **Black** Hat to identify the harmful, insufficient and excessive functions)
- How mature is the current system (where does it and its sub-systems sit on their current evolutionary S-curves?) (White Hat)

- (Optional) Brainstorm and 'Car-Park' initial solution thoughts (**Red** Hat)

SELECT
- Determine the most appropriate problem solving techniques for the particular problem (White Hat)

SOLVE
A variety of options here, depending on which of the TRIZ tools are relevant:
- (Ideality) (White Hat)
- (Knowledge) (White Hat)
- (Contradictions) (White Hat to generate and look up contradictions; Green Hat to translate the generic triggers into specific solutions)
- (Trends) (Hat followed by Green)
- (Trimming) (Hat, probably followed by Green)
- (S-Fields) (Preferably ; probably followed by Green)
- SLP/STC (Green Hat)
- (Subversion Analysis) (**Black** Hat; probably interspersed with periods of **Blue**)

EVALUATE
- Have solutions been generated? If no, then the problem needs to be re-cast (**Black** Hat, possibly followed by **Red**, Green, or maybe **Blue**, probably in that order)
- If yes, then solutions need to be ranked (Hat, systematically followed by **Black** Hat)
- Deciding where to go next (i.e. around the loop again or to finish) (White Hat, but the facilitator should definitely encourage participants to go into **Black** Hat mode one more time if possible)

Of course, the above does not claim to be in any way definitive, rather that it should be judged as a measure of the need for us to shift our mode of thinking both systematically and regularly during a problem session.

Six Thinking Hats and TRIZ-based Software

Some parts of the TRIZ community are strong advocates of TRIZ-based software. While being a frequent user of certain aspects of such software, this author believes that until such times as the software is able to take due account of the different modes of operation found in the human brain, it cannot hope to provide us with anything like a comprehensive problem definition and solving capability. Software tools currently claiming such a capability should be treated with a fair degree of (Black Hat) scepticism.

Conclusions

Successful use of TRIZ tools demands that we recognise that the human brain works in distinctly different modes. Edward DeBono's Six Thinking Hats™ show us the six main modes of operation. We need to ensure that we are aware of the different modes, and, as much as possible, make sure that we match the appropriate Hat to the appropriate parts of the overall process.

3) Psychological Inertia

Much of Edward de Bono's pioneering study on lateral thinking stemmed from the hole-digging analogy he developed in his very earliest work (Reference 3.6). In the analogy, we are trying to solve a problem, the solution to which is a seam of gold buried at some unknown location in a field.

If the problem we're trying to solve is 'similar' to one we've already solved, we are likely to attempt to solve it using what de Bono described as 'vertical' or 'logical' thinking. In such a scenario, we have already started digging a hole, we've already found some gold in it, and we are expecting to find the solution to our new problem simply by digging – vertically, logically – deeper. Whole industries are built on this very principle. The next automobile to emerge on the market is almost guaranteed to emerge from a hole labelled '4-wheeled, internal combustion engine driven vehicle' for example. The next car tyre from a hole labelled 'moulded rubber, radial wound re-enforcement'. The next driver protection system from one labelled 'steering-wheel mounted, inflating bag'. And so on, and so on, at each and every level - from the macro to the micro - of whatever problem it is we're looking at. Each of the products or solutions that emerges will generally have been obtained by digging an existing hole a little deeper.

Figure 3.17: Problem Solving as Hole Digging Analogy

55

Unfortunately, once we've started digging a hole, it doesn't take long for our competitors to find us. In a mature industry like the automobile one, we've probably dug a quarry-sized hole, all the other manufacturers are in there with us, and we're all desperately scratching around for some nugget or other which will discriminate our product from everyone else's for a year or two.

Unfortunately also, we all suffer from what TRIZ calls 'psychological inertia' (PI). In the context of the hole-digging analogy, this is the thing that tells us to stay in the hole we've been digging. It is the thing that tells us that if we just keep on digging a bit deeper, we're bound to eventually come across the solution we're looking for. It is the thing that tells us 'look how much time and energy we've expended digging this hole; how could we possibly let it go to waste?' It is the thing that gives us a quite potent image of industries digging deeper and deeper holes that they are progressively less likely to be able to get out of.

De Bono used the term 'lateral thinking' to denote a different kind of thinking to the vertical/logical variant. Lateral thinking is the thinking that prompts us to set about looking somewhere else in the field in search of a better solution. Lateral thinking is the thing which got us out of a hole labelled 'horse-drawn carriage' into our current '4-wheeled, internal combustion engine driven' one. It will also be the thing that gets us into the next hole, whatever that might turn out to be.

Of course, the difficult part here is knowing where to dig our new hole. In the past, we probably did it to a large extent by accident or hunch or guesswork. Today, we can usually no longer afford either the time or money to embark on this type of random digging exercise. Economic and competitive necessities demand that if we're going to dig a new hole, we'd better have a pretty good idea **where** we're going to start before we pick up a shovel.

De Bono recommends a number of techniques to help locate worthwhile places to start digging new holes – for example PMI or 'Po' or word-association ('pick a random word from a dictionary…') – some more useful than others. None however appear to be as powerful as the opportunities that have emerged through the TRIZ methodology.

In the context of the finding the right place to begin digging a new hole analogy, there is probably no single technique in existence more powerful than the 40 Inventive Principles, 78 Inventive Standards and 35 trends of evolution detailed in this book. What TRIZ is in effect saying is that actually there are only very few places where we might profitably dig a new hole.

TRIZ is an undoubtedly powerful problem solving method. So much so that if we set out to find gold in a field, we can be pretty confident we're going to find it. But, if we actually wanted something other than gold, then being able to locate gold is actually of little use to us. Perhaps a good illustration of this is the air-bag problem solving exercise reported in earlier issues of TRIZ Journal. The exercise was as good as any in demonstrating how TRIZ was able to locate an awful lot of usually good solutions to the 'better air-bag' question. An awful lot of air bag shaped gold, but unfortunately not an awful lot of 'protect passengers in **all** accidents' or, as one letter writer later observed, 'stop drivers taking increased risks as a result of feeling safer' shaped diamonds.

Some applied innovation researchers have suggested that problem definition – determining what it is we're digging for – should be given rather more of our attention than the then comparatively simple tasks of location finding and hole digging. Unfortunately, another depressing human psychological trait – our apparent need to be seen to be 'getting on with the job', to show some shovel-wielding sweat - often means we don't give problem definition nearly enough of the attention it in fact merits. Psychological Inertia, however, also comes into the problem definition equation. Psychological inertia is the thing in this context which says to us 'I've been digging for gold, I'm good at it, people have always bought the gold I find, I'm going to keep right on doing it'. It's the thing which tells us not to even think about the fact that people might one day decide what they actually want is something other than gold.

So, what's this hole-digging analogy stuff all about anyway? What has it got to do with Psychological Inertia? And what is there we can usefully learn from it? We submit three thoughts for your consideration:-

1) Effective gold seam location requires a map. The problem solving tools of TRIZ are probably the best mapping tools available anywhere. Awareness that there are 40 Inventive Principles, for example, and that **any** might be useful to solve a problem gives us 40 extremely effective means of defeating PI.

2) The image of seeing myself stuck at the bottom of a mile-deep, vertically sided quarry is the very best way I know of telling myself perhaps, maybe I've been caught out by the PI thing again, and that perhaps, maybe I'd better start thinking about finding myself a better hole to dig. There is always a better way.

3) Not only does Psychological Inertia try and prevent us from getting out of the holes we dig, it also tells us to assume that what we started out digging for remains constant. It often doesn't, and we therefore need to be aware of **both** problem definition **and** problem solution aspects of the PI problem.

4) Information Structuring – TRIZ and Mind-Maps™

Ask the majority of people to write a report and typically they will attempt to sit down and write it in a linear fashion – starting at the beginning and finishing at the end. A common symptom of this kind of method of tackling the task is that we spend an age trying to work out where to start. Another is that we will get part the way through writing a report and realise we have missed something out. What is happening in both cases is that we are asking our brain to carry out two functions simultaneously – 1) identifying what to write and 2) putting it in the right hierarchical structure and sequence. Most of us find it difficult to conduct both activities in parallel, rapidly becoming saturated by complexity. Mind-mapping™ is a means of enabling us to manage this complexity. It seeks to achieve separation between the 'identify' and 'sequence' functions. It has a particular relevance to the way we define and solve problems within and around TRIZ. It is not essential to the successful use of TRIZ, but is certainly recommended.

Tony Buzan (Reference 3.3) developed Mind Maps as an efficient way of using the brain's ability for structuring information and making associations between different ideas and concepts. Association plays a dominant role in nearly every mental function, and especially creativity.

To make a MindMap, we typically start in the centre of a page by focusing on the overall theme of a problem. We then work outwards in all directions in a branching manner to produce a tree like structure around that central theme. We can develop a hierarchical structure from main branches, to sub-branches to twigs and eventually leaves – each representing different levels of a problem or solution situation.

MindMaps can be usefully applied at a number of stages in the problem definition, problem solving and solution evaluation phases of a problem. We typically use them to help define a problem, analyse resources and constraints, and then provide a structure during the brainstorming of problem solutions. A typical application sees MindMaps being used to record the ideas generated in a brainstorming session. Using the main branches to display the idea concept, lower branches to show ideas, and twigs to record details about the ideas (for example – one of the main points about mind-mapping is flexibility of use) one can easily move between the different hierarchical layers of a problem and its solution possibilities. The MindMap can be enhanced through the use of images, colour, outlining / emphasis, shapes, icons, codes, patterns, and links. This large amount of structured information together with their associations can stimulate us to generate new ideas and associations that have not previously been thought of.

These attributes make MindMaps an ideal partner when using TRIZ for problem solving and inventing. At the end of a typical session, the MindMap is already sorted by area or concept, making it easier to produce a list for ranking, as well as providing a common basis upon which participants, if there are more than one, can see how the big picture is formed from the individual details..

There are several software packages that can be used to produce MindMaps, but the best MindMaps are often produced using pen and paper.

We can use MindMaps to present very large quantities of information in way which is both compact and closely allied to the way in which our brains operate. We can also use MindMaps at a more detailed level to focus in on a part of the problem or, to provide a structure when using the Contradictions and Inventive Principles parts of TRIZ. The following MindMaps (Figures 3.18 to 3.20), for example, illustrate the construction of a hierarchy of mind-maps concerning the classic TRIZ 'liqueur chocolates' case study.

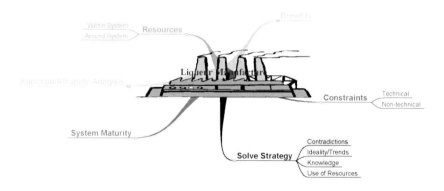

Figure 3.18: Liqueur Chocolate Problem Overall MindMap

The liqueur chocolates scenario, for those unfamiliar with it, involves a limiting contradiction associated with the manufacture of chocolate 'bottles' filled with a liqueur. The contradiction involves our desire to improve production rate ('SPEED' in terms of the Contradiction Matrix). To date we have improved speed by increasing the temperature of the liqueur filling in order to reduce its viscosity and thus improve the rate at which we can pump it into the chocolate bottles. Now we have increased the temperature to a point where we are beginning to melt the chocolate.

The first MindMap (Figure 3.18) illustrates our overall approach to the problem. Being a limiting contradiction, we have identified Contradictions, Trends and Knowledge as the three TRIZ tools most likely to help solve the problem. Used as a foundation, this MindMap serves to prompt us to ensure that we evaluate all identified solution routes rather than, as is common, simply applying one technique.

From this MindMap we proceed to another (Figure 3.19) which we have drawn to help us to think about just the Contradictions part of the problem. In the figure, we have identified a number of contradictions and obtained several Inventive Principle solution triggers. Again the Map serves as a prompt to ensure we consider all possibilities.

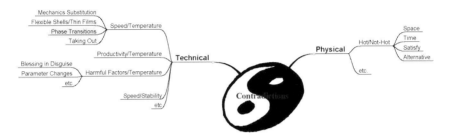

Figure 3.19: Liqueur Chocolate Contradictions MindMap

The final MindMap (Figure 3.20) represents one of the Maps drawn for each of the identified Inventive Principles. In this Map, the Principle is used as the focus for a systematic brainstorm to connect the Principle to the problem.

We would usually take the Figure 3.20 output alongside other similar pictures obtained for other Principles and cascade it upwards to the Figure 3.19 Map until we have explored all of the previously identified branches. Similarly we would cascade the completed Figure 3.19 Map back up to the Figure 3.18 Map along with the other Maps constructed for Trends and Knowledge, until we are able to complete all of the Figure 3.18 branches.

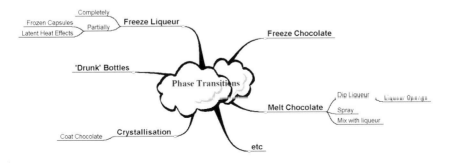

Figure 3.20: Liqueur Chocolate Inventive Principle MindMap

Our brains love solutions and are highly prone to diversion when someone in a brainstorming session derives a 'good idea'. This is an inevitable part of the problem solving process. The framework offered by MindMaps gives us a structured road-map of all the solution routes for a given problem, and thus allows us to maintain a systematic problem solving approach when we wish to return from the euphoria of one good solution in order to continue the search for other – possibly stronger – solutions.

MindMaps can be used with TRIZ and other tools help generate further solutions that you would not otherwise have thought about. In do so it provides a suitable means to record and provide a framework for the ideas and solutions generated during the working sessions. Using the MindMap to group concepts and ideas can help to trigger further ideas and solutions.

Those wishing to find more details about the combined use of TRIZ and Mind-mapping may wish to refer to Reference 3.7.

5) Group Psychology

If the problems of harnessing individual creativity are still largely intractable, issues concerning the effectiveness or otherwise of individuals working together are an order of magnitude more so.

The Six Hats™ idea is an attempt to ensure alignment of thinking modes during a group session ("everybody switch to green hat mode"), and like TRIZ does offer a way of segmenting highly complex phenomena into a commonly understood framework. Anyone who has tried to facilitate a group session, however, is likely to be acutely aware that some people are happier wearing certain colour hats relative to other ones.

In other words, as much as it might be desirable to force someone into green hat thinking mode, if that person is not used to or does not like that type of thinking, no amount of pressure will make that person don the hat. Different character types appear to be happiest wearing just a small number of the available thinking hats.

In the same way that there are an infinite number of ways of segmenting the world, the creativity literature describes a near infinite number of ways of defining personality traits and how those traits mix or don't mix with one another.

We do not attempt to be in any way comprehensive in reviewing these segmentation strategies, merely seeking instead to record that two such strategies have been shown to have a significant effect on group dynamics in creative problem solving situations.

The first is the classic Meyers-Briggs (Reference 3.8) personality profiling method, and the second is the Kirton Adaptor-Innovator (Reference 3.9) method. Both serve to highlight that groups featuring individuals with personalities at different extremes of the profile types (e g a group of extreme innovator types combined with extreme adaptor types) are highly prone to failure during jointly conducted creativity sessions.

The only real remedies to this type of group dynamic problem are firstly to try and select teams with an appropriate clustering of personality types during the relevant parts of the problem solving process, and secondly – more pragmatically in situations where we have no control over who is or isn't a member of the team – to segment that team such that different personality types are tasked with different parts of the overall process. For example, thinking about the thinking hat requirements at different stages in the definition selection-solving-evaluating, it is a good idea to place innovators in green hat tasks and adaptors in black and white tasks and not vice versa. Likewise it is often a good idea to conduct certain parts of the overall process (or at least the first iterations thereof) outside of the group setting. Function analysis (Chapter 6), for example is very difficult to conduct in a group setting as it is difficult to keep everyone actively involved.

Try to encourage people to experience modes different to the ones they instinctively migrate towards. In the short term you might not be thanked; in the longer term you will probably be rewarded with a more rounded team producing higher quality results.

What Do I Do?

1) Awareness of how the brain works is highly beneficial in maximizing the benefits of using TRIZ and other solution triggers; obtain this awareness and (more importantly) experience it.

2) Recognise that different parts of the systematic creativity process demand physiologically different modes of thinking, and take account of these differences.

3) Understand your personally preferred thinking modes and those of the people around you. Try to match the different preferences to the different requirements of the process.

4) Keep psychological issues in mind whenever possible during the systematic creativity process.

References

1) Mann, D.L., 'Case Studies in TRIZ: A Helicopter Engine Particle Separator', TRIZ Journal, www.triz-journal.com, February 1999.
2) De Bono, E., 'The Mechanism Of Mind', (London, Penguin, 1969)
3) Buzan, A, 'The Mind Map Book', (London, BBC Books, 1993)
4) Mann, D.L., 'Case Studies in TRIZ: A Re-Usable, Self-Locking Nut', TRIZ Journal, www.triz-journal.com, March 1999.
5) DeBono, E., 'Six Thinking Hats'. Penguin, 1988.
6) De Bono, E., 'The Use of Lateral Thinking', Penguin, 1967.
7) Care, I., Mann, D.L., 'Mind-mapping and TRIZ', TRIZ Journal, www.triz-journal.com, January 2001.
8) Bayne, R., 'The Myers-Briggs Type Indicator', Nelson Thornes, 1997.
9) Kirton, M.J., 'Adaptors and Innovators: The Way People Approach Problems', Planned Innovation, 3, pp51-54, 1980.

Creativity text bibliography:

10) Boden, M., 'The Creative Mind: Myths and Mechanisms', Basic, New York, 1991.
11) Cooper, L., Shepard, R.N., 'Turning Something Over in the Mind', Scientific American, December 1984, pp106.
12) Regis, E., 'Who Got Einstein's Office?: Eccentricity and Genius at the Institute for Advanced Study', Addison, Reading, MA, 1987.
13) http://www.buffalostate.edu/~cbir/ cbirgenb.htm

14) Hofstadter, D., 'Fluid Concepts and Creative Analogies', Harvester Wheatsheaf, London, 1995.
15) Mitchell, M., 'Analogy-Making as Perception', MIT Press, Cambridge, MA, 1993.
16) Dasgupta, S., 'Creativity In Invention And Design', Cambridge University Press, 1994.
17) Claxton, G., 'Hare Brain, Tortoise Mind', 4th Estate, London, 1997.
18) Root-Bernstein, R. & M., 'Sparks of Genius', Houghton Mifflin, Boston, 1999.
19) Gelb, M., 'How To Think Like Leonardo Da Vinci', Thorsons, London, 1998.
20) Levesque, L.C., 'Breakthrough Creativity: Achieving Top Performance Using the Eight Creative Talents', Davies-Black Publishing, April 2001.
21) Ramachandran, V.S., 'Phantoms In The Brain', 4th Estate, London, 1998.

4.
System Operator/9-Windows

"Start with the universe, any sub-categorisation under that level is purely arbitrary"
Buckminster Fuller

Although the concept of thinking in time and space and its importance in the overall context of both TRIZ and systematic creativity in general has already been described in previous chapters, the existence of the system operator or '9-Windows' tool warrants a chapter of its own. The chapter is placed here, before delving into the details of any of the individual elements of the systematic creativity process, as it is something that, if we are to use the overall systematic creativity process to any reasonable degree of success, we should be aware of and hopefully using at all stages of that process.

The chapter is split into five main segments. The first examines and describes the system operator in its 'classic' TRIZ form; the second examines the tool in a globally holistic sense; the third examines different ways of interpreting and using the classic tool; the fourth examines extensions to this tool that are often necessary in certain problem settings; and the fifth examines how the system operator can be further extended using other existing perspective-based creativity tools.

1) System Operator Concept

The System Operator 'tool' is a simple means of helping users to think in terms of TIME and SPACE. The basic principle of operation divides 'the world' into nine segments as shown in Figure 4.1. The central box of the nine – system, present – is the one our brains naturally migrate to whenever we are given a problem situation. In other words, asked to think about 'designing a better pen', our brains are likely to immediately conjure up the image of a pen ('the system') being used to write ('the present'). What the system operator tool is trying to get us to do is also think about the pen in the bigger ('super-system') context – the person holding the pen, the paper, the desk, etc; the smaller ('sub-system') context – the components of the pen, the ink molecules, etc; the pen in the past – manufacture, shipping, un-packing, preparing to write, etc; and the pen in the future – what happens to the pen immediately after we've finished writing, right through to it's disposal after it has run out. Figure 4.2 illustrates some of the main time and space features that we might like to consider when thinking more completely about the design of a pen. The point of this exercise is to help us overcome the psychological inertia of present and system level only thinking.

We will see this aspect of the tool covered in more detail in Chapter 19. For now, it is important only to be aware of this cruel 'present and system level box' trick our brain often plays on us when we are thinking about a problem situation, and how the 9-Windows tool can help us to overcome the adverse effects of that trick.

In order to use the 9-Windows effectively, the first thing we need to do is define what we mean by 'SYSTEM' and 'PRESENT'. In the pen example we defined the pen being held by a hand, writing as the 'system', and 'writing' as the present.

These definitions then allow us to define what we mean by super-system, sub-system, past and future. It is often a good idea to label these things on a 9-Windows picture – as illustrated in Figure 4.2. Not only does this allow our brains to see how we have chosen to segment a given problem, it also allows us to define the situation for others who may be able to help us.

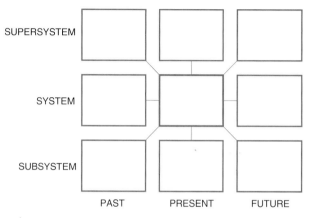

Figure 4.1: '9-Windows' of the System Operator

From a 'pen design' perspective, the system operator is trying to encourage us to think in a much more holistic way about our design task; thus designing a pen is not just about what happens when a user is writing with it, but about **all** of the other aspects shown in Figure 4.2 (and others we might also be able to think of if we were really in the business of designing pens).

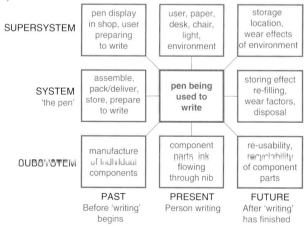

Figure 4.2: Example System Operator Picture for 'Pen Design'

The system operator concept is – as we probably won't be able to state often enough – used throughout the problem solving process (note: as per convention elsewhere in the book, we are using 'problem solving' as a short-hand for the whole problem definition, problem solving, opportunity finding, opportunity exploiting creativity spectrum). We should be using it when we are looking for resources, identifying constraints, specifying the design requirements during the problem definition process (see the problem explorer in the next chapter), we should be using it during idea generation – see the red-eye case study in Chapter 10 illustrating how we use the system operator to focus our thinking when connecting TRIZ solution triggers to our problem situation – and we should also be using it when evaluating our solutions.

An Alternative Perspective

The 9-windows of the system operator offer a simple and effective way of encouraging problem solvers to see their problem situation from different perspectives. The tool in its 9-windows form is, however, relatively crude in many senses. This is acutely evident when, for example, using the 'past' or 'future' triggers to prompt the problem owner to think about the problem in terms of time. Thus in the pen context from above, 'future' might mean a fraction of a second – e.g. putting the pen down – or it might mean several years – e.g. bio-degradation in a land-fill.

A simple way of encapsulating this kind of breadth of consideration is the expanded system operator idea shown in Figure 4.3.

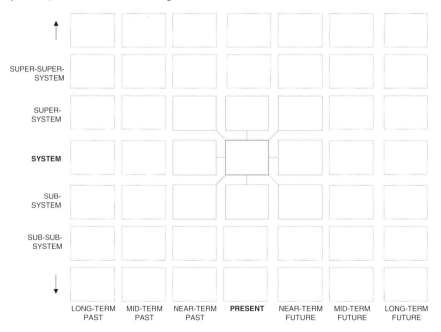

Figure 4.3: Expanded Multi-Screen System Operator

Viewed next to the 'object segmentation' evolution trend uncovered by TRIZ researchers, this kind of re-segmentation is an obvious step. The trend would further suggest that the segmented picture ultimately transforms into a continuum for both time and space considerations. In terms of 'space' such a continuum is analogous to a movie camera 'zooming in and zooming out' on the problem. In terms of 'time', this author has come across several highly creative individuals who effectively 'run a movie' in their minds, tracking the problem situation from its very beginning through to its final end. In fact the movie image seems to be quite an effective one for combined thinking in space and time – with the film running through time and the camera image focusing in or out on micro detail or macro scenery.

2) 9-Windows On The World

While the system operator has existed for some time within TRIZ literature (Reference 4.1), it is not clear whether the concept was first derived by TRIZ researchers or not. Certainly a form of the 9-windows – in actual fact, as we will see in the third section of the chapter, a more comprehensive form – was included in early NLP literature (Reference 4.2).

In this second section we attempt to relate the system operator to a global space and time framework. Rather than this being an attempt to draw any all-embracing philosophical conclusions, our theme is merely to highlight the changing perspectives obtainable during application of the system operator tool.

An 'All-Encompassing' Alternative Perspective

Taking the above 'movie' expanded segmentation idea a little further takes us towards a much more holistic map of the world. A 'complete' (as we know it today anyway!) map of space and time might look something like the picture drawn in Figure 4.4. Sticking with the idea of space being represented up and down a vertical axis and time progressing along a horizontal axis with the past disappearing off to the left, and the future progressing across to the right, as with the 9-Windows, but now expanding those axes to their limits, the figure shows a big time-space framework. The borders of our framework have been drawn to start with the big bang about 10 billion years ago, and an assumption that the future will last as long if not longer (no-one said the thing had to be symmetrical, right?), and, in terms of SPACE, to zoom in to the structure of a proton or electron, and right out to the size of the whole mass of galaxies spawned by the big bang.

The idea takes at least a part of its inspiration from the work of Charles and Ray Eames (Reference 4.3) and their seminal images of how our perspectives change when we zoom in and out from our very human level perspective of the world around us. Like the Eames' model, a logarithmic scale has been used. Firstly as a way of compacting a large space-time information onto a small map, but also because, as many investigators have noticed, our brains are rather better at registering order of magnitude changes than they are small incremental changes.

The figure has been drawn using meter and second scales, with some reference points as a guide – with, for example a year being just over $3x10^7$ seconds, and the emergence of life on earth taking place around 4 billion years (just over $1x10^{17}$ seconds) ago.

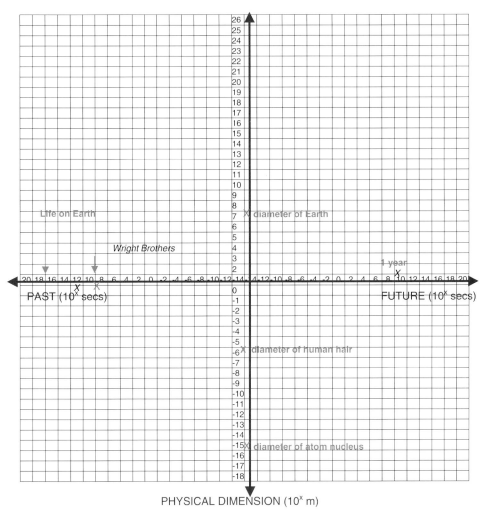

PHYSICAL DIMENSION (10^x m)

Figure 4.4: Comprehensive Time-Space Map

Taking this framework as our start point, we might begin to see how different scientific disciplines see their territory. A mechanical engineer, for example, is generally speaking dealing with objects designed and operated at the 'human' scale. In terms of space, the 'system' is thus likely to be confined to a relatively small range of geometric dimensions. Drawing this in terms of the 9-windows, the sub-system window might see the engineer zooming-in to micro-level consideration of things like tribological effects operating at or around the micron-scale, and zooming-out maybe two or three orders of magnitude to the surrounding environment. In terms of time, the 'present' is likely to mean fractions of seconds – e.g. thinking about transient effects – and a time scale of anything less than a millisecond is unlikely to have any apparent meaning. The 'past' and 'future' horizons are likely to be measured in terms of up to a few years – e.g. thinking about reliability issues.

Thus a mechanical engineers perspective of the 9-windows is likely to look something like that shown in Figure 4.5.

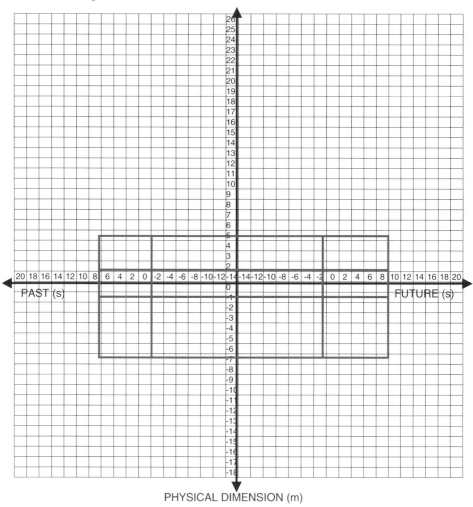

Figure 4.5: Typical Mechanical Engineers 9-Windows Map of the Space-Time Territory

On the other hand – and here is the main point of this section – other engineering or scientific disciplines are likely to have different time and space definitions of what super-system, system, sub-system, past, present and future might mean to them. Thus a physicist conceptualizing future computer chips is increasingly interested in time measurements of 10^{-9} or less – and so to them the line denoting the difference between 'present' and 'future' might be drawn much closer to the central axis, and the idea of thinking of 'past' or 'future' in terms of years might seem ridiculous. The chip design space-time map might look something like the picture shown in Figure 4.6.

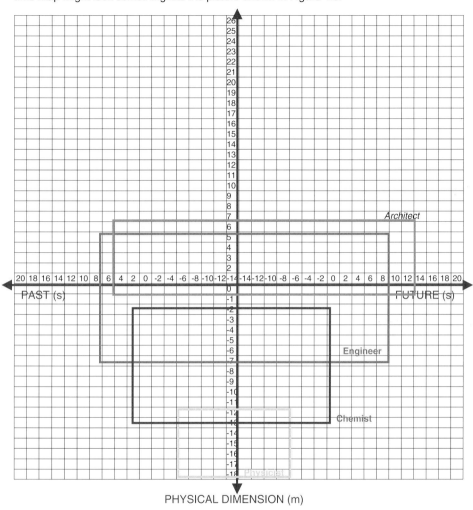

Figure 4.6: Typical 9-Windows Perspectives Map of the Space-Time Territory

Likewise, the map drawn by a cosmologist or an archeologist or a biologist or a chemist or a physicist, or a manager running a department in an organisation will be coloured by different perspectives. This is not to say that any of them are wrong, merely that a) they are different, and that b) in each case they are likely to define their 9 (or however many) window boundaries at different places. Vive la difference.

Furthermore, we are not saying either, of course, that we should all be thinking about the big bang when we're trying to design a new pen, far from it. What such a time-space map it is trying to do is get us to recognise that a) the actual world is much bigger than our personal perspectives on it, and, b) more importantly, that each of us has a potentially different way of thinking about where the boundaries are, and that someone else's perspective may very well help us to solve our problem. As we will see in the next section, this is particularly relevant as our knowledge heads further and further into the sub-system.

3) Between The Boxes – Changing Perspectives

One of the problems commonly associated with the use of the system operator tool emerges from the way we draw it or see it presented to us. Almost inherently in either situation, we are separate from the 9-Windows; we sit above them, looking down on them from a third dimension; we are outside, separate from the windows, looking in. While this can sometimes be a very useful stance to take (indeed in the fourth section, we will be examining this vital three dimensional aspect in some detail), it can also inhibit our understanding of the reality of a problem situation, and –we will hopefully see here – seriously impair our ability to solve a problem in the most effective way.

This second section is thus aimed at examining the consequences of us looking at the 9 windows as outside observers versus what happens when we are able to enter the windows and look at the problem situation from within.

One way to look at this is that we place ourselves 'in' each window and view the other windows from this new perspective. Something like the 9-windows picture shown in Figure 4.7.

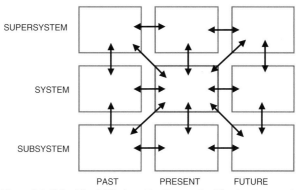

SUPERSYSTEM

SYSTEM

SUBSYSTEM

PAST   PRESENT   FUTURE

Figure 4.7: Using The 9-Windows To Change Our Viewing Perspective

If this picture is difficult to imagine (we do after all live in a three-dimensional world), some people find it useful to recast the windows as 'rooms' they become a part of, and from which they can see each of the other rooms – Figure 4.8.

Figure 4.8: Turning The 9-Windows Into 9 Rooms

In any given problem or opportunity situation, any or all of the viewing directions shown in Figure 4.7 may provide a valuable new insight into a solution. Rather than look at all 16 of the viewing perspective possibilities, we examine some of the ones most likely to be useful in the greatest number of instances. We start with a viewing perspective already likely to be familiar to experienced TRIZ users (otherwise, see Chapter 19) – that found through the eyes of the Smart Little People:

Connections With Smart Little People (SLP) Tool

The Altshuller derived SLP tool – like its earlier precedents independently derived from other sources – was developed as a means of helping problem solvers to empathise with the problem situation by 'becoming the problem. This is in effect changing the viewing perspective of the problem owner; the person (or rather the smart little people) 'becomes the problem'. The problem owner enters the sub-system and re-examines the problem situation from that new perspective – Figure 4.9.

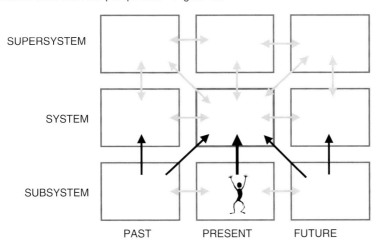

Figure 4.9: SLP Is About Entering/'Becoming' Part of the Sub-System

A classic example of this kind of empathetic viewing perspective change is Einstein imagining how someone traveling on a ray of light would view their surroundings; viewing the bigger picture from the perspective of a small part of it was crucial to the formulation of his theory regarding the speed of light.

In order to demonstrate the value of the SLP tool and the new viewing perspectives they force upon us, we choose to examine a problem somewhat closer to the practicalities of engineering design, that of designing components that are resistant to erosion damage. In trusting that readers will be able to connect a specific example to a much more generically applicable situation, we will examine the case of sand erosion of helicopter rotor blades (Figure 4.10).

Figure 4.10: Helicopter Flying In Sandy Conditions

This is a potentially serious problem for helicopters expected to operate at low altitudes in sandy or dusty conditions – the helicopter rotor blades rotate at very high speed and stir up a lot of air. If the aircraft is close to the ground, this air will cause sand to rise into the air, and potentially be struck by the high-speed rotors. The relative size and strength of helicopter rotors perhaps suggests that such impacts won't cause problems, but the reality of the situation is that the impact of hard silica-based particles onto a plastic and fibre based composite rotor at velocities of several hundred metres per second can cause rotor life to drop by several orders of magnitude.

As recommended by the classic SLP tool, Figure 4.11 sees us zoom-in to the zone of conflict – at a region of the composite rotor blade about to strike a sand particle at very high speed. Although useful, this view is still not going to provide us with too much assistance in developing effective solutions to the problem. In fact the view drawn is quite likely to encourage us to maintain an 'external' view of the problem. A typical solution response to this kind of problem view would be to stick a layer of protective material to the outside of the vulnerable rotor surface. This is indeed a solution we can find many examples of in the patent database, across many industries facing similar impact erosion problems. In the large majority of cases, subject experts know that this type of solution offers little more than temporary relief, and may in the longer term actually make the problem worse than if there had been no protective layer added.

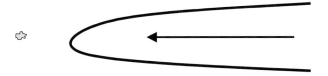

Figure 4.11: Helicopter Rotor/Sand Zone Of Conflict

The SLP view, on the other hand, encourages us to take on a viewing perspective in which we become the problem. In this case we become a group of smart little people sat on the rotor, watching a sharp edged rock approaching us at very high speed.

Given that situation, this author's response as someone looking at this big, sharp thing hurtling towards me too quickly for me to get away is three-fold; 1) I would like something to shield myself with, 2) I would like someone around me to help, and, 3) I and they should brace ourselves, and then try to absorb and/or deflect the energy of the incoming projectile. Thinking about myself surrounded by neighbours (I'm in the system, looking at the rest of the system now) I imagine a situation like that illustrated in the sequence of figures shown in Figure 4.12.

Translating this SLP solution concept back into the real world situation, I might then imagine a blade construction in which a hard outer armour layer is used to cover an inner layer which is able to 'give', elastically absorb energy and then use that stored energy to encourage the sand particle to be deflected away from the blade. This hard layer/soft-layer concept in fact turns out to be a protection technique used quite commonly within nature. It has yet to see any significant inroads into the word of engineering and so there is probably scope for the generation of intellectual property in the concept.

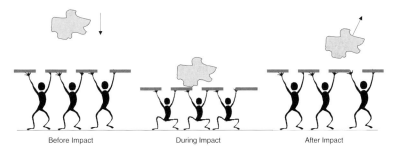

Before Impact   During Impact   After Impact

Figure 4.12: How I Imagine I and My Fellow SLP's Might Solve The Sand/Rotor Problem

What Happens If I Apply The Same Viewing Perspective Change in Different Windows?

So we have seen the 'becoming part of the system' concept produce some different solution perspectives via the SLP tool. What about when we place ourselves in some of the other windows and view a problem from their perspective?

The opposite of the SLP direction is the 'becoming part of the super-system looking in at the system' view. Or, 'what does the system look like, when I view it from the perspective of the outsider?' In crude terms, this perspective might be seen as that of a customer looking at a product. More importantly, from a problem solving perspective, it is not just about encouraging the problem solver to recognize that the super-system exists (which is what the classic 9-Windows tool is trying to do), but encouraging them to adopt the position of that customer and to see the system from their perspective. In some places, this is known as 'empathy'. To many the concept sounds so trite it shouldn't require mentioning. Unfortunately the plethora of 'bad' designs in the world suggests that problem solvers (or more likely the system they are constrained to work within) do not adopt this position as a matter of normal or even occasional practice.

Airports perhaps provide a good example. Most of the systems known as 'airport' appear to have little to do with empathy with the customer. This is especially unfortunate when thinking about airports we might visit in other countries for that establishment gives us our fast and last impression of the country. Anyone unfortunate enough to have to use airports a lot will probably feel that they are very much part of a super-system which has little to do with the smooth running of the airport designed by the architects and managers who organize how they operate.

What if there was a better way? What if the architects and managers saw things from the perspectives of the super-system?

- Would they think it was a good use of passengers' time to have them sitting doing nothing in a departure lounge and then moving them on to an aeroplane to do more nothing for several hours and then force them to endure another possibly several hours (a tie between Moscow and Atlanta for this author) passing through immigration?
- Would they recognize that passenger consumption of electrical power – for laptops, phones, personal stereos, etc – has risen phenomenally in the past five years but that battery power hasn't matched the change? There are a host of passengers who would love (and may even be willing to pay for) recharging facilities.
- Would they recognize that more and more passengers are more and more likely to use carry-on luggage and are therefore less and less likely to want to check their baggage if they can possibly help it?
- Would they recognize that many business travellers travel to get to meetings and that these travellers would be as happy to have that meeting at the airport as locating appropriate ground transportation (in an unfamiliar location) to get them to a meeting somewhere else?

And so on. Not to mention the 'empathy' discussions we might get into if we refocused on the system ('instrument of torture'?) known as the airliner.

Standing In The Future And Looking To The Present

A current favourite example of this kind of empathy comes from a possibly apocryphal, but nevertheless instructive tale relayed at a recent architecture conference. The story relates to an architect appointed by NASA to help think about the design of a possible future manned base on Mars. Such a job no doubt presents an architect with an incredibly enticing combination of freedom and new design challenges – with a good many of the boundary conditions found on earth (gravity, temperature range, atmosphere, etc) considerably altered. The architect concerned apparently reveled in the challenge and proudly presented his design solutions to all and sundry. Among the audience were some astronauts. They were not too enamoured of the chosen solution, especially since at no stage during the design process had they or the equipment they would be wearing been included. Funny but unfortunately also common (one famous architect – a different one by the way – has been quoted on more than one occasion as saying customers should not expect the structures he designs to be functional; his first and foremost role is to make a 'statement'. Oh dear.)

Other examples of benefits accruable from problem solvers standing in the future and looking back – just about every recycling issue currently known ("your customers are your grandchildren"), changing demographics (what will I think about the pension system in twenty years time when I might actually become the recipient?), maintenance issues (this author has direct personal experience of designing components and their ability to be maintained in the field only to find out when actually out in the field that it could be –30°C and the operators are wearing inch thick mittens on their hands), and, thinking about future super-system, a whole host of contradictions that emerge as different parts of society evolve at different rates.

In the next section, we follow one of the TRIZ evolution trends and examining the implications and opportunities arising when we explicitly add a third dimension to the 9-Windows.

4) Another Dimension

In the last section we discussed some of the problems that can occur when we place ourselves 'outside' the 9 windows of the system operator, and how we can overcome those problems. In this one, we look at why this separation takes place and how our understanding of this 'why' can influence a range of problem and opportunity situations. In examining this situation, we will also see how TRIZ can benefit by integrating similar but in many ways more fully developed tools from Neuro-Linguistic Programming (NLP), and how this integration can, in turn, influence how we define and solve problems.

Another Dimension

We use an isometric view of the classical 9 Windows – as illustrated in Figure 4.13 – to begin examining what might happen when we follow the advice of the TRIZ geometric evolution trend, and move out of the two-dimensional model perspective and begin to actively use the third dimension.

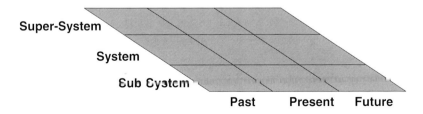

Figure 4.13: Isometric View Of The Classic 9-Windows

A useful first question, then, might be, what can we usefully use this third dimension to express? A very good answer comes from NLP and the work of Robert Dilts (Reference 4.4) who first drew a version of the picture reproduced in Figure 4.14. If the classical 9 windows describe a SPACE – TIME plane, then Dilts suggested that the third plane should describe the different levels of human awareness. The first plane represents physical actuality. Successive planes then represent a hierarchy of awareness of the way we perceive and are affected by that physical reality, from first the way we behave in response to the actuality, right up to how our identity is affected by the actuality.

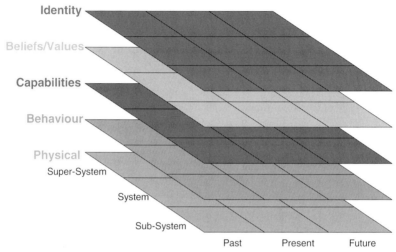

Figure 4.14: Turning The 9-Windows Into 45 Windows

A detailed discussion of the deep philosophical issues potentially raised by this picture is somewhat beyond the scope of this book however; the reference is a far better next step for anyone interested. We, on the other hand will see what we might extract from the image that might help us in a practical problem solving sense.

(By way of a short intrusion, however, Dilts actually uses first, second and third person to represent what the system operator defines as sub-system, system and super-system respectively. This too can add an interesting perspective to the way we use the 9-Windows, albeit one also beyond the scope of this article.)

Many engineers are instinctively comfortable with the 9-windows, 'thinking in time and space' idea. Indeed, the design of physical things is highly amenable to this kind of world-view. Many management and 'people' problems, on the other hand are not so amenable to successful treatment by such a two-dimensional perspective (this is not to say that engineers make bad managers of course!). Such 'people' related problems demand that all of the issues associated with human behaviour have to be considered if we are going to successfully define and solve the real problem. In the NLP view, this means looking at all five levels. In terms of management type problems, just using two would represent a significant advance on the way most problems are viewed and dealt with today.

The Map and The Territory
Using the bottom two of the five system operator 'levels' – the 'physical' plane and the 'behaviour' plane (Figure 4.15) – should straightaway get us to recognize that potential for

differences between the 'actual' and our perception of that actual. In more common parlance, the two planes represent the 'territory' and a 'map'; the territory is what actually exists, while the map represents an opinion of what the territory looks like. Sometimes these two things are closely aligned, and sometimes they are not. When they are not, we have the basis of a contradiction. And once we have a contradiction, we have the ability to use TRIZ and other tools to help improve the situation.

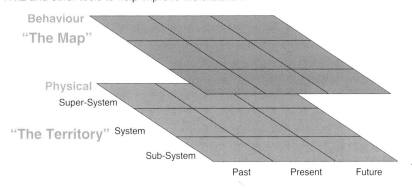

Figure 4.15: The Map Is Not The Territory – Difference Between Physical Plane and Our Perception of It

Common 'Map versus Territory' Differences

The literature is literally full to brimming with examples of contradictions emerging as a result of differences between map and territory. A particularly fine collection of examples may be found in the 'decoding the corporate culture' chapter in Reference 4.5. Author Eileen Shapiro describes the 'internal game':

Espoused Rule ('the Map')	Real Rule ('the Territory')
'Quality comes First'	'Ship product no matter what'
'Never sell the customer something they don't need'	'Get the order; whoever gets most sales gets the biggest bonus'
'We take the long-term view of our businesses'	'Miss your quarterly budget and you're dead meat'
'We have an open environment speak up if you have a concern'	'Accentuate the positive, hide the negative (unless you have a death wish)'
'Developing people is one of our top priorities'	'Managers who spend time developing their people are weaklings and aren't tough enough to be in the job'
'Improve efficiency…'	'…and then we can cut jobs'

Awareness of the 'internal game' contradictions is not a solution of course; but recognition of the map-territory contradictions is at least a start.

Marks and Spencer

M&S have traditionally positioned themselves at the high-end of the high street chain store market. The map of their customer base has traditionally consisted of the aspirant middle-class family, and their competitors are other high street chains. In terms of the classic benefits versus price trade-off of the retail sector, they hold a solid middle-ground position.

Unfortunately in recent times, it has become apparent that the benefits-versus-price map for high-street stores – the map drawn by M&S – is somewhat different from the substantially bigger retailing benefit versus price territory. The difference is highlighted in Figure 4.16.

By no means uniquely – in fact we can observe very similar maps drawn by companies in a variety of markets from household to body-care, from automobiles to airlines – the territory turns out to be a threat to the middle ground business. In the case of M&S, the territory actually also contains private-label goods at the low-price end of the benefits-price spectrum, and a number of niches, but most notably 'little luxuries' at the other end (see Reference 4.6 for more detailed discussion of this trend). In this bigger picture context, M&S is actually a rather small player, and, unless it recognizes the difference between their map and the territory, will get smaller as the private label and 'little-luxury' players gradually encroach further and further onto the M&S map as all associated trends say they will.

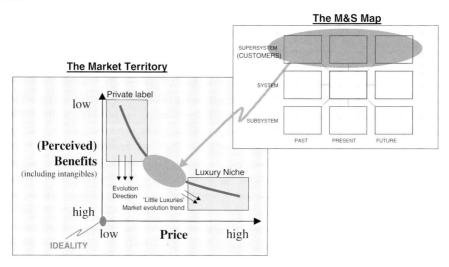

Figure 4.16: M&S - The Map Versus The Territory

(A simple yet surprisingly effective remedy to the type of situation M&S now finds itself in is to use Principle 13 and ask the question 'who doesn't buy our products?' The roots of increased market share usually exist outside the existing customer base.)

John – The Insensitive Line Manager

By way of another example of the problems that can be caused by the differences between map and territory, we look again at a well known TRIZ case study – the insensitive line manager problem first discussed in Reference 4.7. Essentially the problem comes about as a result of the causal map described in Figure 4.17.

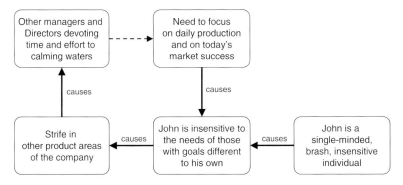

Figure 4.17: The Insensitive Line Manager

The core conflict is that John channels all resources under his control towards meeting the group's goals but he does this in a style that demoralises and renders ineffective other organisational goals. The previous TRIZ analysis detailed in Reference 4.7 presents a rather crude application of Inventive Principles to try and solve the contradiction 'John should be present and not-present'. As subsequently discussed in Reference 4.8, stronger solutions will emerge by obtaining a better understanding of the root causes underlying the contradiction. It is suggested here that understanding of the problem can be further improved by recognising the differences between not just 'map' and 'territory', but also that different participants draw different maps. The point is illustrated in Figure 4.18 below.

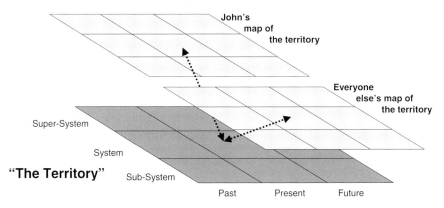

Figure 4.18: The Insensitive Line Manager – Multiple Maps of One Territory

Given this picture, it should become possible to provide a basis for allowing everyone involved in the problem to see what is happening. It also helps us to identify not just the 'John should be present and not-present' contradiction, but also other – perhaps more appropriately tackled – contradictions like John's map versus the territory, and everyone else's map(s) versus the territory.

5) Integrating Other Perspectives

Following on from the previous section examining the introduction of a third dimension dealing with aspects of perception, personal belief and relationships, the start point here assumes that this three dimensional space-time-'interface' (Figure 4.19) viewing system applies to all of the aspects here. For the sake of clarity of illustration, however, we will focus primarily on the conventional space-time plane seen in the classical TRIZ system operator.

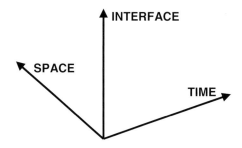

Figure 4.19: Three-Dimensional Space-Time-Interface System Operator Axes

Co-opetition

The Co-opetition idea of a 'value net' previously discussed in Reference 4.9 provides a first example of the 9-Windows being used in conjunction with other ways of scoping and framing a given problem or opportunity situation. The 'value net' idea discussed in Co-opetition (Reference 4.10) is of significant interest when thinking about a holistic approach to business oriented problems – offering a much more broad reaching view than would normally be the case. In effect the 'value net' appears in each of the windows of the system operator tool – Figure 4.20.

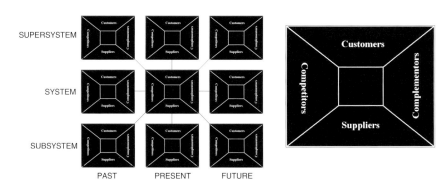

Figure 4.20: Combined 9-Windows and Value-Net Concepts

The importance of integrating the Co-opetition Customer-Supplier-Competitor-Complementor model with the 9-Windows emerges because, as Reference 4.9 suggested, the value net may well change with respect to both SPACE and TIME.

Strengths, Weaknesses, Opportunities, Threats (SWOT) Analysis

By way of a first extension to the co-opetition extension to the 9-Windows, Figure 4.21 illustrates a similar integration of the classic Strengths-Weaknesses-Opportunities-Threats (SWOT) analysis into the system operator space-time framework.

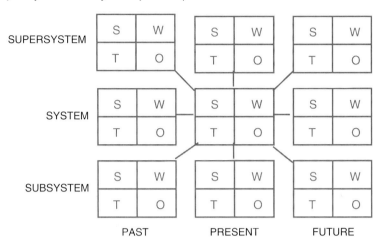

Figure 4.21: Combining 9-Windows and SWOT Analysis

The SWOT analysis idea is used across a wide range of technical and business areas as a means of scoping a given problem, opportunity or innovation situation. It attempts to get the person or team involved in the analysis to look at their situation from a number of different perspectives – namely, what are we good at, what are we not so good at, what are the things that could help us to become good, and what are the things that could stop us from becoming good.

Combining this thinking approach with the 9-Windows offers a number of additional useful perspectives. Of particular interest in many situations are the idea of repeating the SWOT analysis in the 9-Windows 'Future' positions and 'super-system' positions. With regard to the 'future' perspective, the idea of re-thinking the questions on opportunities and threats can be very important because it forces the team to think about not just what they think will happen in the future, but also what they think their competitors and the market will do. In a related manner, asking the same questions from a super-system perspective opens the eyes of the team to other industries beyond their own.

By way of example of both, if we put ourselves in the position of a hypothetical car manufacturer struggling with the idea of developing a commercially viable electric car then, thinking about 'threats' at the system level present (as a conventional SWOT analysis would), io likoly to get us to think about what other car manufacturers are doing. This is likely to put us into a psychological inertia hole (Chapter 3) that will focus our thinking onto hybrid vehicles and fuel cells. While this is undoubtedly necessary, it is far from certain that it is sufficient. Conducting the same SWOT analysis from the perspective of the super-system ought to point us at already viable electric transport systems like golf carts and postal delivery vans. According to Reference 4.11, it is more likely that these things will evolve and improve to take over the electric car market than anything developed by Ford or General Motors. Conducting the SWOT analysis from the 'future' perspective would further force the inclusion of solar energy and battery technology evolution (and, probably as likely, evolutionary limits), and, at the future-super-system level, global warming, choking of road systems and development of better public transport systems.

Thinking about the third 'interface' dimension illustrated in Figure 4.19, it is interesting to note that the idea of integrating the SWOT analysis into the different hierarchical levels of 'interfaces' (environment, behaviour, capability, belief, identity) and seeing how the analysis changes between different viewing perspectives ('the map is not the territory'), is already established practice in certain forms of Neuro-Linguistic Programming (NLP) – see Reference 4.12 for example.

Association/Dissociation

The NLP theme gives us yet another means of using the 9-Windows to better effect when we consider the strategy of association and dissociation. Reference 4.12 discusses the importance and benefits of being able to control whether we examine situations from either an internal (i.e. we are a part of the situation), associated state, or whether we chose to view the situation from an external, dissociated state (we are outside the situation looking in). In many ways this idea is similar to the 9-rooms idea discussed in the third part of this chapter. Figure 4.22 presents the basic idea more explicitly in the context of the 9-Windows tool.

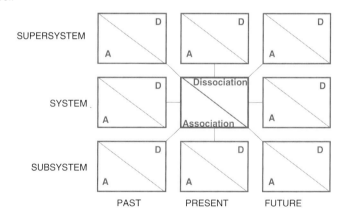

Figure 4.22: Combining Association/Dissociation and the 9-Windows

As described in the reference, the ability to associate and dissociate from any chosen situation is one of the cornerstones of NLP. The model already makes use of the space-time axes by, for example, helping people to solve (primarily) human-relations type problems by anchoring to past successes, and transplanting those anchors into future situations.

VAKOG

VAKOG stands for visual, auditory, kinesthetic, olfactory and gustatory. The acronym is a means of enhancing our ability to remember the five main human senses. The point is that, in a problem-solving context at least, we are often prone to not only forget any of the senses that are not already being used in the system. The use of all senses is important in many problem situations – hence the existence of Inventive Principle 28, Mechanics Substitution – (and its more closely related 'Another Sense' interpretation in a 40 Inventive (Business) Principles context), and the recent uncovering of a distinct trend in technical systems towards increasing interaction with more of the human senses (Chapter 13). The point in the TRIZ/9-Windows context is that if we recognize the five senses in not just the context of the current system, but also in the other 8 windows, we can often create new problem definition and solution opportunities.

The basic idea is illustrated in Figure 4.23 – which hopefully also serves to reinforce the overall theme of this article – that just about any of the problem situation framing tools available to us can be re-framed 9 times into the system operator. 45 times if we chose to use the fully three-dimensional space-time-interface window structure.

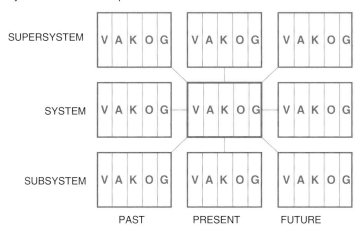

Figure 4.23: Combining VAKOG and the 9-Windows

Too Many Windows?

Anyone that has struggled through a SWOT analysis or an Association/Dissociation or any other analysis, will know that it can be very difficult to maintain concentration (will to live?) through all segments of the process. So what, therefore, are the chances of maintaining concentration over potentially nine times the number of segments as is being advocated by the system operator? Answer; it depends. If done in a single brainstorming session, the answer is probably as close to zero as makes any difference. If done in several sessions, or by splitting groups so that each covers different segments, the chances will increase markedly. The unfortunate truth according to a variant on Murphy's Law is that you can probably bet that the ones you chose not to analyse are the ones that contain the inventive spark that makes the biggest positive difference.

Summary

1) The '9-Windows' System Operator tool is a very effective way of encouraging problem solvers to recognise the importance of and to think in terms of TIME and SPACE. It should be there in our minds throughout our use of TRIZ if we are to get the most out of the method.
2) It is, however, a relatively crude segmentation of a continuous situation. Some people seem to think naturally in this continuous 'zooming-in, zooming-out' film-like kind of way, the rest of us still need some help.
3) The tool explicitly exists to help us avoid the trick our brain plays on us in which we tend to see situations from solely a 'system' level, in the 'present' context.
4) 'The map is not the territory' is a commonly described statement in the context of our frequent failure to effectively solve problems. The difference between the actuality of a situation and our personal perception of that actuality is often significant. We have seen here, however, how the 9-windows concept is a very effective tool for getting us to think in terms of time and space, but that it is also a way, if we're not careful, of also altering our map of the territory; the 'territory' is continuous in both time and space; it is not a series of window segments; the 'territory' is usually also much bigger than even our 9-windows perspective.
5) Different people will draw different maps of the territory. 'Different maps' represent the root of disagreement and contradiction. Awareness of these differences – through awareness of a third 'interface' dimension in the system operator – offers at least the potential of better understanding of how conflicts arise, and thus how we might apply TRIZ and other tools to resolve them.
6) Our brains seem to work naturally over only a small number of orders of magnitude of either size or time at a given time. The 9-Windows idea is useful in helping us to jump deliberately from one mind-set to another.
7) In its original form, the 9-Windows system operator, whether intentionally or otherwise, separates us from the problem; we are encouraged to see it from 'outside' each of the windows; we look into the windows. On some occasions this can be a very useful position to hold. On others, however, it can separate us from the problem in a harmful way. Awareness of this phenomenon is hopefully over half of the solution.
8) The SLP tool is also a way of deliberately forcing ourselves to 'become a part of the problem', but it only does so at the sub-system level; we become part of the sub-system and view the bigger picture from that perspective.

Final Thought

The system operator in whatever form we chose to use it is an important element within the overall TRIZ philosophy. Its presence is (or should be) felt in just about everything we do with TRIZ – hence the reason its image features on every page of this book. The idea of thinking in space and time – which is what the 9-Windows are there to help do – is not unique to TRIZ. The addition of a third dimension called 'interface' or 'relationship' offers an important additional thinking direction. Whether we divide things into 9-windows or 45 or even more, we are simply using the idea of segmentation to help us manage complexity more effectively than we otherwise would. What we have hopefully hinted at in this chapter is that there are many more ways of applying segmentation than just segmenting in space or time. Someone out there has already solved your problem; different people like to segment things in different ways. Some will be more helpful in certain situations than others, but ultimately, the best ones will be those that fit into *your* way of doing things.

The following chapters will demonstrate places where the concept of thinking in time, space and interface are important, and will make suggestions – usually based on the 9-Windows tool – as to how to incorporate the thinking being sought by the tool into the problem definition and solving process.

What Do I Do?

1)   Think about your problem/opportunity situation. Define 'the system'. Define what you mean by 'present' (these definitions can be largely arbitrary).
2)   Draw the 9-Windows. Based on your definitions of 'system' and 'present', define what 'past' and 'future' mean, and what 'super-system' and 'sub-system' contain. In terms of the time elements, it is useful to think in terms of 'before the problem' and 'after the problem'. In the case of process-type problem situations, this may require several time segments as opposed to simply 'past, present and future' as shown in Figure 4.3.
3)   Proceed to Chapter 5.

References

1) Altshuller, G., 'Creativity as an Exact Science', Gordon & Breach, 1984.
2) Dilts, Grindler, 'Neuro-Linguistic Programming Volume 1', Meta Publications, November 1989.
3) Eames, C. and R., 'Powers of Ten Interactive' CD-Rom, "http://www.eamesoffice.com/"
4) Dilts, R., et al, 'Tools For Dreamers', Meta Publications, 1991.
5) Shapiro, E.C., 'Fad Surfing In The Boardroom – Reclaiming The Courage To Manage In The Age Of Instant Answers', Addison-Wesley Publishing Company, 1995.
6) Popcorn, F., 'EVEolution', Harper-Collins, 2000.
7) Kowalick, J., 'THE TRIZ APPROACH Case Study: Creative Solutions to a Human Relations Problem', TRIZ Journal, November 1997.
8) Mann, D.L., Stratton, R., 'Physical Contradictions and Evaporating Clouds', TRIZ Journal, July 1999.
9) Mann, D.L., 'Laws Of System Completeness', TRIZ Journal, May 2001.
10) Nalebuff, B.J., Brandenburger, A.M., 'Co-opetition', Harper Collins Business, 1996.
11) Christensen, C.M., 'The Innovator's Dilemma', Harvard Business School Press, 1995.
12) Merleverde, P.E., Bridoux, D., Vandamme, R., 'Seven Steps To Emotional Intelligence', Crown House Publishing Ltd, 2001.

5.
Problem Definition – Problem Explorer

"In every assumption is contained the possibility of its opposite"
Pam Houston, How to Talk to a Hunter.

In this chapter, we examine one of the essential parts of the problem definition process. The 'problem explorer' is where we will set the context for the problem or opportunity under consideration and lay down the ground rules for what we can and can't do when we start to generate possible solutions. The problem explorer contains four basic parts:-
1) Benefits Analysis
2) Identification of Resources
3) Identification of Constraints
4) Identification of 'Sore Point'

The four parts can be done in any sequence, although it is useful to begin with a Benefits Analysis as this helps set the theme for all subsequent activities.

Appendix 1 at the back of the book contains an example pro forma usable for all types of problem and opportunity situation. Feel free to photo-copy this pro forma for every problem you intend to work on. The pro forma contains elements of Function and Attribute Analysis (Chapter 6), S-Curve Analysis (Chapter 7) and Ideality Analysis (Chapter 8). In this chapter we will just examine those elements of the pro forma relevant to problem exploration and scene setting.

We will detail each of the four parts of problem exploration in turn, before examining a typical example of a completed problem explorer analysis:-

Benefits Analysis

In this first part of the problem exploration process, we are primarily setting the scene for a problem situation. As may be seen from the front page of the pro forma (Figure 5.1), this activity requires us to ask a series of questions:

Firstly, it is often useful to clarify who is involved in the problem – who is the customer, who is the sponsor and who are the people working on the problem. The distinction between customer and sponsor is not always obvious unless explicitly stated. In most circumstances, the customer is the person (or persons) who will receive the output of the problem solving process, while the sponsor is the person paying to have the problem solved. Normally, one is internal and the other external, although, of course, there may be situations where they are both the same. It is important to note the differences that do exist because their motives might be quite different.

We will see whether this is the case when we look at the next groups of questions – 'where are we trying to get to?' and 'how will we know when we've got there?' It is recommended that you begin by answering these questions from the perspective of the customer, before re-asking them from the perspective of sponsor and the team working on the problem.

| Project Title | | Date | |

Project Sponsor	
Project Customer	
Project Team	

Benefits	Where are we trying to get to (what are the goals)?	How will we know when we've got there (measures of success)?
Sponsor		
Customer		
Team		

Figure 5.1: Benefit Analysis Pro Forma

It is recommended (but not essential – hence it doesn't feature on the standard pro forma) that we also think about the 'where are we trying to get to from a 9-Windows perspective. In particular, it is sometimes useful to ask the question 'where will the (customer/sponsor/team) want to get to in the future?' This is really just a means of checking the stability of the problem – and to find out if the solution is likely to change in the future. If the answer to the question implies that the problem and its answer *will* change in the future, we should contemplate re-answering the 'where are we trying to get to?' question accordingly.

Problem Hierarchy Explorer

'The customer is always right, except when it comes to defining the problem' is a common saying among TRIZ consultants. While intended to be flippant, it nevertheless makes the important general point that the human brain has a very strong tendency to believe the *first* defined problem is the *right* problem. The world is full of stories of companies and individuals spending inordinate amounts of both time and money solving what turns out to be the wrong problem. The problem hierarchy explorer is a way of clarifying the space around the originally stated problem definition. The tool framework is based on the work of Min Basadur (Reference 5.1) and the ubiquitous 'ask why 5 times' philosophy of root cause analysis. A schematic of the tool is illustrated in Figure 5.2.

The basic idea underlying the tool is the use of two questions 'why?' and 'what's stopping?' to respectively broaden and narrow the initially stated problem. The outcome of repeating these questions several times is a hierarchical list of problem definitions, from which the problem owner is able to select.

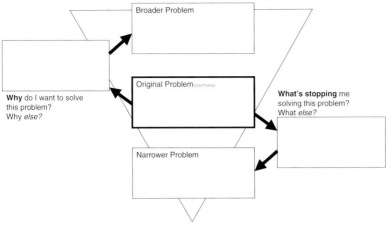

Figure 5.2: Problem Hierarchy Explorer Tool Pro Forma

A simple example should serve to illustrate the mechanics of the tool. Suppose someone approaches us with the problem that they have a bumpy ride to work. This becomes our original problem. We then use the pro forma to broaden and narrow the problem. An example is illustrated in Figure 5.3.

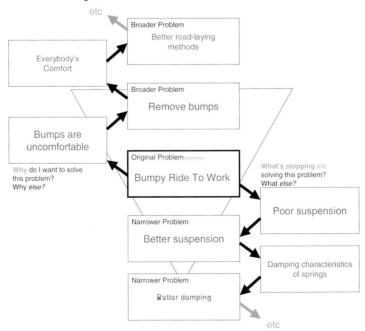

Figure 5.3: Problem Hierarchy Explorer for 'Bumpy Ride to Work' Problem

Thus we see the tool gathering a much more complete understanding of the problem situation and the problem we should eventually be tackling – is it about rebuilding roads, or is it about the detailed mechanics of damper design?

We can of course extrapolate further in both directions, and force ourselves to ask the 'why else?' and 'what else?' questions at each hierarchical level in order to broaden the space even further. The higher we go, the more we will approach the main useful function of what we're trying to do (in this case 'transport from A to work' – which in turn then leads to a still higher level question 'why do I need to travel to work'), while the lower we go, the closer we will head towards the micro-scale understanding of the way things work (e.g. next level down from the 'better damping' problem would be something like 'better hysteresis properties of damping fluid' or 'compressibility of fluid' or whatever else we can think of.

The main thing we will use to determine which of the problems the tool eventually ends up helping us define is the 'right' one will usually be determined by the constraints imposed upon us (for example, if in this problem we decide we only have a small amount of money to spend, we are more likely to solve the problem at the 'better damping' (buy a cushion) level than at the re-building roads level). We will get to the constraint definition part of the problem explorer shortly. In the meantime, our job at this stage is merely to explore the problem space.

(The 'Why-What's-Stopping' tool is also useful from a more general psychological inertia eliminating perspective at other times in the systematic creativity process. An example of the tool in action in this role may be found in Chapter 19.)

Identification of Resources

The next part of the problem explorer involves identification of resources in and around the current system or situation. The general identification of a resource is 'anything in or around the system that is not being used to its maximum potential'; which, especially when thinking about the TRIZ trends of evolution and the concept of 'evolutionary potential (Chapter 13), means there are usually a rather large list of resources locatable.

The main idea at this point in the systematic creativity process is to adopt a systematic approach to help look for resources. As illustrated in the sample resource identification pro formas in Figures 5.3 and 5.4, the search space is best segmented using firstly the 9-Windows tool, and then to look at technical (the things) and knowledge (the people) resource.

As a general rule, it is easiest to conduct this resource identification activity as a brainstorming session. It is also useful to treat the pro forma as a living document – something that lives alongside the problem and which is continuously added to as new resources are identified. In this way, it becomes a document that everyone in a problem team, for example, can use to share the problem in a coherent and consistent fashion.

There are no rules concerning what order to fill the boxes in, or that all boxes have to contain suggestions. What is required is that we at least ask the question for each.

It is useful to refer to the resource trigger lists in Chapter 14 to make sure you have considered all of the different types of resource available. Some find that it is also useful to examine the trends of evolution and to conduct an evolutionary potential assessment at this stage in the process also. Again, there are no rules to say this is right or wrong. What is worth saying, as a final thought on this resource identification activity is that finding something in or around the system that *really* isn't being used to its maximum effect, is an often very important step towards solving the problem. Resources solve problems.

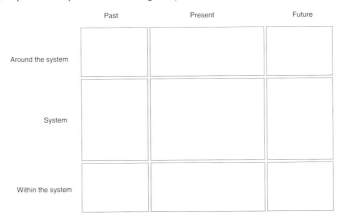

Figure 5.3: Technical Resources Identification Pro Forma

In the search for knowledge resources (Figure below), the main questions to be asking are 'has anybody already solved this problem before?' and 'who knows the real background to this problem?' This examination of people and knowledge around us is often useful in getting us out of another psychological inertia effect in which our brains sometimes trick us into thinking we have to separate ourselves from the outside world when we are problem solving. Someone, somewhere has already solved something like your problem. This part of the process is to help register the existence of both external knowledge bases and the local experts that may be able to help.

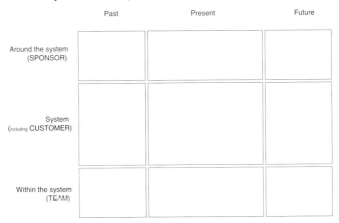

Figure 5.4: Knowledge Resources Identification Pro Forma

Identification of Constraints

Identification of the constraints on a problem situation form the next cluster of things we need to consider in exploring the problem space. All real problems come attached to constraints. These are the things telling us don't touch this, don't touch that, don't move this, only move that when, fit inside this space, cost less than that, and have the implemented solution by then. Some of them will be real and some perceived. Whatever, any real systematic creativity process has to take account of them.

The form of the constraint analysis is similar to that for resources; again the 9-Windows plays an important role, and again it is useful to distinguish between technical and other (in this case 'business') types of constraint. Figures 5.5 and 5.6 illustrate the recommended pro formas. In the case of technical constraint identification, we are primarily interested in things like components we are not able to change, functions that must remain unchanged, processes that cannot be changed and tools and equipment that cannot be replaced.

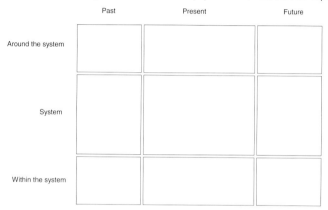

Figure 5.5: Technical Constraints Identification Pro Forma

In terms of definition of business constraints, we are primarily interested in the classic time, cost, risk and specification issues central to successful project management. We should also take due account of any constraints imposed by the availability (or absence) of skills. As with the identification of resources, there may be some constraint boxes that remain empty after the analysis has been completed; the point is that we have at least asked the question for each one.

One very important point concerning all constraints is that very often psychological inertia rears its ugly head and we identify things that, upon further analysis, turn out to not be constraints at all. It is crucial that the constraint pro formas, once completed, are used as a living document by a problem solving team, and that each constraint is periodically challenged for its validity. 'Why is this a constraint?' is a useful question to ask.

Use of TRIZ tends to make people believe there is no such thing as an unsolvable problem. The truth or otherwise of this belief could be argued for an eternity. What is clear, whether it is true or not, is that there are most definitely problems that *become* unsolvable due to the constraints we impose upon them. We should always challenge the constraints we define.

	Past	Present	Future
Around the system (SPONSOR)			
System (including CUSTOMER)			
Within the system (TEAM)			

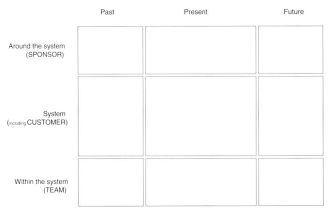

Figure 5.6: Business Constraints Identification Pro Forma

Identification of 'Sore Point'

The 'sore point' of a system is that element which prevents it from delivering the required benefits. The idea is analogous to 'bottlenecks' in manufacture and other processes. According to the Theory of Constraints (Reference 5.2), if we are looking to improve the throughput of a process there is no point in addressing anything other than the bottleneck. The same thing applies with the 'sore-point' in problem solving in general. According to TOC again, there is likely to be only one bottleneck in a process at any one time. It is not clear that this holds true for problems more generally, but it is nevertheless a useful model to help focus thinking on the crux of a problem and why we can't get to where we want to go. There are a number of techniques to help us to identify what the sore point of a system is. The majority emerge from outside TRIZ. The ones that need concern us here are:-

- Energy Auditing – for problems associated with system performance or efficiency issues
- The Theory of Constraints – for process related problem situations
- Subversion Analysis – for reliability centred problems
- Root Contradiction Analysis/Limiting Contradictions

Energy Auditing – is the process of analyzing the energy flows within and around a system. If the problem we are tackling is of the nature 'improve efficiency by x%', it is precisely this kind of audit we need to conduct in order to identify where the inefficiencies occur and thus where we should be focusing our improvement actions. By way of example, thinking of the problem of solar-powered cars, we can construct an energy trail as follows:-

       Energy from sun
       Conversion by solar cells
       Energy store
       Drive motors
       Transmission losses
       Bearing losses
       Tyre losses
       Vehicle drag
       etc

and by supplying quantified data quickly learn that a commercially viable solar-car needs better everything, but most significantly, better solar energy conversion, and better bearings – one perhaps more surprising than the other.

This example is one of an essentially sequential energy flow chain. This is one in which whatever we improve will have a net benefit on the overall outcome. Many systems, on the other hand – particularly manufacturing operations – often feature many parallel flow paths. In these situations improvements to some parts of the system will not result in a net benefit. In these situations, we require a different approach:

Theory of Constraints – includes a variety of tools and strategies for identifying the bottlenecks in a system. Often a simple critical path analysis will help to identify where the bottlenecks are, and hence what the sore point is.

Subversion Analysis – if we are dealing with what appears to be a reliability problem, our equivalent of the energy audit or critical path analysis is a failure modes and effects analysis (FMEA – Chapter 20). Again this type of analysis will contain both sequential and parallel routes to un-reliability and so we need to obtain a view of the big picture to ensure we pick out the issues that are limiting the current level of reliability most. If the reliability of a valve, for example, is determined by seat wear *and* stem wear improving the reliability of the least reliable of the two will improve the overall reliability.

Root Contradiction Analysis – many readers will be familiar with root cause analysis. All of us who are a part of an organization are problem solvers . . . and root cause analysts. As we come to our problems in an effort to control and prevent interruptions, obstacles, errors, and counter-quality occurrences, we are all looking for the same things: root causes of problems that when removed prevent the problem. So, whether our work is Quality, Engineering, Safety, Production, Maintenance, or just about any other function in the organization, we should be comfortable with the concept of root cause analysis, or whatever we want to call the task of finding the root causes and best prevention solutions to our operations problems.

It is useful here to clarify what it is we are talking about when we say "prevention solutions", or rather what we are not talking about. Fixing things, cleaning up, removing, reworking, redesigning, modifying, and fortifying, are not prevention and control steps. They are correction steps. These actions may or may not be a result of prevention actions, but they in themselves are not prevention steps. Prevention has to do with WHY the design was inadequate, WHY the machine needs repair, WHY cleanup is necessary. This is not to say that these correction-step responses are not important to the operation. Certainly we want to discover immediately when things need early repair. Root cause analysis should uncover such opportunities to remedy, but clearly, as our primary goal for analysis, we want to design out of our operation the need for avoidable repair, rework, clean up, and expensive redesign. We are trying to find something that someone can do to keep the problem from ever happening again. Obviously the act of cleaning up the mess every time the problem occurs is not prevention. We must instead design *prevention* and *control* into how we do things. That is what meaningful root cause analysis is all about.

So much for the theory. When we actually get down to the mechanics of root cause analysis, on the other hand, things have a tendency to get out of hand very quickly. Quite simply, root cause analysis requires data. Asking 'why' means we have to understand the system. To understand the system requires data. Very often the cost and time involved in capturing that data can be prohibitive.

One particular example that springs to mind for this author was a case where we were asked to work on regarding a manufacture operation to drill a row of 40 very small (circa 30μm diameter) holes simultaneously through a relatively thick (circa 15mm) structure. The basic problem was that the method used to drill the holes coupled with the length of the holes meant that some of the holes were mis-aligned relative to the others. During the course of finding out WHY this was happening a team of four root-cause analysts spent over 3 months each configuring and running experiments to try and get to the bottom of the matter. Four people times three months each is a lot of man-hours and a lot of money, never mind the cost of running the experiments and all the scrap parts produced.

The team were using a proprietary root cause analysis method (we won't name names) which is both rigorous in its approach and known to generate results in a good many instances.

The problem with it, and root cause analysis in general, is that it only stops when the root cause has been found. If this takes a few hours, this is not a problem. But if it means a man-year and still no answer, we should start to ask whether there is a better way.

The suggestion here is that there is indeed a better way. We call it 'root contradiction analysis'. The key similarity between this method and root cause analysis is that both are built on the question 'WHY?' The first key difference is that, while root cause analysis has a voracious appetite for data, root contradiction analysis requires only that we gain a qualitative understanding of what is happening in a system.

The second key difference – one even more important than the first – is that root cause analysis is a method closely allied to optimisation of processes, while root contradiction analysis is about recognising systems hit fundamental limits, beyond which no amount of optimisation will take them. In other words, you could spend an infinite amount of time gathering data to help optimise something that refuses to be optimised any further.

The Contradictions part of TRIZ is the only systematic way in existence for helping us to jump from one optimised system to a better way of doing things. Root Contradiction Analysis is about helping us to find the key contradictions we need to solve if we are to make the jump to that new system.

In the case of the hole-drilling example, the Root Contradiction Analysis took around an hour to establish that a) the current system was at the limits of its fundamental capability and the root cause analysts were simply pushing it over the edge of a cliff, and b) the root contradiction was quickly traced from the fact we knew that there was no problem when the hole length was only 12mm, or if there were only 30 holes to be drilled. The cliff the system had fallen off was a contradiction between the length of the drill and its stability.

Ten minutes later we had a segmented design solution. Two hours after that we had our first working prototype.

The example is not intended to say that Root Contradiction Analysis works miracles. We still have to do a lot of thinking – 'why' is the most difficult of the 5Ws – but at least we don't have to accompany it with a warehouse full of expensive-to-acquire data, and we know that solving contradictions is fundamentally good direction to travel in any event.

'The most important numbers are unknown and unknowable.' So said W.E. Deming. The quote is particularly relevant to traditional root cause analysis – which often has a seemingly never-ending appetite for data. Finding root contradictions is generally easier, cheaper and quicker than finding root causes.

Root cause analysis is sometimes great for optimising systems. If the system has been optimised to the limits of its capability (as many manufacturing processes have – thanks to years of 'continuous improvement' initiatives), no amount of additional optimisation will improve the result. The only way to improve a fully optimised system is to change the system. Solving contradictions is a good way to achieve this. Root Contradiction Analysis is a good way to find the right contradictions to solve.

Figure 5.7 presents a pro forma designed to help structure our thinking when it comes to finding root contradictions within a system. The fifth example problem in the chapter on Technical Contradictions demonstrates the process in action.

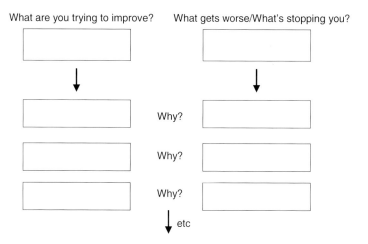

Figure 5.7: Problem Sore-Point Identification Pro Forma

When conducting this kind of root contradiction analysis it is useful to keep the 39 parameters of the Contradiction Matrix in mind in order to help speed the transition from specific problem to generic problem.

Two Final Points

Cruel tricks our brain play, part 67; most of us possess brains that long to get to the solving part of the creativity process. Problem definition might be 90% of the problem, but typically (in true Pareto style), we spend 10% of the available time on it. The problem explorer part of the systematic creativity process is probably the place where our brains feel the longing to switch to problem solving mode most acutely. You are strongly recommended to fight this urge. If necessary, do it on stages, or allocate different parts to different participants. Please stick with it.

A second common experience having reached the end of the problem explorer is that your brain (or collective brains) are bursting with problem solving ideas. It is usually pointless to ask people to ignore these ideas, and to get back to the process. The best strategy in this situation is to add another part to the pro forma called 'car-park'. This is a place where all the initial ideas can be written down so that everyone knows they have been registered and can be returned to later. A short – 10 minute – 'idea dump' session at the end of the problem explorer is highly recommended. If only to demonstrate how many more and how many better ideas will emerge when we do get back to the systematic creativity process.

And Then?

Having completed each of these problem explorer steps, we should continue to examine the other parts of the problem definition process contained in Chapters 6, 7 and possibly (hopefully!) 8. After that, it is time to head towards Chapter 9 in order to find out which problem solving tools are best able to help us solve the problems we have defined.

Before either, here is an example of the problem explorer in action:

Worked Example

Rather than try to explain the background to a problem and then try and show how that background expands into the problem explorer format, we will now simply provide an example of how the pro formas have been completed for a hypothetical situation in order to illustrate the mechanics of the process and likely depth of analysis.

Sheet 1 - Benefits

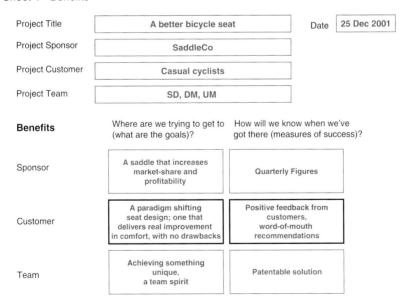

(Note the importance of discrimination between 'customer' and 'sponsor' – both of whom are likely to have different goals and different measures of success. The project should be aiming to satisfy all three benefit goals.)

Sheet 2 – Problem Hierarchy

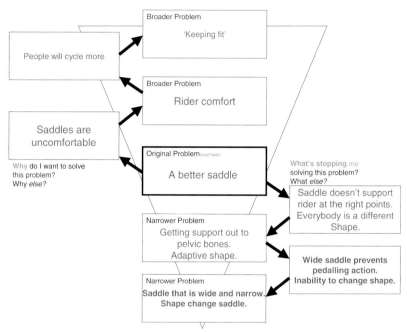

Broader Problem

'Keeping fit'

People will cycle more

Broader Problem

Rider comfort

Saddles are uncomfortable

Why do I want to solve this problem? Why *else*?

Original Problem (start here)

A better saddle

What's stopping me solving this problem? What *else*?

Saddle doesn't support rider at the right points. Everybody is a different Shape.

Narrower Problem

Getting support out to pelvic bones. Adaptive shape.

Wide saddle prevents pedalling action. Inability to change shape.

Narrower Problem

Saddle that is wide and narrow. Shape change saddle.

In this instance, the hierarchy model has helped to transform a vague start point – 'better saddle' into something more tangible. The two problems 'saddle that is wide and narrow' and 'shape change saddle' appeared to both be good problems to solve.

Sheet 3 – Technical Resources

	Past Manufacture, Shipping, Store	Present Cyclist using saddle	Future Reliability, Performance Retention
Around the system	Packaging, in-store presentation	Cyclist, weight, clothing, position relative to other parts of bicycle, bumps on road, gravity, side-forces, torque forces, air, tyres, lights, saddle-bag, space underneath saddle, space at side of cyclist	Sunlight, rain, elements, different riders, change in rider shape, weight,
System 'The saddle plus seat post'	Tooling	Seat-post, seat-post attachment, padding, bag attachment, nose	Fatigue, plastic deformation, leaks, wear, friction
Within the system	Selection of materials	Gel-filling, PVC coating, aluminium frame, plastic trim, quick-release fastener, adjustment features, Interfaces between components	Gel-breakdown

Note that we decided to label what exactly we meant by 'system', 'past', 'present' and 'future' in order that everyone had the same mental image of what was what as everyone else. Note also how even (especially) the harmful things are also listed. In resources terms, 'even the bad things are potentially good things'. In this case, it was decided to conduct a preliminary evolutionary potential assessment on the saddle at the system level.

Sheet 4 – Knowledge Resources

	Past	Present	Future
Around the system (SPONSOR)	Knowledge from shop-floor workers design records, saddle patents, sales figures	Other 'comfortable seating' patents, 'support load' patents, competitor data	Sales projections, bicycle replacement threats
System (including CUSTOMER)	Previous feedback from customers, complaint letters, reject reports, test reports,	Customer trials, 'Working Together Team' design mtg	Market trends – mass-customization, little luxuries, selbstverwirklichung aging population
Within the system (TEAM)	Experience with rheopexic gels, test data on gels, plastics		

Sheet 5 – Technical Constraints

	Past	Present	Future
Around the system		No change to customer adjustment, no change to anything on bicycle, No change of handling characteristics	Upgradability
System	Not design X – which was tried 5years ago	No change to seat-post connection, no additional weight, no change in CofG, no increase of manufacture cost,	Increased duty due to changing off-road role
Within the system		Don't use Gel Y – insufficient Durability	Environmental acceptability of Gel Z ?

Thinking about 'future' constraints can be difficult, but extremely valuable. Think particularly about changes in legislation and availability of materials, etc.

	Past	Present (during the R&D project)	Future
Around the system (SPONSOR)	Take account of previous 'lessons learned'	6 months to market 'Right First Time' No new people 10k maximum budget In-house manufacture In-house test	Mid-life upgradable
System (including CUSTOMER)		Selling price no greater than present	'Money-back' guarantee
Within the system (TEAM)		Everyone has 50% commitment to other projects	Must produce 'lessons learned' log

Sheet 6 – Business Constraints

An interesting one here was that the definition of 'past', 'present' and 'future' changed relative to other sheets; here 'present was defined as the 6 months during which the new saddle development would take place. Also interesting was the fact that the initial perception 'what has the period beyond the 6 months' (i.e. 'the future') got to do with business constraints was proved incorrect simply by being prompted to ask the question.

Sheet 7 – Sore Point

Straight away, examination of the sore-points in the existing system clearly related to the fact that the saddle didn't carry the weight of the cyclist at the points on the cyclist's body (pelvic bone structure) where sitting loads are supposed to be carried. It was decided that adaptability of the saddle to different users was a secondary problem. The root contradiction analysis for the sore point problem was brief and looked like:

What are you trying to improve?   What gets worse/What's stopping you?

Width of saddle	Difficulty of pedalling

↓   ↓

	Shape of saddle

We will return to this saddle example briefly in Chapter 10 when we examine this particular sore point contradiction in more detail.

References

1) Basadur, M., 'The Power of Innovation', Pitman Publishing, 1996.
2) Scheinkopf, L.J., 'Thinking For A Change – Putting The TOC Thinking Processes To Use', St Lucie Press/APICS Series on Constraints Management, Boca Raton, 1999.

6.
Problem Definition – Function and Attribute Analysis

The devil lies in the detail.
Sherlock Holmes

or

"The Earth is moved from its position by the weight of a tiny bird resting upon it."
Leonardo Da Vinci

Function and attribute analysis (FAA) is one of the three essential elements of the problem definition process. It represents a systematic method by which it is possible to analyse the detailed workings of an existing system. Function analysis has its roots outside of TRIZ – with the first versions of the method emerging from pioneering work by Larry Miles (Reference 6.1) at General Electric in the late 1950s/early 1960s. The original Miles-based method recognizes the importance of function and functionality in the design of systems, and undoubtedly, offers benefits to users who are registering this importance for the first time. This version of function analysis can be seen as very much a first generation of capability – it is useful, but its use has not become widespread, because the benefits offered by the method are relatively small beyond the initial function comprehension capability. In this Miles-ian first generation function analysis method, the application process is principally about identification of components within a system, and the definition of the functional relationships that exist between each pair of components.

What can be viewed as a second generation of function analysis (Figure 6.1), emerged when the basic ideas contained in Miles' work were integrated into a TRIZ-based way of thinking. The major innovation to occur in this second generation is that as well as describing the useful functional relationships that exist between components within a system, the user is encouraged to also describe the harmful, ineffective and excessive functional relationships. This simple but profound addition transforms a tool that is 'useful' into one that plays a very big role in the problem definition process.

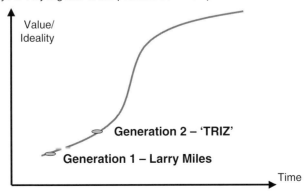

Figure 6.1: Evolution of Function Analysis Methods

Although we view this second generation of function analysis capability as important, it is unfortunately insufficient to allow us to offer it alone as a tool capable of helping in all problem situations. In particular, the method suffers from two significant problems:-

1) an inability to take adequate account of the **attributes** (for example, weight, volume, surface finish, corrosion resistance, etc) of a system component. The consequence of this is that main often key functional relationships are not identified in models.

2) an inability to take due account of the **time** issues surrounding a problem. The essential consequence of this is that the user does not have any value-adding means of defining how a functional model changes with time-based elements of the problem, and thus receives no guidance on how time-based problem solving strategies can be applied, and,

We describe here an evolved version of function analysis – now called 'Function and Attribute Analysis' – that addresses these issues and does in fact allow us to apply the method to a far wider variety of problem situations.

Attribute Modelling

Traditional function analysis modelling techniques allow users to describe the functional relationships between components, but do not take into account the fact that all components feature attributes (size, weight, smoothness, aesthetic appeal, etc), and that it is often the case that the functional relationships occur between component and attribute rather than component and component.

To take the simple example of the system around a piston in an internal combustion engine, a traditional function analysis model would allow the user to describe a functional relationship between piston and oil like 'piston breaks down oil' or one between the oil and an additive 'additive improves oil'. Neither of these descriptions, however, is very useful from a problem definition perspective, nor are they strictly speaking accurate. Far more accurate would be some means of ascribing the functional relationship description to attributes of the relevant components. Thus 'temperature of piston harms oil' and 'sulphur improves lubricity of oil' may be seen as more useful descriptions. Both actually relate attributes to problems.

The FAA method has been designed to allow users to describe such attribute related relationships more readily. In simple terms this capability has been introduced by making the function analysis tool more three-dimensional. In terms of a software implementation, this means clicking on a component to zoom-in and see it's attributes. If the FAA is being done on paper or MagNotes, the '3D' effect comes from either additional cards, or using the other side of the card. Figure 6.2 illustrates the basic idea.

The user needs to be able to connect functional relationships either from or to any combination of components and attributes. As such, the method is intended to not only provide more flexibility of operation, but also to allow fundamentally better access to problem root causes.

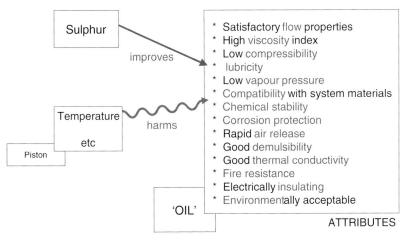

Figure 6.2: Use of Attribute Capability in FAA Modelling Tool

Time and Space –Based Function Modelling

Effective application of TRIZ tools requires a sound appreciation of space, time and interface issues. The system operator or '9-Windows' tool is one explicit means of achieving this kind of thinking in a systematically reproducible way. Traditional function analysis modelling strategies allow users effective means of describing space and interface-based relationships – not only how the 'system' is formed from sub-system components, but also how that system in turn interacts with the bigger picture 'super-system'. On the other hand, time-based problems are not well served by current models. This problem is frequently manifested as a single function analysis model in which several different time images are uncomfortably merged into a single image, often to the confusion of the problem defining team.

The FAA method has sought to overcome such problems by enabling the user to more adequately describe the function analysis model in terms of how it is affected by changes in time. As a minimum, the model assumes the user may wish to describe the functional model situation in the 'past', 'present' and 'future' time slices contained within the system operator. Like the system operator, this structure encourages the user to think about the precise meanings of the past, present and future definitions in the context of the specific problem – i.e. to think about the 'when's of the problem and to establish what the situation before and after the problem has occurred look like.

In many instances, the classic 9-Windows idea has been seen to be somewhat crude (see Chapter 4 for enhancements employed in the FAA methodology). This is especially the case for process-based problems where there may be a whole cluster of time-based changes in the problem situation. Many problem settings – especially those involving manufacture processes – have required the user to make use of many more 'windows' – such as 'distant past', 'mid-past', 'near-term past', etc – in order to properly reflect the problem situation. Chapter 4 further suggests that a more continuous examination of time-change effects – in the form of 'running a movie' of the situation – can further elicit useful situation understanding and problem definition information. The method handles this situation by encouraging the user to select as many different time-slices as are required to model the problem situation above and beyond the three default time-windows. In the interests of efficient use of time, the user is encouraged to think specifically about 'when' problems occur in order to enable function models immediately before, during and after the problem to be drawn rather than possibly drawing a potentially much higher number of models. A useful basic assumption at each time-slice is that the FAA model from the previous time slice is basically the same (Figure 6.3), with perhaps one or two changes to incorporate. This usually helps to save time when drawing the maps. In the case of software-based FAA tools, the software will copy maps easily; in the case of hand-drawn models, the availability of a photo-copier is likely to be useful.

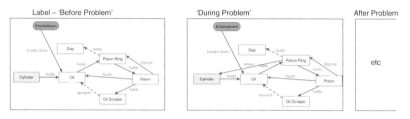

Figure 6.3: Time Modelling Capability of FAA Modelling Tool

As we will see later in Chapter 9, the method will use the differences that occur between different function analysis models as a means of both defining what problems the user should seek to tackle, but also what strategies would be most appropriate to help resolve each defined problem.

For now, the rest of this chapter is divided into four sections:

1) Describing the mechanics and particularly the sequence of events involved in constructing a function and attribute analysis for a simple system
2) Describing the mechanics and particularly the sequence of events involved in constructing a function and attribute analysis for a complex system
3) A case study example of FAA in action on a manufacture process
4) A section on optional enhancements to the process that some readers may wish to consider incorporating into the way they conduct their analyses.

The examples used are sequenced in such a way that they bring out any additional pertinent points about the dos and don'ts of function analysis as we progress through them.

1) FAA For A Simple System

We start examining the mechanics of FAA through the simple system illustrated in Figure 6.4. The system consists of two components; one an optical lens, and the other an abrasive block used to polish the lens.

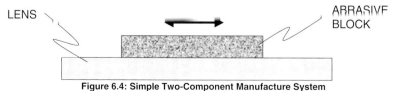

Figure 6.4: Simple Two-Component Manufacture System

The first step in producing a function analysis picture of this system is to identify the components present. In this case it is easy as there are just two. Each of the components is then drawn in a box.

The second stage then involves thinking about what the functional relationships between the different components is and defining that as a directional arrow between the component boxes. Again in this case, there are just two, and so, combining the first stage and this stage, we should end up with a function map that looks like the one in Figure 6.5.

Figure 6.5: Function Analysis Representation of Two-Component Manufacture System

The most important points here are to use simple noun-verb-noun relationships wherever possible (Reference 6.2 incidentally insists on three-word descriptions), and to express the relationship using active verbs. As we will see later, these rules will help us to tap into the solution parts of TRIZ more easily.

Something else which is very important to note at this stage is that we need to think very carefully about the functions present in a system. The function analysis tool is there in no small part to encourage us to think about the interfaces between things rather than the things themselves. This is important from a psychological inertia perspective because our brains are usually configured to think more about the things than the things-between the things.

If we think about the functions present in the Figure 6.5 system (particularly if we combine our thinking with the 9-Windows idea of zooming in and out of a problem), we should register the fact that the system is actually more complicated than the way it has currently been drawn. In actual fact, then, if we focus on the abrasive block, it actually contains two constituents which each have different functions. Those two constituents are abrasive particles plus a binding agent. As shown in Figure 6.6, their functions are, respectively, to polish lens and hold particles.

The distinction between Figures 6.5 and 6.6 can be crucial in using function analysis effectively, and the decision to dissect models into ever more and smaller constituent parts is often one that is hard fought.

Unfortunately there are no absolute rules on exactly how far to segment a model. As we will see later on in the book when the FAA for this lens polishing system is taken to the solution stage, we can get to good answers using either Figure 6.5 or 6.6 as our start-point.

That being said, one thing that is close to being an absolute rule – let's call it a 'good rule of thumb' – is that *the analysis should record all of the functions present*.

In this instance, the recognition that there is a 'hold' function as well as the main 'polish' function has meant that the model has had to be expanded to segment the abrasive block into its two constituent parts.

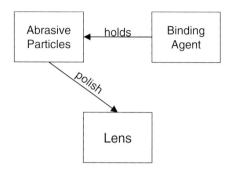

Figure 6.6: Function Analysis Representation of Three-Component Manufacture System

Another useful rule to apply when conducting a function analysis, is to define the Main Useful Function (MUF) of the system and to record this somehow on the FAA picture. This will be shown to be important because it encourages us to focus on the main issues of the system. In the system under consideration here, the MUF is the polish function. Figure 6.7 records this fact. It is important because, if we think about systems evolving towards ideality, we will see all of the functions around the MUF gradually disappearing. For example, in this case, the 'binding agent holds abrasive particles' function exists only because the abrasive particles are not able to hold themselves together. As long as there is a need for abrasive particles to perform the polish function, there will be evolutionary pressure to eliminate the secondary functions and components to leave behind just the MUF-delivering components.

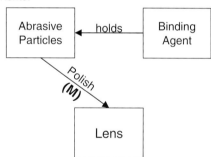

Figure 6.7: Recording of Main Useful Function (MUF)

Having achieved this picture, we have done pretty much what the first generation of function analysis would have us do. The next task required to turn this picture into a useful problem definer is to add in the system functions that are present, but that are the bad ones.

A good way to start this process is to ask the question 'what are the things happening in this system that are harmful?'

Asking this question for the lens-polishing system might get us to the image reproduced in Figure 6.8, where we have drawn red arrows to denote all of the harmful things present in the system. As with the first part of the process in which we were looking for *all* of the good functions, here we should examine each pair of components to identify *all* of the bad things.

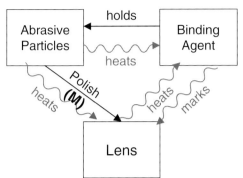

Figure 6.8: Function Analysis of Lens Polishing System Illustrating Harmful Functions

Next in the process of identifying the negative elements within the system comes the questions *'would I like more of this function?'* and *'would I like less of this function?'* Both of these questions should be posed for all of the functional relationships drawn onto the analysis picture. This is particularly important for the Main Useful Function – where we should often be finding ourselves answering the question 'would I like more of this function?' in the affirmative.

The two questions 'would I like more' and 'would I like less' exist to help us identify the insufficient and excessive relationships in a system respectively. We denote either on the function analysis diagram with either a dashed (to denote 'insufficient') or double (to denote 'excessive') line. Figure 6.9 illustrates the identification of an insufficient 'holds' function as a result of asking these questions.

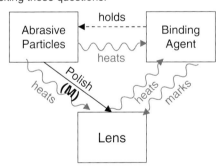

Figure 6.9: Complete Function Analysis Diagram for Lens Polishing System

As we will see later, this picture has helped us to perform a lot of problem definition work. It has done it by segmenting a potentially large problem space into a series of relationships between pairs of components – first positive relationships and then negative relationships.

The next thing segmentation strategy we should look at involves time issues. Remembering at all stages in the FAA process that our aim is the systematic definition of problems, when we begin to consider how time might affect the problem definition, we should be interested in at least three scenarios:

1) the system before any problem occurs
2) the system during a problem, and,
3) the system after any problems

Not all need to be relevant, of course, and by the same token (as we will see in the third example) three time points may be insufficient. For this lens polishing example, thinking about these three time issues should cause is to think about whether there is a time when the system does not exhibit the problems identified in the Figure 6.8 picture.

To take one example, if we think about a time before the above picture when the problems do not exist, we might see that the problem only emerges as we increase the speed of the polishing operation; and that at a lower speed (for example during acceleration of the process) the functional map looks more like that shown in Figure 6.10 below:

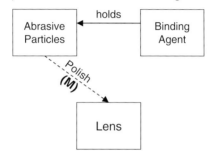

Figure 6.10: Function Analysis Diagram for Lens Polishing System Before The 'Heat' Problem

Again, this time-based thinking has helped to define the problem situation more clearly. The figure now shows that although the harmful 'heat' relationships and the insufficient 'hold' relationship have disappeared, the MUF has now become insufficient. As we will see when we return to this example from a 'select solve tool' perspective in Chapter 9, the two figures have helped significantly to identify not just a bunch of problems, but what approaches we should be applying to solve those problems.

2) FAA For A Complex System

So much for FAA on a simple, two component (although actually, it turned out to be three) system. What happens when we have a system with several or many components? How do we go about analyzing a system like the heat exchanger illustrated in Figure 6.10?

The simple answer is; exactly the same procedure as before – identify the components present; define the positive functional relationships; define the harmful, insufficient and excessive relationships; consider the time-variant issues. Figure 6.11 illustrates the resulting function analysis model. With respect to time issues, it has been decided that because the exchanger operates largely in steady-state conditions, only one time slice is required. If a 9-Windows analysis is conducted from the perspective 'do any of the functional relationships in this system change as a function of time?', we might discover (for example) that the flow impedance produced by the hangers does not cause a problem

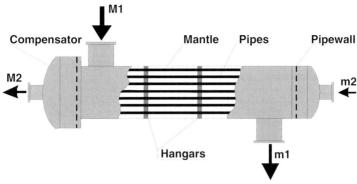

Figure 6.11: Typical Shell-and-Tube Heat Exchanger

during start-up when the flow rate is low. Or we may identify the fact that after several months of operation, there is a new harmful relationship 'M1 corrodes pipes' or 'M1 blocks pipes', we should draw a new functional model at these conditions. As it is, we have identified sufficient problems with the steady state model to suggest we should focus on these for the moment.

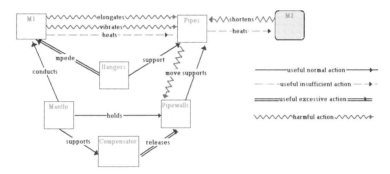

Figure 6.12: Function Analysis Model for Heat Exchanger

Interested readers may wish to examine Reference 6.3 to see how this model was used to generate a considerably improved heat exchanger.

3) FAA For a Time-Based Process System

The basic FAA modeling approach applies to process based problem situations as well as product scenarios. The method requires one or two additions however in order to achieve optimum management botwoon defining the system and transitioning it to the problem-solving parts of TRIZ.

We will examine a typical process-based problem situation in order to illustrate these additions. The process in question is a hypothetical representation of a chemical process in which two constituents, A and B, are mixed together to produce a third compound. A catalyst is added to the mixture in order to accelerate the reaction. After the reaction is complete, the catalyst is removed along with any un-reacted parts of the two constituents. These leftovers are re-processed in order that they may then be returned into the process. A schematic of the process is illustrated in Figure 6.13.

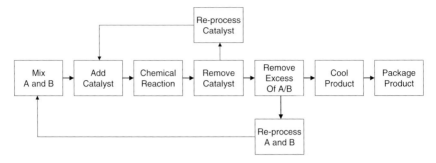

Figure 6.13: Schematic of Hypothetical Chemical Process

The general idea, then, when defining the FAA model is to construct a different model for each of the key time steps in the process. We will illustrate only the most important ones here. For any real problem, it may be necessary to construct an FAA model for each step. The FAA model for the first key step – the chemical reaction after the mixing of the two constituent chemical and the addition of the catalyst – is shown in Figure 6.14.

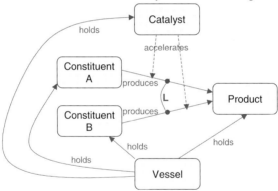

Figure 6.14: FAA Model at Start of the Chemical Reaction Part of Process

This figure indicates the first of the additional things we need to be aware of when modeling process-based systems:-

1) Constituents A and B both have a functional relationship with the product which has been labeled 'produces' in the figure. Neither function is valid without the other as the product is formed precisely because of the combination of the two constituents. The FAA model illustrates the linked nature of the two actions by the joining line labeled with an 'L'. This line is there to remind us that we cannot modify one function without affecting the other.

2) The catalyst is also interesting as it enters and leaves the system unscathed. Its function is to accelerate the reaction between the two constituents. In other words, it is there to accelerate the two linked 'produces' relationships between A and B and the product. There is no unique way of describing the functional

relationship of the catalyst in the system. In some instances, users prefer to connect an 'accelerates' relationship between the box representing the catalyst and the product. In the Figure 6.13 model, we prefer to recognize that the catalyst is actually present to accelerate the function to produce the product rather than the product itself, and have thus drawn the link from the catalyst to the 'produces' relationships between A and B and the product.

Figure 6.15 illustrates another important step in the process – this time at a point towards the end of the chemical reaction. Remember when selecting the times at which FAA models should be driven by when we can identify negative things happening in the system. In the case of Figure 6.14, the negative element was the insufficient action of the catalyst. In Figure 6.15, it is the fact that the chemical reaction has generated heat which heats the vessel containing the chemicals, which in turn causes distortion to the pipes.

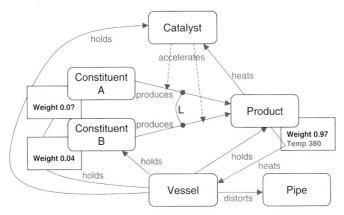

Figure 6.15: FAA Model Towards the End of the Chemical Reaction Part of Process

Note that the heating is caused by the temperature attribute of the product. This is another often useful way of describing this kind of relationship as it offers the ability to allocate the specific source of a negative effect in the system. Note also, how the weight attributes of the two constituents and the product are used to define the relative states of each. The '?' indicative of an attribute that we don't actually know a quantified value for.

Continuing on through the process, let us suppose that after the completion of the reaction, the soup of product, catalyst and any leftover constituents are passed through the pipes to the part of the process where the catalyst is recovered. Figure 6.16 describes the functional relationships present at the beginning and end of this separation activity.

Some of the 'heats' relationships likely to be present have been omitted for clarity.

The main point of showing this pair of models is to illustrate the disappearance from this part of the system of the catalyst. As defined within the figure, the catalyst separation process has been deemed 100% successful – and hence there is no catalyst entering the pipes exiting from the separator. Referring to the overall process map from Figure 6.13, we might chose to draw another FAA model for the catalyst re-processing operation. If the separation operation also removes some of either the un-reacted constituents or the product, then note that the attributes can be used to reflect the amounts of each present in the system.

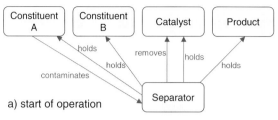

a) start of operation

b) end of operation

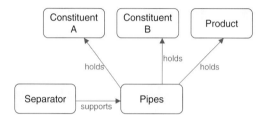

Figure 6.16: FAA Models at the Start and End of the 'Separate Catalyst' Part of the Process

The problem solver would continue to construct other FAA models to represent other parts of the process. We, having made the necessary points about the recommended conventions defining what happens when objects combine or separate, or when objects interact with functions (as opposed to other objects), or when it is the attributes of an object which interact with other components. In short, what this model is intended to illustrate is that functional relationship arrows don't have to just show connections between the components within a system.

Taken together the last three examples should provide a sufficient description of the mechanics of FAA analysis to allow us to construct models for any type of problem situation. Let us no take a look at some of the optional things we might also do to help improve the problem definition information the FAA tool can provide:

4) Optional Enhancements

a) Functional Hierarchies

A simple thought to enhance the information within an FAA is that instead of placing components at random on the page/screen, there are advantages in arranging things in such a way that they communicate more useful information with little if any extra effort, and quite possibly offer even greater structure to the way in which the function analysis process is conducted.

A 'normal' FAA picture might look something like the one shown in the second case study example (Figure 6.12). That picture was constructed using the usual sequence of 1) define components, 2) define the positive functional relationships existing between each component pair, and, 3) define the negative functional relationships.

A revised function analysis illustrating exactly the same information is reproduced below. The only difference between this picture and the previous one is that this new analysis has been conducted after taking into account the idea of functional hierarchy.

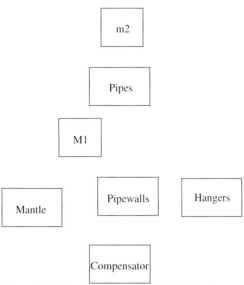

Figure 6.17: Hierarchical Component Structure for Heat Exchanger FAA Model

The revised analysis encourages the user to think more carefully about the functionality of a system. It begins this process by asking what with Main Useful Function (MUF) is. In the case of this heat exchanger example, the MUF is 'pipes heat M2'. This becomes the startpoint for the functional hierarchy – every other function contained in the system existing to serve this one. At the next level down, for example, it is clear that the MUF requires 'M1 heats pipes' to be performed, and likewise (in the current system), the hangers are required to support the pipes.

The completed hierarchical function analysis is useful from several perspectives: At a first most basic level, it has provided more structure to the way the analysis has been conducted, and will consequently offer ease of reading benefits because fewer lines will intersect one another. At a more important level, the functional hierarchy presents a likely sequence for trimming of components from the system – those at the bottom end of the hierarchy being much more likely to be 'trimmable' (Chapter 17) than those at the top.

A useful image to compare with here is the one we often use when thinking about Ideality and the way in which systems evolve. Windscreen wipers are a good example of this sort of hierarchy in action – see Figure 6.18.

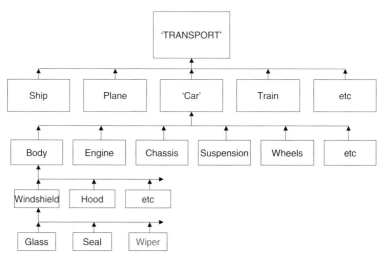

Figure 6.18: Windshield Wipers as Part of the System 'Transport'

Ideality tells us that if the Ideal Final Result windscreen wiper is 'clean windscreens without any wipers', then the most likely way to achieve that IFR will come by having something else already in the system performing the function. In the terms of the hierarchy, it is most likely that such a 'something' will reside somewhere higher up the hierarchical tree.

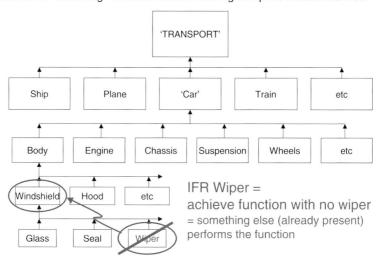

Figure 6.19: Windshield Wipers Likely To Be Replaced By Something at a Higher Level In the System Hierarchy

As shown in Figure 6.19 above, a very useful image to then keep in mind is that things lower down a hierarchy will gradually disappear as things higher up the tree are designed to take over the useful functions of the trimmed items. Thus, to take the example a little further, any replacement to the windscreen wiper is likely to exist only so long as the component 'windscreen' exists – at some stage, evolutionary pressures from the market willing, this too will disappear to in turn have its useful function performed by something higher up the 'car' component hierarchy – as suggested in the figure. See Chapter 18 for further information on this ideality-driven process.

The conclusion we can draw from this hierarchical method of constructing FAA models allows you to structure your thinking better, and gives you a picture that communicates more information for little or no extra effort.

b) Relationship Matrix

In situations where the number of components and functions within a system is large, it can very quickly become apparent that it is difficult to maintain a track on which pairs of components have been analysed and which have not. A simple remedy to this problem involves the definition of a functional relationship matrix. An example – for the heat exchanger case of earlier – is presented in Figure 6.20.

From To	M1	M2	Pipes	Hangers	Mantle	Pipe-walls	Compensator
M1	X		**Heats** (in) Vibrates Elongates				
M2		X	Shortens				
Pipes		Heats	X			Moves	
Hangers	Impedes (ex)		Supports	X			
Mantle	Conducts				X	Holds	Supports
Pipe-walls			Supports			X	
Compensator						Releases (ex)	X

Figure 6.20: Functional Relationship Matrix for Heat Exchanger Example

In addition to offering a checklist ensuring that every pair of components is considered (in both directions between each), the matrix offers the additional benefit of simplifying the process of seeing how many functions any given component delivers (count the number of entries along the row for the component of interest) or receives (count down the column).

c) Cause-Effect Mapping

A common criticism of FAA models is that it doesn't provide any definition of *why* things are the way they are. This has greatest relevance when we are considering the negative functional relationships within a system – why they are there, and what are the causes. The importance of this kind of cause-effect thinking is fundamental to the Theory of Constraints (TOC) (Reference 6.4) which has specific tools and conventions to help structure thinking in this regard. Interested readers may care to check out the Current Reality Tree tool contained in TOC, and discussed in a TRIZ context in Reference 6.5.

For the purposes of this brief discussion, we will make just two points. The first concerns TOC's recognition of the importance of identifying all of the relevant contributory factors to an effect or outcome produced by a component or system. The method talks about necessary and sufficient condition relationships. It is basically a mechanism for increasing understanding of a system, and particularly the relationships between components. Every adverse relationship in a system is caused by something. There may be several things. The necessary and sufficient thinking tool is a way of ensuring all are mapped and the inter-relationship between them are understood. To take a crude example, suppose we examine the 'M1 vibrates pipes' relationship from the earlier heat exchanger FAA model. A conventional root cause analysis of this harmful relationship would tell us that M1 vibrates the pipe because M1 is moving, it is turbulent, it is unsteady and it varies with time, and that it does all of these things because we require the device to be as small as possible, as efficient as possible and able to operate over a wide range of conditions. Although we can see these things as the causes of the harmful relationship, they alone are not sufficient to explain the situation fully. The key question is 'if just these things are present, is the harmful effect present?'. The answer to this question based on the causes we have thus far identified is no. In order for the 'vibrates' action to occur, it is not sufficient for there to be just a moving, turbulent, unsteady, time-variant flow M1; there must also be a propensity for the pipes to vibrate. In other words in this case there are two sets of conditions necessary to create the harmful function. While this is an almost facile example, it does hopefully serve to illustrate the point that our conventional thinking does not naturally encapsulate necessary and sufficient cause thinking, and that thinking about solving the problem we now have two roots to solving rather than just one.

The second point of this short section is to suggest that it is often useful to draw this kind of necessary/sufficient cause model either onto the FAA model, or by extracting and expanding segments, or, if you have access to a software tool, to incorporate the model in an additional screen connectable to each functional relationship in the system. In all of these cases, the model could look something like the image in Figure 6.21.

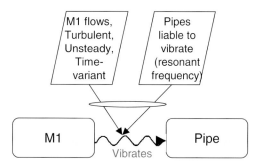

Figure 6.21: Necessary and Sufficient Causes Connected to a Functional Relationship

(The oval shape borrows from the TOC convention and defines that both of the conditions identified are necessary for the 'vibrates' function to occur.)

What Do I Do?

Function and attribute analysis (FAA) is one of the three essential parts of the problem definition process. In terms of managing complexity, it is the most comprehensive of the three. A completed FAA model presents an important lead into knowing how to approach the improvement of systems.

Successful function analysis modelling demands a process in which components are defined and then relationships between those components are established. In terms of defining the positive relationships, the method is useful because in many situations this will be the first time people have viewed the system under evaluation from such a functional perspective. In terms of the subsequent identification of negative - harmful, insufficient or excessive – relationships in the system, this is where the user is identifying where problems exist. Forced questions like 'would I like to perform this function better?', 'would I like less of this function?' and 'is it possible to identify anything harmful in the system?' for each pair of components in the system, and taking due account of the place time takes in affecting these components, are extremely important from a problem and opportunity definition perspective.

Follow the steps detailed in the case studies for simple, complex and time-based process systems in order to construct the FAA model.

A completed FAA model offers a link into the select part of the systematic creativity process. It is also a document that should live with the system as it evolves over time.

References

1) Miles, L.D., 'Techniques of Value Analysis and Engineering', McGraw-Hill Book Company, New York, NY, 1961.
2) Park, R., 'Value Engineering – A Plan For Invention', St Lucie Press, 1999.
3) Busov, B., Mann, D.L., Jirman, P., 'Case Studies In TRIZ: A Novel Heat Exchanger (Use of Function Analysis Modelling to Find and Eliminate Contradictions)', paper presented at 1st Int'l Conf. on Advanced Engineering Design, Prague, May 1999.
4) Scheinkopf, L.J., 'Thinking for a Change: Putting the TOC Thinking Processes to Use', St Lucie Press, Boca Raton, 1999.
5) Mann, D.L., Stratton, R., 'Physical Contradictions and Evaporating Clouds' TRIZ Journal, April 2000.

7.
Problem Definition – S-Curve Analysis

"A long winding road becomes the shortest distance between two ideas"
101 Corporate Haiku

The characteristic manner in which systems of all descriptions evolve has been observed by researchers from many fields of endeavour. Biologists (Reference 7.1), organisational analysts (Reference 7.2), engineers (Reference 7.3), economists (Reference 7.4, 7.5) have all recorded the existence of distinctly s-shaped evolution profiles when some measure of 'goodness' of a system is plotted as a function of time. The generic s-curve characteristic illustrated in Figure 7.1 is seemingly ubiquitous these days.

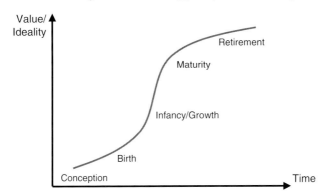

Figure 7.1: Generic S-Curve Characteristic

This s-curve profile is often described in subtly different ways, but all tend to indicate the existence of at least four of the 'conception', 'birth', 'infancy/growth', 'maturity' and 'retirement' stages shown on the figure. These subtle differences are really just symptoms of different researchers segmenting the same space in different ways. For the most part, these differences have little effect on what we actually do with the s-curves for a system once we have defined them.

The s-shaped curve is a characteristic that Altshuller also observed (Reference 7.6), and not surprisingly the s-curve features prominently throughout TRIZ and systematic creativity. In fact, it probably features even more strongly in the 'systematic creativity' process contained in this book than it does in any form of classical TRIZ.

The s-curve in any event is interpreted and used in a much more detailed manner in TRIZ than in any application outside of TRIZ. This chapter examines those differences in the context of an overall description of how the s-curve and s-curve family operates. This overall description is followed by a rationale on why s-curves are important – and particularly so in the context of problem or opportunity definition. Finally, we will examine methods of establishing where a system is positioned within a given s-curve and a given s-curve family.

S-Curves and System Evolution

In the majority of applications outside of TRIZ, the 's-curve' is usually seen to exist as a singular entity – such that any system has 'an' s-curve. In TRIZ, the concept is rather more multi-dimensional. Five dimensions in particular are important in the context of system s-curves and s-curve dynamics. The five dimensions are:-

    1) Labelling of X-axis
    2) Labelling of Y-axis
    3) Relative positioning of s-curves on Y-axis
    4) S-curve system-sub-system hierarchy
    5) S-curve system-function hierarchy

Labelling of X-Axis
The x-axis on an s-curve graph is almost always 'time'. Certainly this is the parameter we will always use when drawing s-curves in this book. The main reason for mentioning the x-axis definition at all is simply to remind readers that the actual time involved for a given s-curve and hence system may be a few minutes or a few thousand years, the timescale could be plotted linearly or (occasionally) logarithmically. Overall, time is not a good indicator of how mature a system is, because market forces drive so much of the dynamic of the s-curve with relation to time. By way of example, the filtration system used on most swimming pools has changed little since Roman times in terms of technology, but this should not be interpreted as meaning the system is 'mature' (it is in actually fact some considerable distance short of mature), merely that the market has not been demanding a better system for the last 2000 years.

Labelling of Y-Axis
There are various forms of defining what is used to define the y-co-ordinates on the s-curve graph. Within TRIZ, they are usually plotted as measures of ideality. Actually, the image of 'plotting' points on the s-curve is not really an accurate description of the mechanics of constructing s-curves, because only in very special circumstances will they be 'plotted' in terms of quantified values. Far more common is that the curves are drawn qualitatively. The definition of ideality used in this book is:

$$\text{Ideality} = \frac{\text{(Perceived) Benefits}}{\text{(Cost + Harm)}}$$

Other equivalent forms of the equation (most commonly; benefits/cost) will also result in curves featuring the same basic characteristic shape. As will the plotting of other forms of s-curve. The most common alternative y-axis labels involve extraction of elements of the ideality equation – most usually measures of 'benefit', but also 'cost' or 'harm' (actually 1/cost or 1/harm to ensure the important characteristics of the s-curve are retained).

As illustrated in Figure 7.2, it can be useful to think of the composite 'ideality' s-curve as an assemblage of elements of the ideality equation. Most importantly with respect to the plotting of s-curves of elements of the 'benefit' side of the ideality equation, it is common to plot the y-axis featuring just elements of the possible array of benefits in a system, and especially parameters concerned with the Main Useful Function (MUF) of the system. We will see this in the form of curves plotting speed for transport systems, or life of a pen, etc.

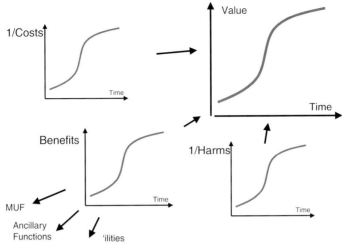

Figure 7.2: Different Forms of Y-Axis Labelling

Now, looking across all of the analyses done on s-curves, it is clear that there is insufficient evidence to justify the claim that any form of y-axis definition will give a precisely s-shaped curve. For a start, in many instances it is simply not possible to extract accurate enough numerical information. Fortunately, this will turn out to be unimportant from the perspective of us actually being able to use the s-curve concept to do something useful in the systematic creativity process.

One thing that is clear, having made the above admission, is that the common feature of all the forms of y-axis construction is that we do obtain the characteristic flattening at the top of the curve. This flattening is characteristic of the emergence of contradictions within a system, and its presence is one of the first indications during any s-curve analysis of a pointer towards which problem solving tools are going to be relevant to improving the system.

In summary – for the purposes of conceptualising s-curve dynamics, the idea that different ways of plotting the y-axis of the s-curve will all result in the same basic s-curve shape is a useful one to keep in mind. While this may turn out to be an over-simplification in some instances, what is clear is that the flattening of the top of the s-curve is generic. This flattening will help guide us during the transition from problem definition to best solution route.

Relative positioning of s-curves on Y-axis
The third dimension of s-curve complexity concerns the positioning – or more specifically the relative positioning of s-curves on the s-curves and in relation to one another. In very simple terms, every different customer of a system could well have a different perception of its overall ideality. Actually, wo oould take this a step further and say that every changing mood of every individual customer could change their perception of ideality. In other words, the positioning of an s-curve relative to any scale defining its y-axis is often extremely dynamic in nature – Figure 7.3.

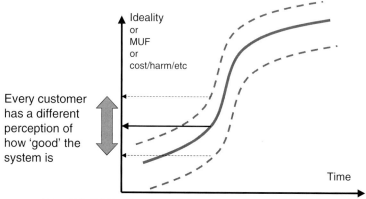

Figure 7.3: Relative Position of S-Curve Depends on Individual Perception

This dynamic curve-positioning phenomenon is of greatest relevance when we are considering the relative position of two different s-curves. How an individual views the relative ideality of two different s-curves will dictate their selection decision. In terms of large numbers of customers, the shifting relative positions of different s-curves will be the principle factor determining the timing of disruptive shifts from one to another.

Given an existing system A at a given time, t (Figure 7.4) any individual customer seeing an alternative system – s-curve B – may perceive it as a relatively more or relatively less ideal option. Different customers will have different perceptions of relative ideality – so that to some customers, option B looks better, while to others, option B appears inferior.

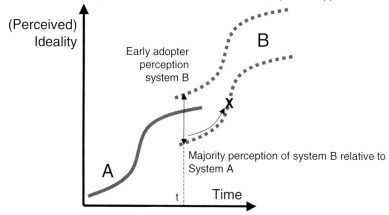

Figure 7.4: Relative Position of Different S-Curves Depends on Individual Perception

The basic mechanics of disruptive shifts from one system to the next are then largely driven by the customers who think the new system is superior and go on to buy it. These 'early adopter' purchases then provide the funds to support the R&D required to improve system B to a point (X) where its ideality is higher than the maximum level achievable by system A in the eyes of to all intents and purposes all customers.

By way of example, if we consider the relative positions of the s-curves for washing powder and, say, the emerging re-usable washing-balls (Reference 7.7), we might see that the inferior washing capability of the washing-balls means that for the majority of customers, this product has a lower ideality than washing powder. For those customers valuing environmental issues and who wash clothes to freshen them rather than because they are dirty, on the other hand, the washing ball may well have a higher overall ideality. If the washing-ball company gets their strategy right, the income they receive from those early adopter purchases will fund the R&D necessary to improve the washing performance of the product to a point where the relative ideality balance shifts from the washing powder to the washing ball. They will then present customers with a fundamentally better ideality offer than can be achieved by the washing powder.

S-curve system/sub-system Hierarchies

One of the most important aspects of s-curve analysis from the TRIZ perspective is that, unlike conventional ways of looking at s-curves where we normally think of there being 'an' s-curve, every component within a system has its own family of s-curves. Thus we should not just consider 'the' s-curve for, say, a diesel engine, but recognise that that diesel engine is made up of pistons, cylinder block, valves, etc – each of which has its own s-curve. This idea is illustrated schematically in Figure 7.5.

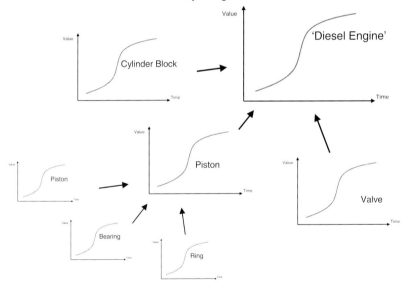

Figure 7.5: Basic System/sub-System S-Curve Hierarchy Model
(Note: Each hierarchical level is actually representable by a chain of s-curves –
only one – the 'current s-curve' – has been drawn at each level for the purposes of clarity)

The figure (simplified for clarity) basically suggests the fact that s-curves have a hierarchical structure, with the s-curve for the overall system emerging from the s-curves for different assemblies, which in turn emerge from the s-curves for their sub-assemblies; which in turn emerge from the s-curves for their components; and so on for as many hierarchical layers as are necessary to draw a representative picture of the overall structure.

It is worth noting that we can take this hierarchical structure a stage further by recognising that every manufacture process for every individual component also has its own family of s-curves. The same also applies to the design process used to design each component. This ever expanding hierarchy of s-curve families represents another example of recursion in action.

The same basic idea of s-curve hierarchy also applies when we add a time dimension to a problem. This is particularly useful when we are conducting an s-curve analysis for a process. Figure 7.6 illustrates how a hypothetical paper processing manufacture operation has been segmented into different constituent manufacture stages, and how each stage can be analysed in terms of position on its current s-curve.

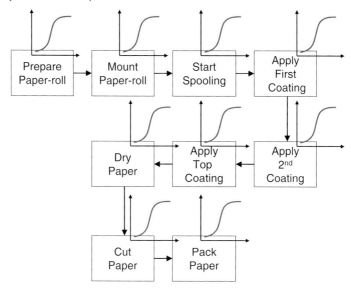

Figure 7.6: Hypothetical S-Curve Segmentation For a Process-Based System

S-curve system-function hierarchy

The other important hierarchical aspect of s-curves worth noting is the distinction between an s-curve for a system and the higher level s-curve describing the function that that system delivers. This is an important distinction to make because our perception of where we are on an s-curve (which we need to help guide us to the right tool to help improve our system) can vary considerably between the two definitions.

The issue is most simply illustrated by means of an example. Say we are in the business of designing tea-bags and are looking to see how to improve our current product. Asked the question 'where are we on the tea-bag s-curve?' we are likely to conclude (rightly) that the current system is at the mature end of the curve. If we make the shift from 'tea-bag' to the function the tea-bag delivers ('make tea') and ask the question 'where are we on the 'make tea' s-curve we are much more likely (rightly again) to conclude that we are some considerable distance away from its mature end.

A schematic representation of the difference between solution s-curve and the higher level 'function' s-curve is provided in Figure 7.7.

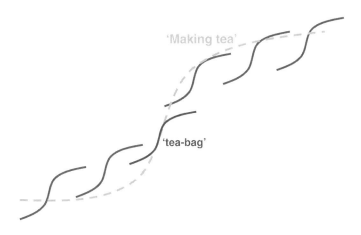

Figure 7.7: Distinguishing Between Solution and Function in Terms of S-Curves

The question being posed by this solution s-curve versus function s-curve distinction is quite simply 'are we interested in improving the current solution, or looking for other ways to deliver the function?'. If we look at how Chapter 9 would direct us in the tea-bag versus make-tea scenario – to contradictions/trends and knowledge/s-fields respectively – you can hopefully see how important it is to understand the distinction between solution and function.

Final Thoughts

If, during this description, any readers have been troubled by the lack of a 'decline' phase – i.e. a downturn after the highest value of the s-curve (Figure 7.8 below), the answer lies in two further basic mechanisms that can be useful in helping our understanding of the s-curve phenomenon:

1) It is actually very rare for an actual s-curve to produce a genuinely marked decline, because few producers will wilfully degrade the benefits produced by a system or increase cost or increase harm – and certainly not when the system is really at the mature end of the s-curve (see 2) below though). What is very common, however, is that customers' *perceptions* (the fourth element contained in our ideality equation) of the system can change. In fact they can change quite dramatically; and so the curve can, if we are plotting 'perceived' elements exhibit this downward curve trajectory. A good example here may be seen with the mobile phone when the public were told about the potentially harmful effect of microwaves from the antennae – nothing had changed about the *actual* ideality of the system (it was the same design as it was before the news broke); but there had been a marked drop in net *perceived* ideality.

2) There are, on the other hand, fairly rare instances when the curve trajectory does genuinely head downwards. These are usually instances where the s-curve that is in the process of replacing the existing system is seen to have an effect on the first

s-curve. A good example of this in action can be seen in cases where the new system causes sales of the old system to drop; which in turn causes the unit cost of the original system to fundamentally rise (manufacture cost and quantity produced being strongly correlated in the large majority of cases). As a specific example think of vinyl records being replaced by CDs – the now much lower volumes of vinyl meaning that that the unit cost of records is forced upwards so that those customers who still wish to buy vinyl are forced to pay more for it – i.e. they have experienced a genuine reduction in ideality of their purchase. Fortunately for the vinyl producers, this actual fall in ideality is such that their overall ideality is still greater than that for CDs for a certain customer niche.

As the two reasons (and particularly the first) have little to do with the actual engineering of the system under examination, we will plot all s-curves without the drooping 'decline' characteristic. Quite simply, from the perspective of engineering a better system (which is the main benefit targeted by the book after all), the decline characteristic is a red-herring.

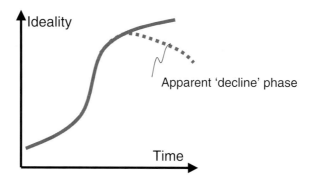

Figure 7.8: Plotting 'Decline' on the S-Curve

S-Curves and Problem Definition

Before examining the mechanisms through which we are able to establish where a system or sub-system is on its current s-curve, it is worth spending a few moments examining why we need this information and what we will do with it once we have got it.

As already stated, the principle purpose of conducting an s-curve analysis during a problem definition exercise is to enable us to better select which of the TRIZ and other problem solving tools are going to be of most help to us. (There are also secondary reasons; better understanding of the s-curve family for the system will help us to better prioritise which problems to tackle, and will help bridge the gap between technical solutions and market requirements.)

As far as linking problem definition to 'right' problem solving tool(s) is concerned, it turns out there are three areas of an s-curve that we can use to help determine what 'right' is:

1) If the system is at the beginning of the s-curve
2) If the system is at the mature end of the s-curve
3) Whether the system is before or after a 'point of maximum complexity'

None of the three require us to acquire precisely quantified definitions of how far up an s-curve we are, merely to identify whether we are close to certain characteristics. Conducting a 'serious' s-curve analysis of a system and all of its components can take several hours or possibly days. Fortunately, this is not the kind of depth or duration of analysis we require, and in fact, for the great majority of cases, what we need to answer the 'right' solve tool question should be acquirable in minutes.

The details of what we will do with the s-curve analysis information is covered in Chapter 9 – which describes the mechanics of the systematic creativity 'select' process. For now, we will simply register the need to identify the above three regions of the s-curves.

System at Beginning of S-Curve
Generally speaking, if a system is at the beginning of its s-curve we are likely to be solving problems involving *improvements* to the system. At the sub-system or component levels it may well be that there is simply no system present to deliver a function, or we may be in the position of looking to add functions. Identifying the need to add functions is an important element of the analysis at this end of the s-curve. An example of this type of identification, picked up later in Chapter 12, comes if we look at the diesel engine again, this time from the perspective of how the oil pumped around the engine tends to all fall into the sump if the engine is not used for a prolonged period. If we ask the question 'how mature is the sub-system responsible for keeping the oil attached to the piston walls?' we are likely to rapidly conclude that, actually, no such sub-system exists at the moment – i.e. the sub-system tasked with the function 'keep oil attached to all at all times' is right at the beginning (if not before the beginning) of its s-curve.

System at Mature End of S-Curve
By far and away the most important aspect of s-curves from a TRIZ perspective is the inherent flattening of the top of the curve as a system approaches fundamental ideality limits. The key word here is 'fundamental' – the limits of a current system are indeed fundamental, and the only way to exceed them is to change the system in some way. Identifying that we are at the top end of an s-curve is a sure way of telling ourselves that we need to adopt problem solving strategies that enable us to make these system-changing leaps. Manufacture processes (which also have their own family of s-curves) are particularly prone to be at this mature end of the s-curve – usually being the object of 'continuous improvement' initiatives that tend to optimize the system performance to the nth degree (see Six-Sigma comment in Chapter 22). Use of an s-curve analysis to justify the decision that further optimization will not produce increases in ideality can offer very powerful arguments for the need for different approaches; at the mature ends of an s-curve, 'optimization' is rarely the right problem solving strategy.

Point of Maximum Complexity
As detailed in the chapter on trends of evolution (13), all systems evolve along a path that sees complexity first increase and then decrease again. We need to know whether our system (and its sub-system components) are in the 'increasing' or 'decreasing' phase of their development, as the two phases require different problem solving strategies, some of which are contradictory and will fundamentally not work if we try and deploy them at the wrong time. A common scenario is that people will try and apply a TRIZ tool like Trimming (which is all about reducing part count) at a time in the evolution of the system when complexity is still in the 'has to rise' phase.

Finding Where A System Is On Its Current S-Curve

Classical TRIZ describes three characteristics that enable problem solvers to establish whereabouts a system 'is' on its current s-curve (Reference 7.6). These three characteristics are the result of analysis of patents and business performance. The first characteristic describes the correlation between position on s-curve and the number of inventions relating to the system; the second correlates position and 'level' of invention (in one of the five categories devised by Altshuller – Reference 7.6 again); and the third correlates position and cash-flow. Unfortunately, although the latter two appear to have a degree of validity in certain situations, they cannot be used to ascertain s-curve position with any degree of reliability in general. They are also very difficult to identify and calculate. As such, we will not discuss them further here. Readers are advised to check out either Reference 7.6 or 7.8 if they wish to know more about either. The first characteristic relating to number of patents, on the other hand, is a sufficiently reliable indicator to warrant inclusion as a tool to help identify where a system is on its current s-curve. Figure 7.9 illustrates the characteristic in generic terms.

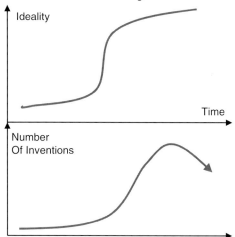

Figure 7.9: Generic Correlation Between S-Curve Position and Number of Inventions

Basically, the finding uncovered during the TRIZ research was that the number of inventions filed by an industry increase markedly during the maturity phase of the evolution of a system. A simple search of on-line patent databases is often sufficient to confirm the validity of the correlation for anyone wishing to observe it for themselves. The most useful correlation point to be gathered from the characteristic occurs when the number of inventions characteristic begins to decline – which is a sure sign that the retirement phase of the s-curve has been reached.

The curve characteristic is usually driven by competing companies within the industry attempting to squeeze the last few increments of improvement out of a system that is beginning to hit some fundamental limits. The rise in number of inventions can also be driven by the emergence of a disruptive new system s-curve and the resulting (ultimately futile) attempts of the incumbent industry to prolong the life of the original system. See Chapter 13 for more on the dynamics of disruptive technologies.

The health warning carried by the curve is that as the world of intellectual property changes (some companies/industries choosing to not patent, others to saturate the arena with large quantities of 'smoke-screen' patents for example), this characteristic may begin to shift.

Beyond this correlation there are other means of establishing position on an s-curve that come from work outside of TRIZ. We will discuss three in particular that are helpful and more reliable indicators of s-curve position than the original TRIZ research:
1) Technical focus of inventions
2) Design Process
3) Market and Competition Dynamics

Technical Focus of Inventions

The simplest means of identifying where a system is on its current s-curve is to examine the general focus of the intellectual property being created. Research conducted during the preparation of this book has identified a number of generic steps in the types of patents being granted for a given system over the course of its evolutionary life. The summarized form of these focus shifts is illustrated in Figure 7.10 below.

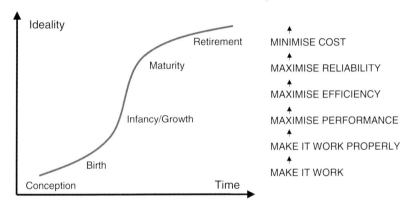

Figure 7.10: Correlation Between S-Curve Position and Invention Focus

The stages shown heading up the right hand side of the figure describe a progression from first getting the system to deliver its main useful function at all, and then adequately ('make it work' and 'make it work properly' respectively). Then when customers are receiving enough of the function, the focus shifts towards maximizing performance and then efficiency, and then, when the customer appetite for these has been sated, the focus is seen to shift again to reliability issues. Finally, when the system has delivered all of the benefits that it can, and efficiency and reliability foci have minimized the harm aspects of the system, the only remaining focus is cost.

Thus, by tracking these progressions (see also the related 'Customer Focus' trend in Chapter 13), we are able to obtain a reliable estimate of overall system maturity. In order to obtain the maximum confidence, it is necessary to examine sufficient invention disclosures to achieve statistical significance. This is most pragmatically achieved by focusing on the patents of the industry leader (if known). If the title of the patent does not provide enough information, it is usually possible to obtain a good idea of the inventor's motivation by reading through the section of patent text describing the background to the invention.

Patents relating to cost are often the easiest to identify – often mentioning improvements in manufacture processes and/or describing reductions in part count. In addition to helping identify the position on the s-curve, these patents are also strongly indicative that the s-curve for the system in question has also passed the point of maximum complexity, which, as described in the previous section will have an important role to play in our choice of problem solving strategy.

Figure 7.11 – also derived from research conducted for this book (Reference 7.9) – highlights the presence of considerable variability in the position of the point of maximum complexity relative to the s-curve. The position does appear to correlate to the relative complexity of the system – such that for complex systems featuring several hundred or more components, the point of maximum complexity will be towards the center of the s-curve, whereas, for a relative simple system, the maximum complexity point may be pushed well over to the right of the s-curve. This variation means that when we have obtained a reliable estimate of the position of the system on its current s-curve, we haven't necessarily answered the question about whether this point has been reached or not. Consequently the focus of patents on manufacture, cost reduction and/or part count reduction patents is the surest sign that the point of maximum complexity has been passed.

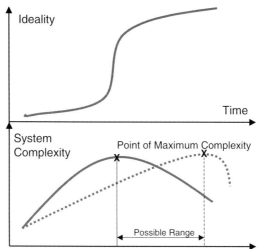

Figure 7.11: Variation in Maximum Complexity Point Relative To S-Curve.

Design Process

Although not an absolute rule, a thought that is well worth keeping in mind when analyzing s-curves – particularly the curves for the components within a system – is the role of the designer in the definition of those components. The job of the designer is very often one of pushing a component to the limits of its capability (with due allowance for inclusion of safety (fudge) factors of course). By way of example think of a designer designing a system to meet a certain duty and the parallel drive to achieve that duty with the minimum amount of material (equals minimum cost and/or minimum weight). This kind of limit pushing happens throughout design – often driven by the fight that takes place between the top half and the bottom half of the ideality equation.

The simple image that emerges from this design motivation scenario is that designers will tend to push their designs to the top end of an s-curve (Figure 7.12). In other words, they will design to the edges of a contradiction. This is particularly evident at the component level. When asking the question 'where is this component on its current s-curve?' therefore, it is always worth connecting the question back to the motives of the original designer – who, more likely than not, will have pushed the design to a limit that is fundamental, and which will only be excedable by changing to a new component s-curve.

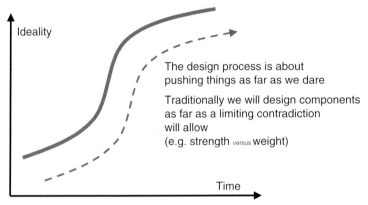

Figure 7.12: Design Drive Towards The Limit of System Capability

Market and Competition Dynamics

The original Soviet TRIZ researchers were not the only ones interested in understanding the dynamics of innovation. Reference 7.4 contains the fruits of a considerable programme of analysis into what the underlying principles of innovation are. One of the findings described in the book can be modified to give us yet another indicator to help us identify where a system (this time at the 'system' as opposed to sub-system or component levels) is on its current s-curve. That modified finding is illustrated in Figure 7.13 below.

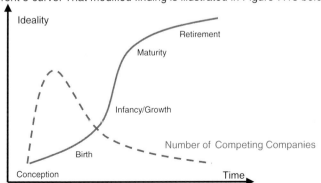

Figure 7.13: Correlation Between S-Curve Position and Number of Competitors

What this characteristic shows is that during the initial stages of evolution, there is a tendency for many players to enter the development race. Then as the system being produced gradually matures, a small number of 'winners' will emerge – either because the weaker companies fail, or because the ones with most money buy others. At the 'mature' end of the s-curve, the market is usually dominated by a 'big-5' or similar number. At this point in time, we can see the automobile industry very much in this final phase; while e-Business and the Internet are very much still in the explosion of companies phase – suggesting that automobiles and e-Business are at opposite ends of their respective s-curves.

What Do I Do?

This chapter is primarily about using s-curves to guide the choice of tools to help solve a given problem. Position of a system, sub-system or component on its current s-curve will affect solution strategy. There are three main positions we need to be aware of – is the system at the beginning, end or before or after its point of maximum complexity?

We do not need to be quantifiably precise when identifying these positions. The chapter describes a number of simple ways of determining s-curve position – either from a) number of patents/time period, b) technical focus of the current patents, c) the design process being employed, and d) the number of players involved in producing the system under consideration.

A secondary purpose of the chapter is to encourage the reader to become familiar with the concept of s-curves as they play an important linking role across the whole of systematic creativity.

If you are looking to use the chapter simply as a means of structuring an s-curve analysis and then identify current position on s-curve, we recommend you construct an s-curve hierarchy like that shown in Figures 7.5 and/or 7.6, and then use an on-line patent database in conjunction with Figures 7.10, 7.12 and 7.13 to identify position.

If you are looking to gain a broader understanding of s-curves and s-curve dynamics, you may care to peruse the whole chapter and check out the quoted references.

References

1) Hofbauer, J., Sigmund, K., 'Evolutionary Games and Population Dynamics', Cambridge University Press, 1998.
2) Handy, C., 'The Empty Raincoat, Making Sense of the Future', Hutchinson, London, 1994.
3) Burgelman, R.A., Maidique, M.A., Wheelright, S.C., 'Strategic Management of Technology and Innovation', Richard D Irwin Inc., Burr Ride, IL, 2000.
4) Utterback, J., 'Mastering The Dynamics of Innovation', Harvard Business School Press, 1993,
5) Nelson, R.R., Winter, S.G., 'An Evolutionary Theory of Economic Change', Harvard University Press, 1990.
6) Altshuller, G.S., 'Creativity As An Exact Science', Gordon & Breach, New York, 1984.
7) Re-usable washing ball – www.ecozone.co.uk

8) Slocum, M.S., Lundberg, C.O., 'Technology Forecasting From Emotional To Empirical', Creativity and Innovation Management Journal, Blackwell Publishers, Vol.10, No.2, June 2001.

9) Mann, D.L., 'Trimming Evolution Trends in Complex Technical Systems', TRIZ Journal, June 1999.

8.
Problem Definition – Ideality/Ideal Final Result

Today I am a small blue thing.....
Suzanne Vega

The concepts of ideality as an evolutionary direction, and the existence of an 'Ideal Final Result' (IFR) are very important philosophical elements of TRIZ and 'systematic creativity'. We discuss both in this chapter in the context of their applicability during the problem definition process. In Chapter 2, where we overviewed the complete systematic creativity process, we identified ideality and IFR as 'recommended' rather than compulsory elements of the problem definition process. Strictly speaking, of course, this 'not-compulsory' position is forced by the pragmatic demands a given problem situation; put simply, many problems do not permit us the freedom to throw away all that has gone before in order to pursue what, inconveniently, turns out to be a more ideal solution route. As you can probably imagine, such a pragmatic stance carries with it considerable dangers – as we will see later, history says that organizations that don't tackle the issues arising from ideality thinking tend to go out of business. At least a part of this chapter, therefore, will seek to convince the reader of the importance of at least examining what an ideality-based thought process does for the problem they end up defining.

The chapter itself is divided into three main sections. The first section details the mechanics of an ideality/IFR based problem definition tool. The second section then works through a series of case study examples showing how others have successfully defined 'better' problems using the tool. A shorter third section then offers some additional thoughts on how the concept of ideality links to other TRIZ tools, and how we might use the concept to enhance the way we deploy those tools.

The chapter is very much about the use of ideality in the context of problem definition. Certain elements contained within the concept also make it amenable to application in a problem solving context. Such applications are detailed in Chapter 18.

1) Ideality/IFR as a Problem Definition Tool

The basis of ideality as a problem definition tool begins from a logic which works something like the following: Increasing ideality is the overriding trend of technological evolution. We can define ideality in several ways, but the most useful one tends to be:-

$$\text{Ideality} = \frac{\text{(Perceived) Benefits}}{\text{(Cost + Harm)}}$$

And so, if we accept increasing ideality as an evolutionary direction, it is basically saying that as systems evolve, it delivers more of the benefits (the top half of the equation), and progressively less of the bad things – the costs and harms (the bottom half of the equation). If we evolve a system to its furthest limits, the thinking goes, the system would deliver *all* of the good stuff we require and literally *none* of the bad stuff. Such an evolutionary state becomes our Ideal Final Result. The next part of the thinking then says, 'okay, if everything is evolving in this direction, why don't I start by thinking about that end-point rather than from the baggage of today?' This simple thought process represents a subtle but actually rather profound shift in the way most organizations (and many individuals) think. Most organizations actually think in the direction illustrated in Figure 8.1. This is the direction that uses the 'current system' as its start point. All improvement effort is then based on this starting model. The 'continuous improvement' phrase most engineers have drummed into them is a direct consequence of this kind of 'start from the present' thinking. As we probably know, the law of diminishing returns (but actually the fundamental dynamics of evolutionary s-curves) says that as time progresses, we will achieve lower and lower levels of improvement in a system for ever greater levels of effort.

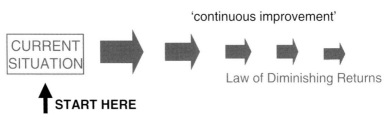

Figure 8.1: The Way Most Organisations Think

The next thing that tends to happen is that someone then finds a better way of doing things. This new way of doing things is, in TRIZ terms, the emergence of a new s-curve – Figure 8.2.

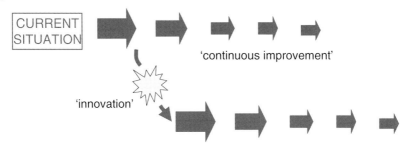

Figure 8.2: The 'Flash of inspiration'

The interesting fact found by TRIZ researchers looking at these major flashes of inspiration was that they almost always came from someone outside the current industry. The finding has since been independently observed by James Utterback (Reference 8.1) who records that for major product innovations (things at the level of jet-engines, carpets, refrigerators, ice manufacture, radial tyres, ball-point pens, diesel locomotives, incandescent lamps, transistors, celluloid film, calculators, parallel super-computers, etc) it was always the outsider who made the innovative jump. Put another way, based on history, the likelihood that your current organization will develop the product that puts your current product out of business is **zero**.

The ideality and IFR concept is a systematic way of at least seeing what these yellow innovation flashes are going to be.

There is an interesting paradox in the shift in thinking provoked by ideality. Convention says we should solve problems by starting from the current situation and that is in fact the way most people seem to think. But at the same time ask an engineer or anyone for that matter how to solve the puzzle illustrated in Figure 8.3 and the almost immediate answer that comes back is 'start from the prize and work back'.

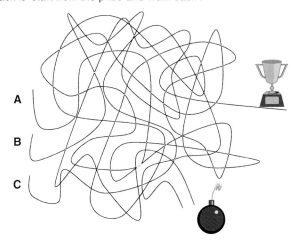

Figure 8.3: 'Which Line Leads to the Prize' Ideality Analogy

This simple model turns out to offer an extremely simple analogy of what the Ideal Final Result problem definition tool is trying to achieve; if we equate IFR to prize, then start from the prize and work back to the answer, we have a much more efficient way of doing things.

Of course, the actual tool is not quite that simple. But almost. The basic idea contained in the tool is illustrated in Figure 8.4.

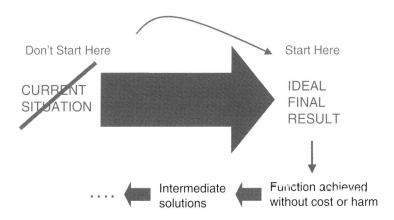

Figure 8.4: Ideal Final Result Problem Definition Strategy

The additional requirement when using the tool is, having started by defining the IFR, the process then works back in (usually) a series of conceptual steps back. The basic thinking required to make this work goes something along the lines 'if I can't achieve the IFR specification then what is the smallest step back I could make?', followed by 'if I can't achieve a solution from that small step back, what is the next smallest step back I could teak?', and so on until a conceptual solution that is realisable is obtained.

One final important point before examining the mechanics of the actual IFR problem definition tool is the image illustrated in Figure 8.5.

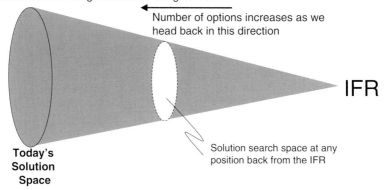

Figure 8.5: Conical Search Space When using IFR

This figure illustrates the almost inevitable widening of the search space as we head back from the IFR (which is after all a very definite – conceptually at least – end point). In practical terms, the implications of this broadening are that as we step back from IFR to other conceptual solutions, we will tend to create an ever increasing number of conceptual directions the more steps back from IFR we take. We will see this phenomenon in action in some of the examples in the next section.

As a small aside, it is also worth considering the cone idea in the context of the problem-solving-as-hole-digging analogy in section 3) of the chapter (3) on psychological aspects of TRIZ, it is sometimes useful to draw the cone in a vertical orientation (Figure 8.6) – to symbolise the search for buried treasure, with the deepest hole being the location of the ideal treasure.

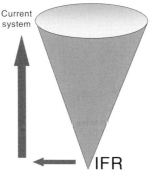

Figure 8.6: Vertical Cone/digging-for-Treasure IFR Image

In either image, the main point is the widening of the search space as we retreat away from IFR to the current situation.

So let us now examine a simple tool to show how the IFR concept can help guide our problem definition thinking. The tool is based on a simple questionnaire originally configured by Altshuller as a way of structuring thinking. The questionnaire is illustrated in Figure 8.7.

1) **What is the final aim of the system?**

2) **What is the Ideal Final Result outcome?**

3) **What is stopping you from achieving this IFR?**

4) **Why is it stopping you?**

5) **How could you make the thing(s) stopping you disappear?**

6) **What resources are available to help create these circumstances?**

7) **Has anyone else been able to solve this problem?**

Figure 8.7: Ideal Final Result Problem Definition Questionnaire

The sequence of questions is important. The first question represents the first challenge. This question demands that the problem definer thinks about the FUNCTION(s) required to be delivered by the system – functionality being the key to why systems exist, and so the 'final aim' should accurately reflect that.

The second question – what is the IFR – is something of a no-brainer, certainly on the first iteration through a problem definition exercise. The answer to this question will be something along the lines of 'deliver the function/final-aim/benefit with zero cost or harm.

The third question is the first of what may be seen as the big challenge questions. The answers to this question may be both non-obvious and multitudinous. The main point of the questionnaire at this stage is to provoke what Altshuller has called 'strong thinking'. Be sure to record all of the answers found.

The fourth – why? – and fifth – how? – questions are equally challenging from the required thinking quality perspective. The underlying provocation provided by the question is to challenge the answer of the previous – what? – question. Sometimes the answers generated by these questions can appear to give an argument that becomes somewhat circular, but don't let this detract from the overall purpose of the tool – which is to help you explore the problem space as fully as possible.

The sixth question seeks to make an explicit link between ideality and the resources that should previously have been identified during the problem explorer part of the overall problem definition process. Ideality and resources are very closely linked; if there is something already around a system that can perform the function of the system instead of the system, it will provide us with a very good route to achieving IFR. This ideality-resources link is discussed in more detail in Chapter 18 – where we examine the use of ideality in its problem-solving role.

The final question in the questionnaire is there to provide a connecting link to downstream solving tools. The very large majority of all ideality-centred problem definition thinking will lead to either a knowledge/effects problem or a contradiction. This final question is intended to help formulate which. It is also there to guide thinking away from the specific towards the generic.

Having answered all of the questions, the general idea is that the problem situation has become much clearer. It is by no means a one-off thing however. The ideality problem definition process described here offers two possible exploration routes should the first time through the questionnaire result in the definition of a problem that cannot be solved:-

1) we cannot achieve the stated IFR and wish to explore other problem definitions with a less challenging IFR definition, or
2) there are more than one things stopping you from achieving the IFR and you wish to explore each one in more detail.

The first instance, is equivalent to us stepping back towards the current situation to the 'intermediate solutions' denoted in Figure 8.4. The second is equivalent to the broadening of the cone as we seek to explore the search space at a given IFR definition.

The net result of the two different exploration directions is that we may end up with several questionnaires, each with its own position on the conical search space – as illustrated in Figure 8.8.

The general idea then is that we use the resulting collection of questionnaires as a way of mapping the available solution space for a given problem, and use the triggers provided by the questions at the end of the list of questions as the means by which we tap into the solution parts of TRIZ.

The next section illustrates examples of this process in action.

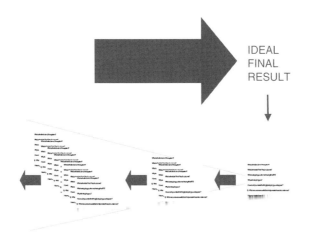

Figure 8.8: How The IFR Questionnaire Fits With The Conical Search Space

2) Case Study Examples

a) Washing Clothes

There has been a noticeable shift in the thinking of certain forward thinking washing powder manufacturers in recent times from a business strategy built on 'sell more washing powder' to one built on 'sell more clean clothes'. The simple but profoundly important difference between the first and second objectives being that the first represents a solution and the second a function. The distinction is important because, solutions change and functions stay the same. In other words, any organisation that thinks it is in the washing powder business is likely to find themselves out of business when someone works out a more ideal (think 'benefits divided by the sum of cost and harm') way of delivering the same function as their washing powder.

This 'solutions change, functions stay the same' phenomenon applies across all industries not just washing powder – people want a hole not a drill, 'communication' not a mobile phone, and so on. This shift to building business strategy around function fits in very neatly with the first question of the IFR problem definition tool; 'what is the final aim?'

In the case of the washing powder business, the final aim (the function being delivered) is 'clean clothes'. A good IFR definition having made this solution-to-function connection is then 'clothes clean themselves' or 'clothes don't get dirty'. Running this definition through the IFR questionnaire for the first time should give us something like:-

1) **What is the final aim of the system?**
   Clean clothes
2) **What is the Ideal Final Result outcome?**
   Clothes that clean themselves
3) **What is stopping you from achieving this IFR?**
   Cloth fibres are not able to perform this function
4) **Why is it stopping you?**
   If the fibres can't perform the function, the clothes aren't cleaned
5) **How could you make the thing(s) stopping you disappear?**
   If there was a fibre or fibre structure that was able to clean 'itself'
6) **What resources are available to help create these circumstances?**
   Fibre, atmosphere, wearer, wardrobe, sunlight,
7) **Has anyone else been able to solve this problem?**
   The 'self-clean' function is possible in nature (Lotus Plant), but the only man-made Self-clean structures (e.g. ovens) use resources that are not present in this case. Alternative; disposable clothes.

Figure 8.9: Example IFR Questionnaire For 'Clothes that Clean Themselves' Definition

The net result of going through the questionnaire this first time is that, while we might have a few leads on how to achieve self-cleaning clothes, at this point in time we do not know how to achieve a practical solution. When this happens, the IFR definition process asks us to take a small step back from our ideal, and to define an alternative – as illustrated in Figure 8.10.

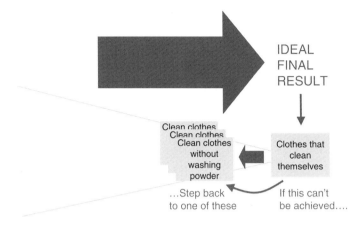

IDEAL
FINAL
RESULT

Clean clothes
Clean clothes
Clean clothes
without
washing
powder

Clothes that
clean
themselves

...Step back
to one of these

If this can't
be achieved....

Figure 8.10: IFR Definition Space For 'Washing Clothes'

The basis of our new IFR definition having made a step back may actually be several options. Essentially, if we are unable to achieve 'self-cleaning' clothes then the step back we take must involve some external cleaning mechanism. We could pick various different concepts – 'clean clothes without washing machine', 'clean clothes without water', and so on. As we are (for the moment) examining the problem from the perspective of the washing powder manufacturer, we will select from the possible options, 'clean clothes without a powder', or, more formally, 'clean clothes without external agent'. The washing machine manufacturers might well pick the 'without machine' option initially. Either way, if we were *really* in the clean-clothes business, we should examine all of the conceptual scenarios emerging from this IFR definition tool. Meanwhile, we will stay with 'clean clothes without external agent' for the purposes of illustration. This new IFR definition thus forms the basis of a new questionnaire:

1) **What is the final aim of the system?**
   Clean clothes
2) **What is the new Ideal Final Result outcome?**
   Clean clothes without the need for an external agent
3) **What is stopping you from achieving this IFR?**
   The external agent is required to break down the bond between the dirt from the clothes
4) **Why is it stopping you?**
   If the bond isn't broken, the clothes aren't cleaned
5) **How could you make the thing(s) stopping you disappear?**
   If there was some other way of breaking the bond between dirt and clothes
6) **What resources are available to help create these circumstances?**
   Water, clothes, dirt, washing machine, other household products electricity, etc
7) **Has anyone else been able to solve this problem?**
   Only the washing powder industry has to solve the 'clean clothes' problem, but many industries have to solve the more general 'clean' or 'remove dirt' problem.

Figure 8.11: Example IFR Questionnaire For 'Clean Clothes Without External Agent' Definition

This time the questionnaire has taken us to a point where we have identified a 'knowledge problem'. We know that other industries are able to perform the 'clean' function, but as yet we don't know how. This kind of end to the questionnaire should be the prompt that takes us to some kind of knowledge/effects database. We might use the information in Chapter 15 as a start of this search, and we might use one of the growing number of on-line knowledge repositories. In either case, we are likely to find that there are several ways of delivering the required 'clean clothes without external agent' function – not least of which would be ultrasound. Now, we might not like this finding, but at least we now know the threat is there, and that if ultrasound (say) turns out to be a better way of delivering the 'clean clothes' function than a washing powder, we are in trouble. Hence the reason some organisations don't like using the IFR approach during problem definition; it is never good news when you find that someone may come along and supersede all of your invested time, effort and money.

The story doesn't end quite at this point, however. Although this IFR definition has realised possible future options, for the moment, that is exactly what they are; future. What happens if we need a better solution more quickly than is achievable through any of the 'clean clothes without external agent' options? Answer; take another step back along the IFR definition space – Figure 8.12.

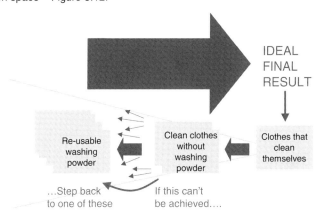

Figure 8.12: IFR Definition Space For 'Washing Clothes' – New Iteration

(Note how each of the conceptual stages can and usually does branch out into a multitude of options as we head back closer to the current situation. This is why the solution search space is drawn as a cone.)

Stepping back from 'clean clothes without external agent' can result in several conceptual definitions. The figure highlights 're-usable washing powder' as this is one that certain sectors of the industry appear to be working towards, but other options might well include – 'more concentrated powders', 'concentrated liquids', 'field-based additives' and so on.

Taking another step back from any of these options is likely to get us back to the current situation. At which point, we may be seen to have fully mapped, if not the breadth of conceptual definitions, at least their depth from ultimate IFR back to the present.

(As a hopefully interesting aside to this case study, the switch from selling solutions to selling 'functions' is also beginning to happen in the washing machine industry. Again, the theory goes, customers want clean clothes, not a washing machine. Find more on this story at Reference 8.2, and see some of the design implications of so-called 'functional sales' in Chapter 20.

b) Planting Seeds

Commercial agriculture is an area ripe for ideality-oriented thinking processes. The following is an example of application of the IFR questionnaire to re-examine the way one of the bottleneck farming problems is defined.

1) **What is the final aim of the system?**
   Planted seeds
2) **What is the Ideal Final Result outcome?**
   Seeds plant themselves
3) **What is stopping you from achieving this IFR?**
   Seeds need to be under the ground before they will germinate
4) **Why is it stopping you?**
   Currently, we have to drill a hole to drop the seed into
5) **How could you make the thing(s) stopping you disappear?**
   If the seed drilled its own hole
6) **What resources are available to help create these circumstances?**
   Seeds, ground, air, atmosphere
7) **Has anyone else been able to solve this problem?**
   Nature solves the problem itself, but too slow and unreliable for commercial planting. Several industries have solved the more generic problem 'pierce through a hard thing' without damaging the piercing object.

Figure 8.13: Example IFR Questionnaire For 'Seed Planting'

It turns out that a very elegant solution to this 'self-planting' seeds problem definition involves projecting the seeds into the ground at very high speed (via a very simple rotating drum). About 400m/s to be precise. If this sounds counter-intuitive (the seed gets damaged, right?), think again. We like this example for two reasons:-
1) it is a great example of finding and using existing resources. In this case, the resource comes in the form of the 400m/s value – which happens to be supersonic; which in turn means that as the seed is projected a shock wave is formed immediately in front of it, which then serves to protect the seed during impact with the ground.
2) It is also a good example of the 'opportunity finding' (as opposed to 'problem solving') side of problem solving; an industry that has knowledge of high speed projectile motion seeking to apply that knowledge in another sector.

c) Aerosol Sprays

A similar IFR problem definition approach can be applied to the subject of aerosols used in, for example, deodorant applications. We will start this example a couple of conceptual steps back from what we might regard as 'actual' Ideal Final Results; that is 'armpits don't produce odour', or 'armpits protect themselves'. This may be because we have already explored these options, or simply that the constraints of the problem dictate that, for now at least, we are going to stay in the deodorant business.

Starting from this 'it will be an aerosol' constraint, we can hopefully show how the IFR problem definition strategy can still help us to define the 'ideal aerosol'. Firstly we need to examine some of the aspects of aerosols that we would like to improve. There are probably several (environmental, safety, disposal, durability, etc), but we will focus on one in particular – that of waste of product. Should we choose to examine any of the other problem areas, we can use exactly the same process as for this waste example. The waste problem with deodorant sprays can be quite large – with a considerable proportion of the spray leaving the nozzle missing its target. The consequences of this are a bathroom full of deodorant fumes, a user with an unevenly protected armpit – lots of deodorant in some places; not enough in others – and a generally dis-satisfied customer. Figure 8.14 details what the IFR definition strategy questionnaire has to say about the problem:-

1) **What is the final aim of the system?**
   Even dispensing of deodorant particles onto armpit
2) **What is the Ideal Final Result outcome?**
   Deodorant particles control their position themselves
3) **What is stopping you from achieving this IFR?**
   Deodorant particles are dispensed from the can by gas pressure and can only be projected in a straight-line trajectory from the nozzle
4) **Why is it stopping you?**
   The nozzle spray pattern and the (variable) shape of the target are different
5) **How could you make the thing(s) stopping you disappear?**
   If the deodorant particles were able to move in different directions, and knew how to 'find' an uncovered area on the target zone – if the particles were 'self-seeking'.
6) **What resources are available to help create these circumstances?**
   Particles, nozzle, gas pressure, user, atmosphere, moisture, bathroom
7) **Has anyone else been able to solve this problem?**
   Only the deodorant industry has the specific problem of moving deodorant particles. Several industries have the problem of wanting to cover things with an even coating without leaving gaps, and without wasting product.

Figure 8.14: Example IFR Questionnaire For 'Aerosol Spray'

The end-point of this questionnaire again points to a question about knowledge from other industry sectors. In this case, a search of patent databases soon revealed that, as in so many instances, someone out there has already solved something like your problem.

Figure 8.15 reproduces the front-sheet from US patent US6199766: 'Targeting of flying insects with insecticides and apparatus for charging liquids' as an example of exactly such a 'someone else' – in this case someone looking to solve the same problem in the insect spray business (except a more extreme version of it – insects are very small and fast moving, oo typically a lot more product gets wasted trying to get some to stick to the insect).

(12) **United States Patent**
Fox et al.

(10) Patent No.: US 6,199,766 B1
(45) Date of Patent: Mar. 13, 2001

(54) TARGETING OF FLYING INSECTS WITH INSECTICIDES AND APPARATUS FOR CHARGING LIQUIDS

(75) Inventors: Rodney Thomas Fox, Hull; Neale Mark Harrison, Burton-on-Trent; John Farrell Hughes, Southampton; Lindsay Faye Whitmore, Winchester, all of (GB)

(73) Assignee: University of Southampton, Southampton; Reckitt Benckiser (UK) Ltd., Windsor, both of (GB)

(*) Notice: Subject to any disclaimer, the term of this patent is extended or adjusted under 35 U.S.C. 154(b) by 0 days.

(21) Appl. No.: 09/446,489
(22) PCT Filed: Jun. 29, 1998
(86) PCT No.: PCT/GB98/01898
§ 371 Date: Mar. 7, 2000
§ 102(e) Date: Mar. 7, 2000
(87) PCT Pub. No.: WO99/01227
PCT Pub. Date: Jan. 14, 1999

(30) Foreign Application Priority Data

Mar. 29, 1996	(GB)	9804133
Jul. 4, 1997	(GB)	9714231
Oct. 28, 1997	(GB)	9722611

(51) Int. Cl. ... A61G 23/10
(52) U.S. Cl. ... 239/3; 239/690; 239/708; 239/337; 43/132.1
(58) Field of Search ... 239/3, 690, 690.1, 239/708, 337; 43/132.1, 125, 129
(56) References Cited

U.S. PATENT DOCUMENTS

4,776,515 *	10/1988	Michalchik	239/708
4,071,257 *	11/1990	Birge	239/708
5,090,633 *	2/1996	Jeffries et al.	239/691
5,010,265	9/1998	Comelius et al.	239/691

FOREIGN PATENT DOCUMENTS

278 204	1/1952	(CH)	
615322	5/1919	(GB)	
1 482 332	5/1989	(SU)	B05B/5/00
WO90/10505	9/1990	(WO)	B05D/1/02
WO97/28883	8/1997	(WO)	B01D/47/00

OTHER PUBLICATIONS

Copy of International Search Report for PCT/GB98/01898 dated Oct. 30, 1998.
Kleber W. et al.: "Triboelectrically charged powder coatings generated by running through holes and slits", Journal of Electrostatics, vol. 40–41, Jun. 1997, pp. 237–240.
Electrostatics: Principles, Problems and Applications by Jean Cross, Adam Hilger, Bristol, pp. 17–22.
Electrostatics: Principles, Problems and Applications by Jean Cross, Adam Hilger, Bristol, pp. 61–69.

* cited by examiner

Primary Examiner—Andres Kashnikow
Assistant Examiner—Dinh Q. Nguyen
(74) Attorney, Agent, or Firm—Hoth & Richardson P.C.

(57) ABSTRACT

A method of killing flying insects which method comprises spraying into the air in which insects are flying liquid droplets of an insecticidal composition, a majority of the droplets being imparted to the said liquid droplets by double layer charging and charge separation during spraying, the unipolar charge being at a level such that the said droplets have a charge to mass ratio of at least +/-1x10^-4 C/kg. An aerosol spray device which is capable of imparting a unipolar charge by double layer charging and charge separation to liquid droplets of a composition sprayed therefrom has a spraying head in the form of an insert in an actuator, the spraying head having a bore through which liquid is expelled having an outlet, preferably with a tortious periphery, having an 1/a ratio of at least 8 (preferably at least 10) where 1 is the length of the periphery defining the bore outlet in mm and a is the cross-sectional area of the bore outlet in mm² and the apparatus being constructed such that the droplets are expelled from the spraying head at a flow ratio of at least 0.4 (preferably at least 0.5) grams per second and have a charge to mass ratio of at least +/-1x10^-4 C/kg.

28 Claims, 15 Drawing Sheets

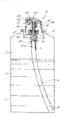

Figure 8.15: 'Self-Seeking' Aerosol Spray Patent

In this example we have seen how it is possible to 'zoom-in' on just a part of a problem (i.e. self-moving aerosol particles as opposed to the bigger 'prevent smell' function) and still use the IFR problem definition strategy. This aerosol example also provides a useful link to one of the ways we can also use the ideality concept – and particularly the word 'self' (as in self-seeking, self-planting, self-cleaning) – as a problem solving strategy. See Chapter 18 for more on this subject.

3) Links to Other Tools and Additional Thoughts

Who's Ideal Final Result?

One of the biggest challenges during use of the ideality/IFR tool as a problem definition mechanism is discriminating between what the customer wants and what the manufacturer/supplier is willing to offer. In the large majority of instances, the difference between these two perceptions of what Ideal Final Result means can be widely different between each of the different parties involved in the value chain.

To take a simple example, think about the different elements of the value chain involved in the manufacture, supply and use of lawnmowers. The following is a hypothetical ideal final result definitions from the respective stakeholders:-

Lawnmower manufacturer	-	A machine that cuts grass effectively, that is aesthetically pleasing, is silent, requires no user-maintenance, no user effort, burns no fuel, profitable, and (in the short term at least) needs replacing the day after the guarantee runs out.
Lawnmower dealer	-	A product that sells itself, has excellent profit margin, and requires servicing or replacing the day after the guarantee runs out
Energy supplier	-	A machine that uses lots of fuel or electricity, and oil
The lawn owner	-	An attractive, no maintenance lawn

The point being that while companies have one set of goals, the ultimate customer quite often has a very different set. The mind-set of the lawnmower manufacturer is that one day, given enough R&D effort, they will produce their ideal machine. Unfortunately, their idea of 'ideal machine' is some considerable distance away from the ideal machine desired by the customer; the customers ideal machine is the one that delivers the required function without cost or harm (in other words, it doesn't exist). From another perspective, what the customer probably wants is grass that knows how to make itself attractive, and maintains itself.

The reason this is important (if it is not already obvious) is that whereas in the past the poor old customer was generally at the mercy of the manufacturer, and basically got what they were told to have, the increasingly globally market means it is increasingly likely that someone, somewhere will supply those customers with exactly what they want. Historically, as stated earlier, that someone else has been a newcomer with no vested interest in maintaining the status quo. As companies become more enlightened, it will be increasingly the case that the organization that delivers the customer the customer's IFR will be the forward looking one.

In summary; the customer is always right; the customer's IFR is always right. It is increasingly likely someone will offer it to them.

As a general customer IFR direction, the phrase 'free, perfect and now' (Reference 8.3) makes an excellent, customer-friendly statement of what ideal final result means. What do customers want? They want something that fits their personal needs perfectly, they don't want it to cost anything, and they want it now. Simple.

Okay, so maybe there are one or two contradictions to solve along the way (how does a company achieve the 'free' part and manage to stay in business is a good one!). But that's another chapter.

IFR as a Function of Time

An often useful extensive to the basic ideality/ideal final result concept is to incorporate an element of time into the IFR definition process. This achieves two things; first of all it encourages a more holistic view of the ideality picture, and second it recognise that our definitions of ideality can (and often do) change as a function of time. The ideality equation

$$\text{Ideality} \quad = \quad \frac{\text{(Perceived) Benefits}}{\text{(Cost + Harm)}}$$

can be a very dynamic one. The 'perceived' word is very important in this context, with the fickle customer frequently seeming to change their perspective on what's 'good' and what isn't at the turn of an eye. This is not to say that they are wrong of course (the customer is always right, right?), merely that we should wherever and whenever possible try to anticipate how their views will change. Fortunately the focus on FUNCTION, provides some stability to this process – function being the thing that stays the same.

A good example of how the balance of the ideality equation can shift comes with the mobile phone. Initial drives towards increase in ideality came in the form of phones that were ever smaller, weighed less, had increased talk-time, and increasing numbers of features. That dynamic was shifted significantly when people became aware of the potential harm caused by radio waves heating the brain.

Although this one is a difficult one to predict (although having said that, the ideality equation does specifically prompt the problem definer to think about what 'harm' might mean), a simple lesson we can draw from it, and a simple tool we can employ to help structure our thinking on IFR definition, is a combination with the 9-Windows tool.

Figure 8.16 outlines how we can use the 9-Windows to force us to define what the Ideal Final Result might be from the perspective of each of the windows in turn. Sometimes we will find that the IFR definition stays the same as we look at it from each box, but often we will find it changes significantly. The most likely windows within which we will experience this type of definition change are:-

- Sub-System Future – from the perspective of individual components within a system, the future will see them increasingly evolve to their IFR and hence disappear from the system – i.e. have their function delivered by something else in the system. Conducting and IFR assessment of each component in a system can thus be useful in seeing which components will continue to be present in the future and which ones won't.

- Super-System Future – how things around the system will evolve can have a profound influence on how we define the IFR of the system under evaluation. The big questions are – is something at the super-system level going to make the system redundant?, and (more difficult) is some change in the super-system going to change how we define our IFR?

- System-Future – the big issue here is whether the IFR definition for the system under evaluation would be different at different times in the future.

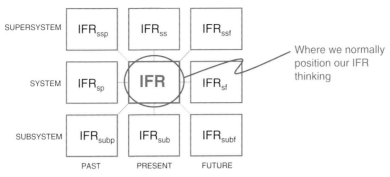

Figure 8.16: IFR In Relation to the 9-Windows

Expanding on this last point a little, it is also worth remembering that the 9-Windows tool is a way of segmenting what is actually a time-space continuum. An additional level of sophistication in IFR thinking is to position yourself at various points along a time-line into the future, and see if your perspective of IFR changes at those different points – Figure 8.17.

Figure 8.17: Does IFR Change as a Function of Time?

Another way of looking at this image involves mimicking the back-to-front thinking shift at the center of the ideality thinking paradigm shift. First imagine the ultimate Ideal Final Result definition; then put some kind of estimated timescale on this (remember we're trying to think at a conceptual rather than definitive detail level), and gradually step back from this point in the future to the present in order to see how the IFR can be redefined at each time point to fit with the prevailing constraints.

Example;   Whilst I might have an ultimate IFR definition of a mobile phone that goes something along the lines of 'I want to be able to speak to anyone, anywhere, from anywhere, at any time without having to carry around a phone', and be working towards this, it is often essential in a business context at least to have some more tangible, realizable goals in the interim – like for example a fourth generation phone in 5 years, a third generation phone in the next year. IFR-based milestone setting in other words.

Links To Trends of Evolution

Some users find it difficult to imagine what the different conceptual steps back from ideal final result might be for a given system. This would not be without good reason – as the available solution space can often be very large. We recommend two strategies if this type of thinking does not come naturally (and it almost certainly won't for most people at first).

The first strategy links to the 'Trimming' trend to be found in Chapter 17. The trend suggests that systems will eventually evolve to achieve the same or greater levels of functionality with progressively fewer components. We can turn this phenomenon the other way around when we are thinking about IFR and working back from it – in that the number of components in the systems will gradually increase as we return from IFR to the current system. A crude, but nevertheless useful way, therefore, of thinking about conceptual solutions is the image illustrated in Figure 8.18.

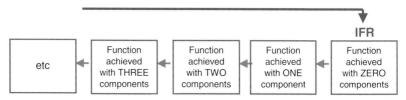

Figure 8.18: Crude Connection Between IFR Problem Definition Strategy and Trimming Trend

An example of this model in action comes from a car wheel nut case study in which the required function ('lock wheel onto safely and reliably onto axle') was attempted, first using zero components – with the resulting concept of some kind of smart or adaptive wheel or axle attachment – then stepping back to allowing the use of one component – a self-locking nut – then stepping back to permit the use of two components, and so on. Further details on this case study can be found at Reference 8.4.

This component count based model also has something in common with Axiomatic Design (Reference 8.5), which in simple terms defines 'good design' as one component per useful function. (Actually, the IFR model suggests that we can do better than this!).

The idea of using the trends to help guide the IFR problem definition space can also be applied to some of the other trends. The object segmentation trend in particular – which is effectively, again, about 'doing more with progressively less' – can act as a very useful guide. The evolution from mechanical to fluid to gas to field and beyond described within the trend offer very useful conceptual maps:-

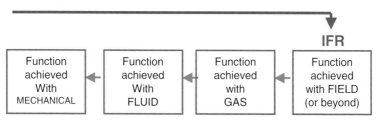

Figure 8.19: Object Segmentation Trend as an IFR Definition Guide

What Do I Do?

Although conducting an Ideal Final Result analysis is not a compulsory part of the problem definition process, it is nevertheless very strongly recommended that one is carried out.

The concept of defining an ideal result (especially one as far-reaching – achieve the function without cost or harm) and then working back from it to something that is achievable does not come naturally to most people. It is nevertheless a very potent strategy for achieving the oft-sought goal of 'thinking out of the box'.

In order to make most effective use of IFR as a problem definition tool, the basic questionnaire illustrated in Figure 8.7 is recommended as a start point. Use this questionnaire multiple times as you gradually step back and broaden outlook (Figure 8.8) coming back in conceptual design stages to the current situation.

This kind of conceptual thinking can be guided by the TRIZ trends of evolution – particularly the object segmentation and trimming trends.

References

1) Utterback, J., 'Mastering The Dynamics of Innovation', Harvard Business School Press, 1993.
2) Electrolux - functional sales web-site, http://www.corporate.electrolux.com/
3) Rodin, R., 'Free, Perfect and Now', Simon & Schuster, New York, 1999.
4) Mann, D.L., 'Case Studies in TRIZ: A Self-Locking Wheel Nut', TRIZ Journal, November 1998.
5) Suh, N., 'The Principles of Design', Oxford University Press, 1990.

9.
Select Solve Tool

As has already been stated in the early introductory chapters of the book, one of the biggest problems newcomers face when first exposed to TRIZ is knowing how to sort through all of the tremendous richness and depth to find the parts of the whole relevant to their particular situation. The purpose of this chapter is to achieve precisely that knowledge; to make a bridge between the problem(s) we've defined and the use of the 'right' problem-solving tool.

It is rarely the case that only one of the solving tools within or around TRIZ are relevant. It is also likely that many readers will be unfamiliar with (or not be interested in) certain parts of the total toolkit. With both of those things in mind, and recognising the need for a degree of overlap between the different tools, the chapter presents tool selections in the form of ranked menus. In other words, the intention of the chapter is to provide you with the sort of route map that says, 'for problem type X, first try tool Y, then if that doesn't work, try Z, and if that doesn't work, try A' etc. The general idea behind this strategy is that if you happen not to be familiar with tool Y, you should still be able to generate good answers from tools, Z, A and any of the other recommendations.

There are many types of problems and opportunities, and so the menu of options is quite large. The chapter is structured in such a way that each problem type is described individually, and a matrix at the end of the chapter then summarises the whole select strategy into a compact, easy to read form. Some readers may prefer to head straight for this summary table. For everyone else, what follows is a logically ordered sequence of questions and answers we should go through when we are seeking to select the most appropriate problem-solving tool for the problem we are in the process of tackling.

Again, there is no absolutely unique logical involved in the sequence of these questions; if you are happier adjusting the sequence to fit better into your way of doing things, then please feel free to do so.

We will start here with the first big solve tool selection discriminator; the s-curve. Figure 9.1 illustrates the typical s-curve characteristic discussed in detail in Chapter 7. As detailed in that chapter, the relative position of the system (or sub-system or component) at the heart of the problem on its current s-curve will have an influence on both the type and sequence of problem solving tools employed. The main characteristics to examine are whether the system is at the conception/birth/growth or mature/retirement end of the s-curve and whether the point of maximum complexity has been passed.

Some of the first questions we should therefore be asking when transitioning from defined problem to solving tool is where is the system under consideration – or, more specifically, the part of the system with the problem – is on its current s-curve.

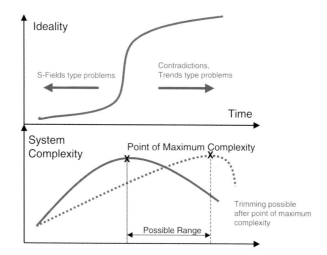

Figure 9.1: How Position on S-Curve Influences Problem Solving Tool Selection

Limiting Contradiction?

If either your s-curve analysis or your assessment of the sore point in the system has revealed the existence of a limiting contradiction, you should head directly towards the contradiction resolution parts of the method. Your route could take you to either the physical or technical contradictions part of the method. Let your definition of the contradiction determine which route you take. If you are in a position where you can identify both physical and technical contradictions, you are advised to start by looking at the physical contradiction.

If this route proves fruitless, your next best option is to head towards the Trends of Evolution (Chapter 13) in order to establish whether there is some unused evolutionary potential in your system that might reveal means of overcoming the limiting contradiction. A third option is to examine the chapter on Knowledge/Effects (15) to see if anyone has already solved your problem. Some people will instinctively head down this route before the other two. While this is certainly not 'wrong' it does present significant potential for becoming embroiled in psychological inertia issues – if you find something that might be relevant, the very specific nature of a patent – and the pictures presented within it – can often cause our brains to jump into 'satisfied mode'. Hence, the process recommends you try Contradictions and Trends first.

Other Contradictions

As Figure 9.1 suggests, systems which have evolved to the top half of their current s-curve are highly likely to contain contradictions. Our FAA models will help us to identify the existence of these contradictions in the system. Contradictions can be identified by the existence of components which feature both positive and negative interactions with other components. The piston ring illustrated in Figure 9.2, for example, should suggest that we have a technical contradiction associated with the component – in that it produces a useful 'holds' function, but also creates a *different* harmful function 'wears'.

There are many combinations of possibilities here, but the real key lies with arrow direction (where we should focus on arrows directed out of a component) and the presence of 'good' and 'bad' functions.

Figure 9.2: Manifestation of Technical Contradictions in FAA Model

Physical Contradictions

The FAA model can help us to identify the presence of physical contradictions. Related to Figure 9.2, the presence of functions or attributes with both positive and negative effects (for example 'temperature reduces viscosity' (useful) and 'temperature breaks-down polymer chain' (harmful) should suggest the existence of a physical contradiction linked to a desire for temperature which is both high and low.

Physical contradictions separated in time are visible by looking at FAA models drawn at different times – Figure 9.3.

Figure 9.3: Manifestation of Physical Contradictions in FAA Model

All of these FAA model representations of positive and negative relationships can also be used to help define s-field type problems:

Insufficient Actions

Wherever an FAA model indicates the existence of insufficient actions in a system, there are two primary options to help increase the action – Knowledge/Effects and the Trends of evolution. Selecting between the two will largely depend on the constraints attached to the problem; if there are no constraints to prevent you from looking to alternative means of delivering the function, you should start with knowledge/effects to scope the range of possible other available ways to see if any are capable of delivering the function to better effect. If the constraints imposed on the problem situation are such that it is not permissible to change the means of function delivery, the Trends of evolution should be used to establish means of enhancing the capability of the current function delivery means. The presence of insufficient actions also warrants investigation of the S-Fields part of TRIZ and the relevant Inventive Standards. We don't recommend this route as being among the 'primary' options, because many of the Inventive Standards suggested for insufficient actions are very abstract for the large part, and overlap with some of the Trends in any event. Nevertheless, S-fields will make a useful third port of call if the first two options do not bear fruit.

Excessive Actions

The presence of excessive actions in an FAA model suggests similar solution strategies to those recommended for insufficient actions. We recommend that the Trends should be the first port of call, followed by Knowledge/Effects (if the constraints of the problem present the freedom to consider other ways of delivering the function. S-Fields make a useful third option if required.

Missing Actions

Indications of a missing action suggest the use of S-Fields – as the delivery of an action (function) demands the requisite minimum two substances plus a field. Also check out Knowledge/Effects to establish other known ways of delivering the action. If both of these routes suggest that something needs to be added to the system, use the Resources trigger lists in Chapter 14 to see if there is something already in the system that can be harnessed to help deliver the missing action.

The above list of problem types all build from s-curve analysis or an FAA model. There may be situations where the problem we are looking to tackle is more general:

System and/or Function Doesn't Currently Exist

If your FAA model is a blank piece of paper, and the problem explorer full of blanks, chances are that the function you are looking to deliver does not exist yet. Alternatively, a system may already exist, but it doesn't deliver the function you require from it. In either of these situations, the recommended problem solving strategy is to first try the IFR tool to help define and scope the situation, then try either the Knowledge/Effects or S-Field parts of TRIZ. The first of these two is recommended as a means of scoping the range of available means of delivering the required function; the second as a means of gaining a more fundamental understanding of the system that will need to be created in order to allow the function to be delivered.

No Problem?

If you have constructed a function and attribute analysis model and it contains no harmful, insufficient or excessive relationships, the best suggestion would be to don a black hat, think explicitly about the 9-Windows and try harder. Are you sure you wouldn't like more of the Main Useful Function of the system? If you still can't see a way forward, you should definitely take a(nother) look at using the IFR tool to re-define the problem. If that reveals nothing, Trimming (Chapter 17) should be your next port of call (check first that the system is at an evolutionary state where trimming is a viable option – Figure 9.1).

Measurement Problems

TRIZ generally takes a view of measurement problems different to the prevailing view. The TRIZ view is that the best form of measurement is no measurement at all. Or that a measurement makes 'itself'. If you are facing a measurement problem, we recommend that you first examine the specific class of measurement Inventive Standards in the s-fields part of the toolkit (Chapter 12). You might complement this with a look at Ideality (Chapter 18). If neither of these offers anything useful, your next port of call should be the chapter on Knowledge/Effects (15), and the table of known ways of measuring different attribute types to see if anyone has already thought of a way of solving your problem. You could complement this with a patent search as suggested later in Chapter 15. If none of these approaches bears any fruit, you might care to evaluate the possibility of solving the problem as a technical contradiction (thing you are trying to improve – Measurement Accuracy or Loss of Information).

Reliability Related Problems

Employ the strategies recommended in Chapter 20. These will already contain elements of contradiction solving and the design methods technology evolution trend.

Reduce First Cost?

If the problem definition part of the process confirms that the requirement of the problem is to reduce first cost, the most obvious place to start is trimming. This tool will certainly provide some initial provocations consistent with movement in the right – cost reducing – direction. You might also consider combining the 'self' idea from the solving version of the Ideal Final Result tool (Chapter 18) in with the trimming tool. Either from the trimming provocations – which will often introduce a contradiction that something gets worse if we take out a certain component – or because it is simply a good thing to do, application of the Contradictions tools is also recommended in this type of problem. Provided the system in question is beyond its point of maximum complexity, you might like to consider focusing on the Inventive Principles specifically targeted at reducing part count within a system – see Chapter 10, part 2) of the section on 'what to do when the Matrix doesn't work'.

Specifically Searching for a Disruptive Shift

There are occasions when we are specifically looking to jump from a current s-curve to a new one. This may be at the system level, or for a sub-system or individual component. In the case where we are looking to evolve at the system level, we should first of all examine the main useful function delivered by the current system and then examine the knowledge/effects part of the toolkit to establish whether there are alternative means of delivering that function. If the answer is yes, then these should act as the start of an exercise to determine how the particular knowledge and/or effect could be translated into the specific requirements of the system being replaced – this may well necessitate another complete cycle of the systematic creativity process. If no suitable alternative means of delivering the function can be found, the next best strategy is to examine the TRIZ trends of evolution in the reference section at the end of Chapter 17 in order to see if any of these offers new insight.

If we are looking to find new s-curves at the sub-system or component level, it is usually preferable to begin the search by exploring the evolutionary potential of the existing sub-system or component, rather than starting from knowledge/effects. A search of knowledge/effects can be conducted as a secondary route – but care needs to be taken if there are significant integration issues regarding other components within the overall system.

Zero Risk

There are certain occasions where the innovation requirement demands a 'zero risk', right first time approach. To some, the combination of 'innovation' and 'zero risk' might sound like an oxymoron. Whether it does or not, the most effective strategy if the imposed constraints really do necessitate zero risk, inevitably have to involve some kind of 'here's one I prepared earlier' solution search. Knowledge/effects is the most appropriate start-point. Preferably using an in-house knowledge source. The global patent database makes an often-suitable second choice, albeit there may be issues of infringement if a solution that cannot be used for whatever reason is found. A sometimes-valid subsequent option is to conduct a resource analysis to establish whether there is something already in the system that can be used to greater effect.

Designing Around Someone Else's Patent

There may be situations where it is necessary to invent an alternative to an existing patented solution. This is not an area of specific focus for this book, but nevertheless, it is fair to claim that the systematic creativity process can be used for this sort of application without modification. A comprehensive FAA model of the invention under investigation is an essential start point. Something else that will also be useful is a Claims genealogy. The

Claims section at the end of an invention disclosure is the important aspect of the patent from a design-around perspective. These Claims usually form a hierarchical structure highlighting the dependencies between the different claims present.

The following represents a hypothetical example (extracted from Reference 9.1). Firstly here is the list of Claims:

1) A door hinge wherein is included a mechanism for the provision of torque on the door when it is in any position other than closed, so as to cause it to become closed automatically

2) A door hinge according to claim 1 wherein one portion of the hinge is located on the door frame and a second portion is located on the door itself.

3) A door hinge according to claim 1 in which the whole of the automatic closing mechanism is located on the door

4) A door hinge according to claim 1 in which the whole of the automatic closing mechanism is located on the door frame.

5) A door frame according to claim 1 in which a first part of the automatic closing mechanism is located on the door and a second part of the said mechanism is located on the door frame

6) A door hinge according to any of the preceding claims in which the automatic closing mechanism incorporates a spring.

7) A door hinge according to claim 6 wherein the said spring is made of metal.

8) A door hinge according to claim 6 wherein the said spring is made of material other than metal.

9) A door hinge according to claims 6, 7 and 8 wherein the said spring is of spiral construction.

10) A door hinge according to claims 6, 7 and 8 wherein the said spring is in the form of a cantilever.

11) A door hinge constructed and arranged substantially as herein described with reference to and as shown in any of the accompanying drawings.

The resulting Claims genealogy showing how the claims relate to and depend upon one another is illustrated in Figure 9.4.

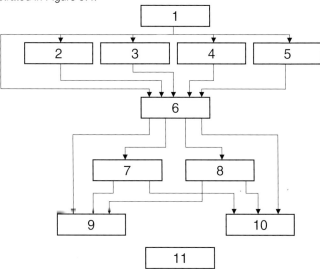

Figure 9.4: Invention Disclosure Claims Genealogy

The main purpose of constructing this genealogy is to identify all of the Claims that need to be designed around. In the above case, all of the other claims except 11 are dependent on Claim 1 and so if we cab design around Claim 1, we have also designed around Claims 2-10.

The mechanics of actually designing around other patents and patent claims are essentially two-fold. The first route involves examining the FAA model and the functions contained within the system. Here there are three main considerations:-

1) *Are There Other Ways to Deliver the Function?*
   (if there are, I may be able to use them to design around the current IPR)
   In order to answer this question, we should use the knowledge/effects part of TRIZ (Chapter 15)
2) *Do I Need the Function?*
   (Can I trim it? – if I can I may have generated new IPR)
   Use Trimming – Chapter 17.
3) *If I Eliminate Harmful or other Negative Functions, Does That Generate Design Around Opportunities?*
   Contradictions, S-Fields in that order.

The second route involves comparison with the Trends of Evolution with the aim of evolving the system (or the top level Claims) to a new s-curve.

Finally, and most important of all, the recommendations here are intended as a complement to the recommendations of a registered Patent Agent, and should not in any way be interpreted as a substitute.

Strengthening a Patent/Patent Application
The same comment about use of a registered Patent Agent applies to those situations where we wish to strengthen one of our own patents. In many senses the activities required to achieve this are similar to those for designing around someone else's patents, and certainly those suggestions apply in this context.

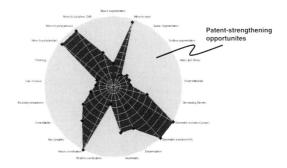

Figure 9.5: Using 'Evolutionary Potential' as a Patent Strengthening Guide

The idea of patent strengthening, however, also includes the consideration of 'improvement patents'. These are inventions that build-on an existing patents rather than trying to supersede them. The main tools to help us to make sure we have the opportunity to protect the possible improvements to a basic invention are firstly the evolutionary potential parts of the Trends tool (where all unused evolutionary potential represents the opportunity to evolve an existing system – Figure 9.5), and consideration of the 'opportunities' aspects of TRIZ (see below, and Chapter 2). The main desire in this second regard is to find answers to the basic question 'who else might be able to use the useful functions delivered by the current invention?'

Opportunity Finding

If the situation you are working through is of the 'opportunity' type ('where is the best place for me to exploit solution X?' for example) the comments at the end of Chapter 2 are worth re-reading.

The key to successful opportunity identification is the recognition of the useful functions and attributes being delivered by your solution. Suppose, for example, that we have discovered a way of producing an electrically conductive paint which is able to very reliably, efficiently, homogenously and accurately translate an electrical input into heat, and we now wish to exploit this in the most effective manner. The first thing we need to do is recognize that the function we are delivering is primarily one of 'heats X', where X is any sub-strait we care to paint the material onto. This recognition should be the prompt to examine the knowledge/effects part of TRIZ to see what other methods exist of delivering the function.

We then need to examine the main attributes of our solution (in the above description, these are reliability, efficiency, homogeneity, and accuracy) in order to compare them with other alternatives. As shown in Figure 9.6, it is often useful to do this graphically – in this case we have plotted two of the four main attributes of our solution. If we were doing it for real, we should construct similar comparison means for the other attributes. If we choose to use the graphical approach, our 'opportunities' are represented by anything to the left and lower on the graph than our capability.

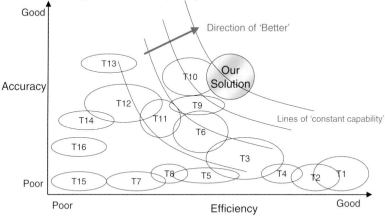

Figure 9.6. Schematic Difference Between 'Innovation' and 'Optimization'

In this hypothetical case, all of the other methods T1-T16 are inferior to our solution for the chosen attribute comparators. The next step is to then establish what the applications of the inferior function delivery methods are. The best ways of achieving this are to use on-line patent databases to see which inventions are using a given effect. For any that we find using a particular effect, we then need to establish whether the improved attributes that our solution is offering are relevant to the users of that effect. Those where the improvement would be helpful to users of the effect are thus 'opportunities' for insertion of our solution. (This process is of course simpler to describe than to implement; please remember that this kind of opportunity identification exercise can be quite time consuming.)

We can also use the Trends to help identify opportunities – any system that is at an earlier evolution stage on any of the trends than our solution is potentially threatened by the advance we offer. The key to successful deployment of the Trends in this opportunity finding role is working out 'why' the evolutionary advance in our system offers a benefit to the users of the other system. See the 'reasons for jumps' reference section in Chapter 13.

Optimization

There are situations where 'optimization' is an appropriate solution strategy. We might define optimization as the task of finding the absolutely best balance between the conflicting parameters within a system in order to achieve the best possible output. A useful way of visualizing the optimization process is connects back to the 'problem solving as digging for treasure' analogy described in Chapter 3: Optimization is the technique that helps us to find the deepest possible hole. Figure 9.7 illustrates the idea, while also showing the potential dangers if it turns out there are 'better' solutions in another direction.

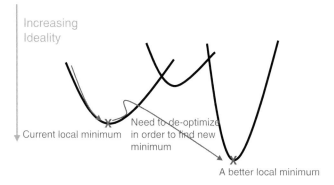

Figure 9.7: Schematic Difference Between 'Innovation' and 'Optimization'

(Read more about this analogy in Reference 9.2). Another potentially useful image relates to the fluid-filled bag model used in the next chapter to describe the importance of contradiction-solving in the innovation process. In this model, innovation is about changing the size of the bag, while optimization is about massaging the bag to get it to the best possible shape.

Drawing a line between what is optimization and what is innovation is probably a pointless exercise, nevertheless it is clear that TRIZ specifically and systematic creativity in general are not well suited to the bag-massaging optimization role. Optimization is largely about mathematics, and these days some undoubtedly sophisticated mathematics geared towards taking the human out of the optimization process altogether (another distinction with creativity and innovation – where we are not as yet able to automate the process).

The advice here is to seriously ask yourself whether the problem you are tackling is *really* about optimization, or whether you might not be better thinking about changing the size of the bag. If you genuinely believe the answer to be that optimization is what is required, the world is full of better techniques than TRIZ. Some of the places we suggest you look for help are listed in the optimization bibliography at the end of this chapter.

Don't Know

If, having been through the preceding problem definition steps you cannot make a connection to the problem types listed in this chapter, head in the direction of Chapter 16 and ARIZ.

No Solutions?

If you have tried all of the recommended strategies for your given problem situation, consider using the Psychological Inertia tools to first help clarify that you are solving the right problem, and then to explore alternative solving routes.

Prioritisation of Problems

It is possible – likely even – that having been through the problem definition part of the systematic creativity process a large number of problems and opportunities for improvement have been identified. Although there are no absolute rules for prioritising problems, this section examines some general strategies for helping us to prioritise which problems we should tackle in what order.

For existing systems, generally speaking, contradictions should receive the highest priority. Eliminating physical contradictions generally gives more powerful solutions than technical contradictions – with a strong likelihood that un-anticipated benefits will emerge if the contradiction can be successfully challenged (on the down-side, physical contradictions can be more difficult to solve). After this, the priority should usually shift to the elimination of harmful functions, then insufficient and excessive. It is a good idea to begin by focusing on main useful functions, and gradually working away to the ancillary functions.

If the system doesn't currently exist, or we are looking to exploit one in a new role, the priority should generally begin with recognition of the useful functions required and the use of functional-benchmarking (Figure 9.6) that will determine what we do next and in what order.

Ultimately, it will be the marriage of defined problem and the constraints that have to be accommodated that will determine which solution routes will be tackled in what sequence.

We end the chapter with an overall summary table. The general idea here is that you work your way down the problem/opportunity situation column until you meet a description matching your situation:

Tool Selection Summary Table

Problem/Opportunity Situation	1st Choice Solve Tool	2nd Choice Solve Tool	3rd Choice Solve Tool	4th Choice Solve Tool
Limiting Contradiction	Physical Contradictions	Technical Contradictions	Trends	Knowledge/ Effects
Other Contradictions	Physical Contradictions	Technical Contradictions	Trends	

Insufficient Actions	Knowledge/ Effects	Trends	S-Fields	Contradictions
Excessive Actions	Trends	Knowledge/ Effects	S-Fields	Contradictions
Missing Actions	S-Fields	Resources	IFR	
System Doesn't Exist	IFR	Knowledge/ Effects	S-Fields	
System Improvement/ 'No Problem'	IFR	Trimming	Contradictions	
Measurement Problem	S-Fields	IFR	Knowledge/ Effects	Technical Contradictions
Reliability Problem	Chapter 20			
Cost Reduction	Trimming	IFR	Contradictions	
'Disruptive Shift' (system level)	IFR	Knowledge/ Effects	Trends	
'Disruptive Shift' (sub-system level)	IFR	Trends	Knowledge/ Effects	Contradictions
'Zero Risk'	Knowledge/ Effects	Resources		
Designing around a Patent	Knowledge/ Effects	Trimming	Contradictions	S-Fields
Strengthening a Patent	Trends	Knowledge/ Effects		
Opportunity Finding	Knowledge/ Effects	Trends		
'Optimization'	Optimization Methods			
'Don't Know'	ARIZ			
'No Solutions'	PI Tools			

What Do I Do?

Start with the above summary table in order to identify a logical sequence of problem solving strategy options. Use the preceding text as support if you require it.

Remember above all that the general idea behind this selection part of the systematic creativity process is to guide thinking, and not to replace it. The more you put into thinking – as in really thinking – about problems/opportunities, the more you will get out of both the process and the solutions you generate. 'Process' does not mean 'panacea'. It does mean that there should be a structured framework. We hope that is the part we have succeeded in delivering.

References

1) Thring, M.W., Laithwaite, E.R., 'How To Invent', MacMillan Press, London, 1977.
2) Mann, D.L., 'Klondike versus Homing Solution Searches', TRIZ Journal, February 2002.

Optimization Bibliography

- Ahuja, R.K., T.L. Magnanti and J. B. Orlin, 'Network Flows. Theory, Algorithms and Applications', Prentice Hall, Englewood Cliffs, NJ, 1993.
- Avriel, M., 'Nonlinear Programming: Analysis and Methods', Prentice-Hall, Englewood Cliffs, NJ, 1976.
- Bazaraa, M.S., Sherali, H.D., Shetty, C.M., 'Nonlinear Programming', John Wiley, New York, NY, 1993.
- Bertsekas, D.P., 'Nonlinear Programming', Athena Scientific, Boston, MA, 1995.
- Birge, J.R., Louveaux, F., 'Introduction to Stochastic Programming', Springer, New York, NY, 1997.
- Chvatal, V., 'Linear Programming', W. H. Freeman and Company, New York, NY, 1983.
- Duff, I.S., Erisman, A.M., Reid, J.K., 'Direct Methods for Sparse Matrices', Oxford University Press, Oxford, 1986.
- Gill, P.E., Murray, W., Wright, M.H., 'Practical Optimization', Academic Press, London, 1989.
- Gondran, M., Minoux, M., 'Graphs and Algorithms', Wiley-Interscience, Norwich, UK, 1986.
- Horst, R., Pardalos, P.M., Thoai, N.V., 'Introduction to Global Optimization', Kluwer Academic Publishers, Dordrecht, 1995.
- Horst, R., Tuy, H., 'Global Optimization: Deterministic Approaches', Springer Verlag, Heidelberg, 1996.
- IBM Corporation, 'IBM Optimization Solutions and Library', QP Solutions user guide, 1998.
- Kall, P., Wallace, S.W., 'Stochastic Programming', John Wiley & Sons, Chichester, England, 1994.
- Minoux, M., 'Mathematical Programming. Theory and Algorithms', Wiley, New York, 1986.
- Nemhauser, G. L., Wolsey, L.A., 'Integer and Combinatorial Optimization', Wiley, New York, NY, 1988.
- Nesterov, Y. Nemirovskii, A., 'Interior-Point Polynomial Algorithms in Convex Programming', SIAM, Philadelphia, PA, 1994.
- Papadimitriou, C. H., Steiglitz, K., 'Combinatorial Optimization. Algorithms and Complexity', Prentice Hall, Englewood Cliffs, NJ, 1982.
- Rockafellar, R.T., Wets, R.J.-B., 'Variational Analysis', Springer-Verlag, Berlin, Germany, 1998.
- Schrage, L., 'Optimization Modeling with LINDO', Duxbury Press, Pacific Grove, CA, 1997.

10.
Problem Solving Tools -
Technical Contradictions/Inventive Principles

"Every coin, I now realise, has at least two sides, but there are pathways through the paradoxes, if
we can understand what is happening and are prepared to be different"
Charles Handy, The Empty Raincoat.

Contradictions – or rather the elimination of contradiction, conflict, paradox, trade-off, or whatever we prefer to label them as – are a central part of the TRIZ philosophy. While many authors have begun to recognise and report the importance of not accepting the contradictions we normally take for granted, TRIZ is unique in that it offers problem solvers tangible tools to help to actually 'eliminate compromise'.

The Contradictions toolkit has two parts; technical and physical. A technical contradiction occurs when we have two different parameters in conflict with each other –for example 'I want high strength, and low weight', while a physical contradiction defines a situation in which we are looking for conflicting values of one parameter ('I want high weight, and low weight'). This chapter examines the technical contradiction aspects of TRIZ, while the next chapter examines physical contradictions.

Before we delve into the detail of technical contradiction definition and 'elimination', it is worth spending a few moments examining the expression 'eliminate compromise', which is used often in and around TRIZ. The expression is both useful and dangerous. It is useful because it is deliberately trying to get us to think about doing things differently than the ways most engineering schools and colleges teach things. It is dangerous because it carries with it the implication that we can literally eliminate contradiction. While there are indeed cases where this can be shown to be the case, it should be viewed as a good **direction** to travel rather than as a specific destination.

Both points are worth exploring a little further, because there are important philosophical elements at play here which will have a significant impact on the way we use this part of TRIZ. A useful analogy is the fluid filled bag concept illustrated in Figure 10.1.

In the analogy, the bag is filled with an incompressible fluid representing all of the parameters we are typically expected to think about when we are designing a system; there are the physical things like area, volume, weight, etc; there are the performance related things like power, force, speed, etc; there are the efficiency related things; there are the 'ility things – like reliability, manufacturability, maintainability, etc; there are environmental aspects; and probably top of the list in most of manufacturing industry, cost aspects.

The vast majority of the methods we are taught about designing systems tell us that the size or amount of fluid contained in this bag is pretty well fixed. Thus, if we are tasked with improving one aspect of a design, something else must get worse. Or, in the analogy, if we

squeeze the bag in one place – say to reduce the cost – then it must bulge out somewhere else – the reliability gets worse, or the performance drops, or whatever. Engineering mathematics does a very good job of enabling us to make the trade-offs between all these battling parameters; it is very good at optimizing the shape of the bag we eventually present to the customer.

What the contradictions part of TRIZ is about, on the other hand, is 'wouldn't it be great if we could change the size of the bag?' If the amount of fluid in the bag is a measure of 'bad'ness or non-idealness; wouldn't it be great if we could reduce that amount.

This is the real essence, then, of 'eliminating compromise'. The TRIZ contradiction tools are there to enable us to reduce the amount of fluid in the bag. If we are literally able to 'eliminate compromise', this is equivalent to removing all of the fluid in the bag. We probably won't be able to achieve this, at least not straight away (but see Chapter 18 on Ideality and Ideal Final Result), but, again, it is the direction of removing fluid that is important.

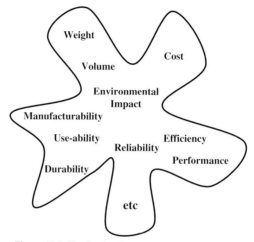

Figure 10.1: The Design Process As A Fluid-Filled Bag

The Contradiction part of TRIZ is about using the successful strategies of other designers and inventors who have not followed the normal route of massaging the shape of the bag, but have instead found ways of reducing the amount of bad stuff.

As we will see, it may not be easy – the process of 'eliminating compromise' almost inevitably means inventing something new – but the benefits if we can promise to be substantial.

If we accept for the moment that it is in fact possible to change the size of the bag – to in effect have your cake and eat it, then this should encourage us to think about design in a very different way. If the size of the bag can be changed by eliminating compromise, we should be looking to find those compromises. In TRIZ terms, if the system exists; it contains contradictions.

And one final point on this theme and analogy before we actually look at how TRIZ enables us to achieve this compromise 'elimination' feat, is that we may well have to think about *successive application* of the tools. This means that one application of the tools might allow us to squeeze the bag in one area (solve one problem), but at the same time

introduce another (hopefully smaller) bulge in another area. We should then look to use the tools again to tackle this new bulge, and so on until the size of the bag has been reduced sufficiently. We will see several instances of this 'contradiction chain' idea in the following case study examples, before returning to the subject in a summary after the examples.

In graphical terms, technical contradictions – the fight between two different parameters can be seen as a hyperbolic curve as illustrated in Figure 10.2.

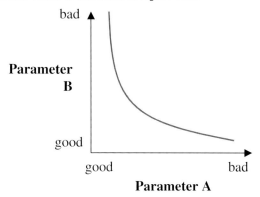

Figure 10.2: Graphical Representation of a Technical Contradiction

The hyperbolic curve on the graph is not usually drawn explicitly, but most of our engineering mathematics and design calculations are helping us to find the point on this line where we achieve an 'acceptable' value of the two conflicting parameters. We might see this as a line of constant design capability, or designing to the established rules.

What the Contradictions part of TRIZ is trying to do is get us to alter and shift the line towards the origin of the graph; the point where, again, the contradiction has been eliminated. The basic line shifting idea is illustrated in Figure 10.3. For those that like a graphical image of what Contradictions is about, this is the thing to keep in mind.

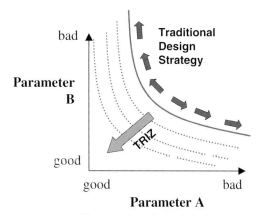

Figure 10.3: Graphical Representation TRIZ Being Used To Eliminate Technical Contradictions

So now let us have a look at exactly how TRIZ allows us to conduct this compromise elimination process:

The Contradiction Matrix

Thinking about the fluid filled bag from Figure 10.1, it should be possible to see that the parameters contained in the bag are the ones that just about every engineer, scientist or designer has to think about when defining a system.

In broad terms, they are the collection of parameters the original TRIZ researchers used when they were formulating a way of classifying problem types. Given the importance of eliminating contradictions, the basic form for the tool generated was a two-dimensional matrix, each side of which featured the aforementioned parameters relevant to the solving of engineering, scientific or design problems. The resulting matrix structure contained 39 different parameters. This 'classical' Contradiction Matrix is reproduced in the fold-out insert provided with the book.

The manner in which the Matrix is used involves selection of a pair of parameters in conflict with one another (we will show several examples shortly); firstly a parameter we are trying to improve, and then a second parameter which either gets worse as we try and improve the first, or somehow stops us from making the desired improvement. The first (improving) parameter we look up in the left hand column down the side of the Matrix; the conflicting parameter then being taken from the list across the top of the Matrix. The selection process is summarized in Figure 10.4.

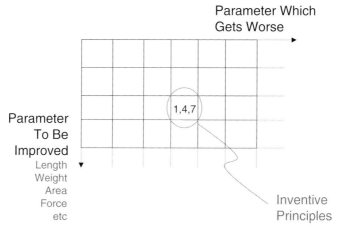

Figure 10.4: Segment of Matrix Illustrating Principles of Operation

The box then denoting the intersection of the improving and conflicting parameters contains the numbers of the Inventive Principles that other problem solvers have used most successfully to tackle the contradiction in question. A quick scan around the Matrix will soon highlight the fact that there are very few such Principles; in fact, as far as this classic Matrix is concerned, just 40. This is not to say that there aren't other Principles out there waiting to be discovered, simply that so far – from all the patents and inventive solutions studied (hundreds of thousands) – only these Principles have been observed. A section at the end of this chapter lists each of the 40 Principles along with details of how they have been interpreted by problem solvers, and a list of examples of the Principle being used.

In the same way that there may be more Principles (actually some people prefer the words 'strategies' or 'triggers'), the three or four contained inside each box of the Matrix should in no way be considered to be the *only* ones potentially relevant to a given problem – see the section on 'what happens when the Matrix doesn't work' below. Experience across a wide variety of problems, on the other hand, justifies use of the Matrix as an excellent start point.

Though conceptually quite simple, the actual mechanics of using the Matrix can appear a little unnatural at first. This can be particularly so with respect to the process of mapping your specific problem onto the 39x39 framework of the Matrix. The best advice here is to write the thing you're trying to improve and the thing stopping you, or that gets worse as succinctly as possible and then try and make connections to the 39 possible links to the Matrix. Sometimes the links will be obvious, but other times you may find that several 'may' be relevant to your problem. The simple advice in this scenario is to not try too hard to pin the contradiction down to one pair; if you're not sure whether your desire to improve 'efficiency' maps better to 'loss of energy' or 'waste of energy' or 'loss of substance' or even 'duration of action', look them all up. (You will often find if you do this that the uncertainty you have experienced is resolved by the Matrix by having some of the suggested Principles occurring several times.

That being said, the following table should provide you with useful guidelines on how best to interpret the 39 parameters.

Moving objects - situations where there is any degree of relative motion between two or more parts related to the problem. This may be linear or rotational, a few microns or a considerable distance.

Stationary objects - situations where there is no relative motion between different parts relevant to the problem.

Parameter Number	Parameter Name	Interpretation
1	Weight of moving object	The mass of or gravitational force exerted by a moving object.
2	Weight of stationary object	As above.
3	Length of moving object	Any linear dimension. Applies equally well to 'width', 'height', 'depth', etc.
4	Length of stationary object	As above
5	Area of moving object	Any dimension related to surface or surface area. Internal or external. May include contact area as well as actual surface area.
6	Area of stationary object	As above.
7	Volume of moving object	Any dimension related to the cubic measure of space occupied by an object or the space around it.
8	Volume of stationary object	As above.
9	Speed	The velocity of an object or the rate of any kind of process or action. Relative or absolute speed; linear or rotational.
10	Force	Any interaction that is intended to change an object's

		condition. Can be linear or rotational; the term applies equally well to torque. Applies to static and dynamic forces.
11	Stress or pressure	Force exercised on a unit area. Stress is the effect of forces on an object. Also, tension, compression. Includes static and dynamic effects, fatigue, creep. Also strain – provided length is not the main issue.
12	Shape	The external contour, and/or aesthetic appearance of a component or system.
13	Stability of the object's composition	The integrity of a system; the relationship of a system's constituent elements. Wear, chemical decomposition, dissociation, and increasing entropy should all be interpreted as issues concerning 'stability'.
14	Strength	The extent to which an object is able to resist changing in response to force. Resistance to breaking. Can mean elastic limit, plastic limit, or ultimate strength; tensile or compressive; linear or rotational. Also includes toughness and hardness.
15	Duration of action by a moving object	The time that an object takes to perform an action. Mean time between overhaul, maintenance or failure are all measures of duration of action, as are 'life' related issues. (see 27 also)
16	Duration of action by a stationary object	As above.
17	Temperature	Measured or perceived thermal condition of the object or system. Loosely includes other thermal parameters, such as heat capacity, conductivity, radiation, and convection parameters.
18	Illumination intensity/Brightness	Light flux per unit area, also any other related characteristics of the system such as colour, light quality, etc.
19	Use of energy by moving object	The measure of an object's capacity for doing work. This parameter focuses on the actual amount of energy (rather than the efficiency of its use – see 22).
20	Use of energy by stationary object	As above.
21	Power	The rate at which work is performed. The rate of use of energy. Rate of energy output.
22	Loss of Energy	Use of energy that does not contribute to the useful function being performed. Inefficiency. (See 19).
23	Loss of substance	Loss of elements of a system – substances, materials, sub-systems, product, etc. Can be partial or complete, permanent or temporary.
24	Loss of Information	Loss of data (or access thereto) from or to a system. Includes data associated with any of the five senses – visual, auditory, kinesthetic, olfactory or gustatory (VAKOG). Can be partial or complete, permanent or temporary.
25	Loss of Time	Time inefficiencies – waiting periods, slack-time, etc.
26	Amount of substance	The quantity or number of a system's materials, substances, parts, fields or sub-systems.

27	Reliability	A system's ability to perform its intended functions in predictable ways and conditions. Also includes durability and issues related generally to the ability to use of an object or system over prolonged periods. (see 15, 16 also)
28	Measurement accuracy	Degree of precision. The closeness of a measured value to an actual value of a property of a system. Measurement error.
29	Manufacturing precision	The degree to which the actual characteristics of a system or object match the specified or required characteristics.
30	Object Affected Harmful Factors	Susceptibility of a system to externally generated harmful effects. Includes safety related issues.
31	Object-generated harmful factors	Aspects of an object or system that produce and adverse effect on external elements. Includes environmental issues like contamination, emissions, noise as well as things like things like vibration.
32	Ease of manufacture	Issues related to manufacture, fabrication and assembly issues associated with an object or system. Also includes ease of inspection.
33	Ease of operation	Simplicity of operation by the intended user.
34	Ease of repair	Quality characteristics such as convenience, comfort, simplicity, and time to repair faults, failures, or defects in a system. Includes issues associated with need for special tooling or equipment required to achieve repair. Also think about conditions associated with in situ repair
35	Adaptability or versatility	The extent to which a system/object is able to respond to external changes. Also, relates to a system capable of being used in multiple ways or under a variety of circumstances. Flexibility of operation, use. Customizability.
36	Device complexity	The number and diversity of elements and element interrelationships within and across the boundaries of a system. The user may be an element of the system that increases the complexity. Includes issues like use-ability, train-ability, number of functions, excessive number of components.
37	Difficulty of detecting and measuring	Complex, costly, time-consuming, labour-consuming inspection or analysis operations. Increasing cost of measuring to a satisfactory quality level.
38	Extent of automation	The ability of a system or object to perform its functions without human interface or intervention.
39	Productivity	The number of useful (value-adding) functions or operations performed by a system per unit time. The time per unit function or operation. Useful output per unit time. Cost per unit output, or amount of useful output. (see also 'speed' – 9 – which is more focused on issues of mechanics rather than output of product)

Table 10.1: Explanation of the 39 Parameters of the Contradiction Matrix

The most common question asked by newcomers to the Matrix is 'why is there no 'cost' parameter. The simple answer (provided here because it provides further useful insight into the Matrix construction philosophy) is that 'cost' is too generic. The Matrix contains instead the parameters 'manufacturability', 'use of energy', 'reliability', etc as ways of prompting the problem solver to think about whether it is first cost, running cost, maintenance cost, or some other element of 'cost' that is at issue. In other words, the Matrix is trying to force the user to transform vague and woolly thinking into something more focused. 'Cost' can mean many things, particularly in an engineering context; the Matrix asks you to think about which of them is relevant to your problem.

Following on from the chapter on psychology, what the Matrix seems to help achieve is to keep our brains in 'define' mode for longer than most of us would naturally choose: if, as stated in the old adage, '90% of the problem is defining what the problem is', the Matrix works to help us concentrate on the 90% for as long as is necessary to adequately translate our specific problem into the generic framework provided by the Matrix.

That being said, the classical Contradiction Matrix has not been updated for at least fifteen years, in part because certain parts of the TRIZ community have shifted their efforts to other parts of the method, and partly because the analysis is lengthy and time-consuming.

An updated version of the Matrix will be available at Reference 10.1 in the future. This new Matrix presents the fruits of a renewed program of comprehensive analysis of the patent database from the last 15 years.

In the meantime, the overall advice is that the current Matrix still makes a very good start point. A section at the end of the chapter provides suggested strategies when the Matrix doesn't work.

So now let's have a look at a few simple examples to illustrate the process in action.

1) Pipe Flange Joint

Many casing or pipe-work structures employ bolted flanges to join adjacent sections that at some point are required to be dis-assembled. Casings on gas-turbine engines (Figure 10.5) are a particularly good example. Flanged joints between casings in such applications are required to seal against extremely high temperature and high pressure conditions across a wide range of operating conditions and loads. A typical gas-turbine flanged joint may require over a hundred bolts to ensure adequate functionality.

Of course, the presence of such large numbers of bolts presents a considerable penalty to operators in terms of both the amount of maintenance time required to dis-assemble an engine and also a not inconsiderable weight penalty.

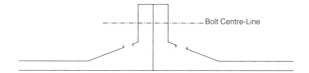
Bolt Centre-Line

Figure 10.5: Typical Flange Cross-Section

From a design perspective, we may see flanges as a classic compromise situation; one in which the designer is trying to strike a delicate balance between a requirement for a large

number of bolts to ensure adequate sealing **and** a desire for a small number of bolts in order to improve maintainability and reduce weight. The vast majority of the rules configured to help design flanges is based on optimising precisely these kinds of trade-off. Sometimes, these rules and this 'optimisation' strategy is fine, but not if we'd like to do a better job.

The technical contradictions part of TRIZ gives us a tool through which we might eliminate such compromise situations. Right from the start, thinking about 'eliminating' contradictions should encourage us to register the possibility of doing things a better way. The first thing we need to do after registering the concept, is to begin identifying possible contradictions. In the case of the bolted flange the contradiction we are looking to remove may be expressed as our desire to achieve:-

GOOD SEALING, PREVENTION OF LEAKS **AND** LOW WEIGHT, SMALL NUMBER OF BOLTS

Sometimes it is useful to think of the conflicting parameters we have identified in graphical terms as previously illustrated in Figure 10.6:

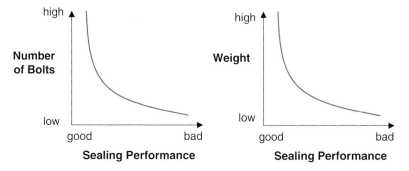

Figure 10.6: Graphical Representation of Flange Joint Contradictions

This graphical form can often be useful in helping us to confirm that the parameters we are interested in are in fact in contradiction with one another – allowing us to confirm for example that a form of the hyperbolic line exists in some form between the chosen parameters.

The next thing we have to do once we have identified some contradicting parameter pairs is to translate our specific problems into generic ones that TRIZ has identified as contradictions that other problem solvers have successfully tackled. The job to be done here is to map our specific words onto the 39 possible categories defining the axes of the Contradiction Matrix.

By way of example, one of the specific parameters we are interested in is 'sealing performance'. Unfortunately, the Matrix does not feature a parameter with this name, and so we have to make the best matches we can. In this case, looking through the list of possibilities, there appears to be several that might fit – Loss of Substance, Harmful Side Effect, and Reliability might all be connections our brains might make. At this stage, if we make a connection, we should include it in our investigation.

On the other side of the contradiction, we have 'number of bolts'. This per se is not something that gets worse in our system, but, mapping it onto the Matrix, we should be able to make connections to things like Convenience of Use – thinking of the person who has to fasten and unfasten all the bolts – or weight or possibly even productivity.

Translating all of the other relevant contradicting parameters in terms of the Contradiction Matrix we should get something like:-

Things we are trying to improve:-	Loss of Substance
	Harmful Side Effect
	Reliability
Things which tend to get worse:-	Weight of Stationary Object
	Convenience of Use
	Ease of Repair

Strictly speaking, this then gives us 9 (3x3) possible contradictions to look up in the Matrix. If we do this, the matrix recommends quite a large number of Inventive Principles. The list includes the following (if we were doing this for real, we would examine them all of course):-

Parameter Changes	Another Dimension
Segmentation	Taking Out
Local Quality	Flexible Shells and Thin Films
Intermediary	Composite Materials

The next part of the problem solving process then requires us to translate these generic solutions into something we can use on our specific problem. The best way to do this is to examine the list of Principle with examples reference section at the end of the chapter to see how we can best interpret the solution suggestions. We will go through precisely this operation in our fourth case study. For now, however, we will jump to just one good solution emerging from the suggestions derived from one of the above Principles.

In the fullness of time, these suggestions may operate collectively to achieve an Ideal Final Result flange joint design (for example it is already possible to seal a relatively low duty flanged joint with one bolt – using a V-band clamp type arrangement). We should also examine closely (our thus far assumed necessary) functional requirement for a breakable joint at all. In the meantime, however, Inventive Principle 'Another Dimension' was used to profound effect in offering the potential for possibly halving the number of bolts around a flange whilst maintaining the sealing performance.

One of the great beauties of the elegant idea contained in US patent 5,230,540 (Figure 10.7) is that it manages to solve the design contradiction without the need for any additional parts or complexity. In essence, all that has changed from a manufacturing standpoint is that the faces of the flange are formed at a slight angle to one another rather than being parallel (hence the 'another dimension' solution trigger).

Tests on an prototype flange (reported at ISABE 1989 in Athens) demonstrated the ability of the design to not only seal a flange with around half the number of bolts of the traditional parallel surface flange, but to do it more effectively across the entire range of operating conditions a gas-turbine may be expected to face.

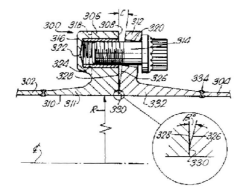

Figure 10.7: Improved Flange Joint Design Emerging From 'Another Dimension' Principle

Some solutions are better than others. The best ones – irrespective of their degree of novelty – seem to possess a simplicity and elegance that makes them not only a powerful example of the Inventive Principles of TRIZ, but a spark in their own right to a host of inventive solutions to other problems.

Clearly, despite the fact that this design concept allows us to halve the number of bolts required to achieve the desired function, there are still bolts present. We have successfully 'challenged' the contradictions present in the original design, but we can't claim to have 'eliminated' them. We will return to this later in the chapter when we examine 'contradiction chains'. For now, the most important information to take from the example is the mechanics of actually using the technical contradiction part of TRIZ.

2) A Comfortable Bicycle Seat

Bicycle seats are uncomfortable. The state of the art in today's world of bicycle seat engineering is the bicycle seat design that tends to look something pretty close to the one illustrated in Figure 10.8.

Look in any bike shop, or any bicycle saddle patent on the US database and there are literally hundreds of tiny variations about the same set of design principles. Each one a subtly different balance between the trade-offs inherent to the concept of a product that is required to give both weight support and the freedom to pedal. All in all, the bicycle seat may be seen as a classic example of how the traditional 'design is a compromise' philosophy produces a product that ultimately satisfies no customer; bicycle saddles indeed being uncomfortable at best, health-damaging at worst.

The search for, and elimination of contradictions is a fundamental principle of the TRIZ method. The search for design trade-offs like those found with the bicycle seat – in other words the search for contradictions – is an often potent means of defining the 'right' problem to be solved. It is clear from the prevailing bicycle saddle design paradigm that no-one in the industry has thought to define the problem as a contradiction. Anytime we see a situation like this – where the whole industry is busy optimising designs that are all essentially the same – we can be pretty certain that finding and then solving a 'good' contradiction will, from an engineering context at least, be a very good thing to do.

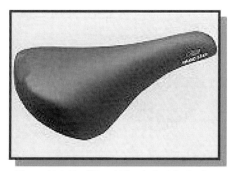

Figure 10.8: Traditional Bicycle Saddle Design

In the case of the bicycle seat, the fundamental design trade-off may be seen to be a conflict between the desire for a WIDE seat in order to achieve comfort for the cyclist, and the fact that the wider the saddle becomes, the more difficult it is to provide freedom of movement of the legs during pedalling.

Seeking out the best compromise between these two conflicting requirements is clearly here not solving the 'right' problem. The right problem is more likely to be how we might achieve

A BICYCLE SEAT THAT IS BOTH WIDE **AND** DOESN'T IMPEDE LEG MOVEMENT.

In order to use the Contradiction Matrix to solve this conflict in a better way than the traditional trade-off approach, we need to transform the two sides of the conflict into the framework of the 39 Matrix parameters.

In terms of the desire to improve 'WIDTH', we should quickly establish that although there is not a parameter explicitly called 'width', there is one called 'length'. The mapping between the specific (width) and the generic (a linear dimension, length) is fairly straightforward in this instance. The only thing we still need to do in fact is decide whether we should be mapping to parameter 4 'length of stationary object', or 5 'length of moving object'. As stated at the top of Table 3.1, if there is any degree of planned movement in the system, we should use the latter; if there is none, we should use the 'stationary' parameter.

The translation of our specific worsening parameter 'doesn't impede leg movement' is a little more difficult. Looking down the list of parameters the possible matches could be deemed to include 'shape', 'object generated harmful effect', or 'convenience of use'.

For the sake of brevity, we will consider only the first conflicting pair of 'length of stationary object' versus 'shape'. In practice, we would examine all of the pairs of conflict parameters we have identified. For our LENGTH/SHAPE technical contradiction, the Matrix recommends.▪

    13 THE OTHER WAY ROUND
    14 CURVATURE INCREASE
    15 DYNAMIC PARTS, and
    7 NESTED DOLL

as inventive principles used by others to solve this kind conflict, 13 being the most commonly applied strategy, 7 being the 4th most likely based on analysis of other solutions. Our task now is to translate these generic solution triggers into a specific solution to our saddle problem. The table of Inventive Principles at the end of the chapter suggests some more detailed interpretations of the triggers. In particular, for inventive principle 'the other way round' is the suggestion:-

"make movable parts fixed, and fixed parts movable"

And for 'dynamic parts':-

"divide an object into parts capable of moving relative to each other"

and

"if an object is rigid or inflexible make it movable or adaptable"

Which almost immediately (based on the experiences of doing this as an exercise in presentations to TRIZ newcomers) gives rise to an idea very much like the following concept from ABS Sports in the US:-

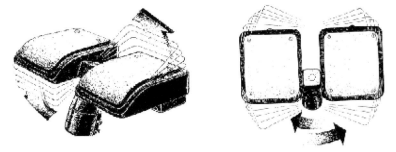

Figure 10.9: Alternative Bicycle Saddle Design Resulting From Length-Shape Contradiction Elimination

It seems almost immediately clear that here is a solution to the bicycle seat problem that not only uses the two inventive principles recommended by TRIZ, but is also fundamentally 'right'; not only giving cyclists support where the body desires support to be found, but also – thanks to the moving seat components - giving the possibility of zero-chafe pedalling action. Our length versus shape contradiction has indeed been eliminated in this particular case.

On the other hand, even cursory analysis of the design should indicate that we have clearly made some aspects of the design worse than they were before. Some of these are obvious – it looks to be fundamentally more expensive to manufacture – and some less so – the designers, for example have failed to recognise that the saddle performs functions other than the main function 'support rider'. In particular they have failed to recognise that the horn of a traditional saddle has the function 'help high-speed cornering'. In either instance, an important point of the example is the reducing fluid bag concept and the fact that we while we have squeezed the bag in to areas, we have clearly made it bulge somewhere else. As described in the overall systematic creativity process (Chapter 2), we

should always look to go around the process again. Our brains – or, the brain of the ABS designer in this case – fell into the usual trap of being too easily satisfied by an attractive concept. Again 'if the system exists, it contains contradictions'. The smart money goes around the loop at least twice.

3) A Better Wrench

Many of us have struggled to undo an over-tightened or corroded nut at some point in our lives. Conventional wrenches are not well-suited to such situations, and chances are that they will damage the nut in some way, and make it even more difficult to remove. This is especially so if the wrench is not 'exactly' the right size to fit the nut. The damage occurs because the majority of the fastening or un-fastening loads are focused on the corners of the nut as shown in Figure 10.10.

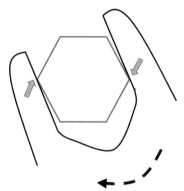

Figure 10.10: Conventional Wrench Focuses Loads on Nut Corners

If we look to TRIZ to improve the design of this simple, in evolutionary S-curve terms, relatively mature system, the Technical Contradiction problem solving tools offer a good start point. As we know from previously discussed TRIZ findings, if we are to improve the design of a system at or close to the top of its current S-curve, we are going to have to identify and eliminate a contradiction. The damage causing traits of the current wrench are a symptom of the current (fundamental) limitations of the current design paradigm. These traits give us a good lead in helping to identify what contradictions we should tackle in order to improve the design. If we are to tackle this contradiction successfully, we need then to map our 'reduce the likelihood of damage to the nut' desire onto one or more of the parameters in the Contradiction Matrix. 'Object generated harmful factors' – parameter 31 – thus appears as a very good correlation. So, we know what it is we want to improve, we now need to work out what gets worse as we reduce the nut damage. This is often a more difficult task than identifying the parameter we are trying to improve. One common strategy is to work through the list of 39 parameters until one appears to fit the problem. Another, more systematic, approach involves a process by which we force ourselves to put all the solution constraints we know to exist to one side. A good question to ask is *how might I achieve the improvement goal if there were no obstacles?*

Asking such a question for the Figure 10.10 wrench, we might come up with answers like:-

a) I would make the sides of the wrench fit the sides of the nut exactly so that **all** of the flat face of the wrench touches **all** of the flat face of the nut.

b) I would add a 'gizmo' that allowed me to move the sides of the wrench so that they fitted the sides of the nut (or a gizmo that allowed the sides of the wrench to move by themselves)

c) I would make the wrench out of a softer material so that it was damaged instead of the nut

None of these is anything that 'gets worse' per se about the design of the wrench, so in order to be able to use the Contradiction Matrix, we need to map the answers to a generic worsening parameter from the list of 39. The first of the three answers – make the sides of the wrench fit exactly – is probably the most pragmatically practical one. In terms of relating the idea to 'something that gets worse', we might well here make a correlation between our desire for very good dimensional accuracy to the 'manufacturability' parameter (i.e. if I make the manufacture tolerance tighter, the manufacturability becomes worse).

We now have a very good technical contradiction:-

Thing we are trying to improve:- OBJECT GENERATED HARMFUL FACTORS

Thing which gets worse:- MANUFACTURABILITY

Matrix recommends:- 4 ASYMMETRY
17 ANOTHER DIMENSION
34 DISCARDING AND RECOVERING
26 COPYING

From Another Dimension we get 'move an object in two or three-dimensional space' or 'use a different side of the given area', or, in layman's terms, 'anywhere we see a straight thing, make it not-straight'. From Discarding & Recovering, we get 'make portions of an object that have fulfilled their function go away', and from Asymmetry, 'if an object is asymmetrical, increase the degree of asymmetry'. All of which give very strong pointers to the solution found in US Patent 5,406,868 from 1995 (Figure 10.11).

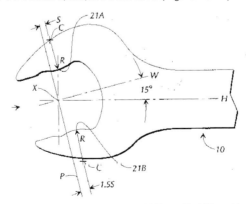

Figure 10.11: US Patent 5,406,868 'Open End Wrench'
(NB: This invention represents a step beyond the conceptually similar design currently marketed by 'Metrinch')

The motivation for this (and similar) inventions is precisely to eliminate the nut-damaging harmful side-effects of all conventional wrenches. The 5,406,868 solution achieves this objective by profiling the working faces of the wrench such that the points of contact with the nut avoid the damage-prone corners.

Closed-End Wrench

Moving from an open-ended to a closed ended wrench design – especially if we include the good design practices identified in the Figure 10.11 or Metrinch designs – largely overcomes the objective generated harmful factors found in the open-ended design. We might consider this closed-end wrench design to be a good solution. TRIZ however is there to help prompt us to look for ever better solutions, and in particular to continue to tackle the contradictions present in any design – see 'Contradiction Chains' later in this chapter. Examining the Figure 10.12 design below, we might observe, for example, the fact that although theoretically the loads in the wrench and on the nut being tightened or loosened are distributed evenly on each contact face of the nut, in practice, irregularities in manufacture mean that the loads are not evenly spread. As with the previous discussion of open-ended wrench designs, this uneven load profile can cause damage to either the wrench or – more likely – the nut.

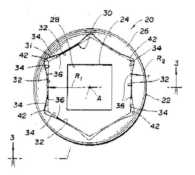

Figure 10.12: Closed-End Wrench Design, US Patent 4,930,378

In this case, we might see that in beginning to formulate a new contradiction, the parameter we are trying to improve is the stress distribution around the nut. In terms of the Contradiction Matrix, what we are trying to improve is TENSION, PRESSURE.

Thinking next about what gets worse as we try to improve the stress distribution, we see immediate parallels with the previous open-ended wrench discussion in that, we see that tightening the manufacture tolerances will allow us to assist the stress distribution. Thus we have a TENSION, PRESSURE versus MANUFACTURABILITY contradiction. Looking then to the Matrix we have:-

Thing we are trying to improve:- TENSION, PRESSURE

    Thing which gets worse:- MANUFACTURABILITY

        Matrix recommends:- 1 SEGMENTATION
                        35 PARAMETER CHANGES
                        16 PARTIAL OR EXCESSIVE ACTION

Both Inventive Principle Number 1, Segmentation and Number 35 Parameter Changes ('increase the degree of flexibility') have been combined in the novel solution illustrated in Figure 10.13 (more details also at Reference 10.2).

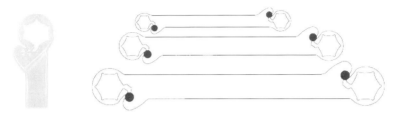

Figure 10.13: Liquid Levers Advanced Wrench Design

The novel design overcomes the contradiction by allowing the wrench to flex in such a way that the loads and stresses around the nut tend to become equalised. Thus a high load on one face causes a high degree of flexure and consequent re-distribution of loads to other faces.

The recommendation of the 'Segmentation' solution trigger is particularly interesting in the light of the otherwise non-instinctive step of introducing a cut into the closed wrench: 'conventional' design thinking would tend to suggest that segmenting a fundamentally strong closed structure would inevitably weaken it. In practice, of course, the novel wrench design overcomes the decrease in structure strength by adding an existing resource, such that now the nut becomes a part of the structural system. (Note: the invention is also a very good example of the identification and use of previously un-exploited resources in a system.)

The recommendation of Parameter Changes, and particularly the accompanying trigger 'increase the degree of flexibility', is likewise non-instinctive in this case. And yet the solution offered by adopting the Principle is considerable in terms of overcoming the stress contradiction.

4) Anti Red-Eye Flash Photography

Anyone who has taken photographs using flash photography will be aware of the phenomenon known as 'red-eye' – Figure 10.14 illustrates a typical example. Although there are several well known 'solutions' to the red-eye problem, the phenomenon has by no means completely disappeared.

Figure 10.14. Red-Eye Phenomenon

Red-eye is a flash photography phenomenon. It is caused by light reflected off the subject's retina. Research has shown that if the angle of reflection is less than 2.5 degree, red eye will occur – Figure 10.15.

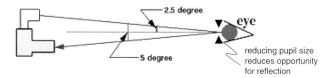

Figure 10.15: Red-Eye Phenomenon

There are several known means to remove the red-eye problem. The basic mechanism for overcoming the effect is to ensure that the angle of reflection will be larger than 2.5 degrees. This can be achieved by moving closer to the subject, or by increasing the distance between flash and lens. Another well known means to achieve the 2.5 degrees or better requirement is to encourage the subject's iris to reduce in size (typically the pupil opening will be large prior to the photograph being taken as there will be little light around (hence the need for flash! – Ideality would tell us of course that ultimately the red-eye problem will disappear because the need for flash will disappear)). The size of the pupil is mainly governed relative to the amount of light present.

Effective use of the TRIZ Contradiction Matrix demands a sound definition of the contradictions present. It is usually advantageous to conduct this definition in a number of separate stages (as previously described);

1) define the elements of the design that are required to be improved
2) map these into the terms of the 39 parameters of the Matrix
3) identify the solution directions that will help remove the problem
4) identify which of these elements is in contradiction with the feature to be improved
5) map these into the terms of the 39 parameters of the Matrix to get pairs of improving-worsening features.

From this red-eye example, we might follow these stages as follows:-

Elements to be improved – red-eye

Mapping 'red-eye' on the Matrix – 'Object Affected Harmful Factor'

Solution directions - reduce distance between subject and camera
                      - increase separation between flash and lens
                      - change the amount of light

Identify whether these are in contradiction:
                      - distance – reducing distance between camera and subject means the shot has to be re-framed and not as much of the subject can be included; so distance *is* something that gets worse as red-eye is improved
                      - separation – increased separation means the camera and lens may no longer be able to be mounted together, or there may be synchronization problems, or the flash may generate unwanted shadows; so this too may be seen as a

worsening feature in contradiction with red-eye improvement
- amount of light – increasing the amount of flash light present would tend to worsen red-eye and so is not seen here as a useful solution direction. On the other hand, reducing the amount of light would improve red-eye, but we can't do this because if we do, there will no longer be sufficient light to make the photograph. Hence the amount of light is in contradiction with our desire to improve red-eye.

Map these onto the Matrix –
- distance → 'Length' ('of Moving Object' – because there is relative movement between camera and subject)
- separation → 'Length' again, although this time we might chose to use 'stationary object' because there is currently no relative movement between lens and flash unit.
- amount of light → 'Illumination Intensity'

In total, then, these contradictions give us a number of Inventive Principle solution triggers:-

Object Affected versus Length of Moving   - 17, 1, 39, 4

Object Affected versus Length of Stationary - 1, 18

Object Affected versus Illumination Intensity - 1, 19, 32, 13

We may immediately see the relevance of these Inventive Principle solution triggers to some well established remedies to the red-eye problem.

Inventive Principles 32, Colour Changes, is perhaps not so useful, but does suggest use of black and white photography, or points towards the plethora of after-the-event remedies like anti-red-eye pens for touching up photographs or, for digital photography, anti-red-eye features in photo manipulation software. There are also one or two patented solutions where the 'colour change' is remedied by software processing within the camera when the photograph is being taken (undoubtedly clever, and an effective transition from a mechanical to a field based solution to the problem).

Inventive Principle 1, Segmentation occurs several times and thus should suggest it is likely to be highly relevant to the problem at hand. The most obvious interpretation of the trigger is the solution adopted by most professional photographers; that of segmenting the camera and flash (and, in fact, also segmenting the flash to utilize several flashes). More practically from the perspective of the amateur photographer are patents in which the segmentation between camera and flash occurs more locally – pop-up flashes, flash units driven away from the camera body using linear motors, and even velcro-attachable flashes are all available or patented solutions.

Principle 1 might also to suggest the idea of segmenting the light emerging from the flash, which in turn relates to the next solution trigger:

Inventive Principle 19, Periodic Action, emerging specifically from the contradiction associated with illumination intensity, offers a direct lead into the anti-red-eye flash

solutions incorporated into the majority of current integral camera designs. This is the idea of a double (or more) flash action – in which the first flash prompts the pupil to contract such that when the second flash is fired to coincide with the taking of the picture, the pupil is usually small enough to allow the 2.5 degree rule to be satisfied.

So, the Matrix may be seen to be offering clearly appropriate solution directions for the red-eye problem.

Of course, TRIZ always recommends that we don't just satisfy ourselves with the first group of solutions that emerge. Our brains tend to fight this direction particularly if it looks like the emerging solution – e.g. the now prevalent double flash idea – possesses a high degree of elegance, and so we usually have to force ourselves to remember that '*if the solution exists, it contains contradictions*', and to look to tackle the remaining or emerging contradictions after we have solved the first one – as discussed in the 'contradiction chains' section later.

In the case of the double-flash idea, any user of this solution will be clearly aware of other contradictions that have emerged as a result of solving the red-eye problem. New problems relate to the phenomenon that we tend to find dilated pupils more attractive than small ones, and, more seriously from a practical point of view, to the fact that when we press the shutter to take a photograph, the timing of the double flash means there is a delay of up to a second between action and the resulting photographic image – in other words we're not taking the photo we intend to take.

Translating this particular new problem into the terms of the Contradiction Matrix, we may see the 'duration of action' as a definite feature we would like to improve. We could thus repeat the TRIZ process for contradictions related to this situation.

Rather than doing this, however, we will take another direction as a way of highlighting another important feature about using the Contradictions part of TRIZ. This feature we will call 'solution mapping'.

In many senses, the double-flash idea has been seen as so attractive a solution in the compact camera market that it has provoked the whole industry along the same direction (see the large range of highly similar patents in the area on the patent database). Solution mapping gets us to remember that there are other solution routes available and to question whether solving the next round of problems with the double-flash is the right thing to do relative to travelling along one or more of the other available routes. In other words, it gets us to question whether the double flash idea is actually an evolutionary cul-de-sac.

One way of thinking about the solution map is the tangled string game found in children's puzzle books and described in more detail in Chapter 8. In these puzzles, the reader is asked to choose from a number of loose ends of string (usually three or four – in real life, there will be many more!) and to trace the chosen string through the tangle of other strings to hopefully reach the 'treasure' at the other end. All but one of the start points, however, ends up not leading to the treasure, but to some cul-de-sac with anything but treasure at the end of it. If we extend the analogy so that 'treasure' becomes 'ideal final result', we obtain a useful image of how systems will evolve – with lots of dead-ends and cul-de-sacs, but (at least) one route through to IFR.

(We might also note that anyone who spent any time at all playing with these puzzles during childhood, pretty soon learned it was more effective to start from the treasure and work back to the start. Back then, it was called 'cheating'; today it's called an 'IFR tool'.)

Coming back to the real world again, a partial solution map for the red-eye problem is illustrated in Figure 10.16.

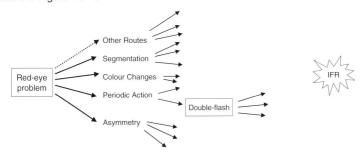

Figure 10.16: Partial Solution Map For 'Red-Eye' Problem

One of the questions provoked by drawing this type of picture is 'am I correct to continue down this path, or should I go back and investigate whether other paths might offer me a more effective route to ideality – including, incidentally, solutions from other parts of the TRIZ toolkit above and beyond those prompted by the Inventive Principles.

It should also be encouraging us to examine how different solution routes might be combined and distilled.

With little justification other than the desire to travel down a different route to see how to make the journey most effectively, and to see what happens along the way, we will now examine the thus far un-explored 'Asymmetry' route (from the above contradiction solution suggestions) out of the red-eye problem:

The translation of the TRIZ generic solutions like 'Asymmetry' into specific solutions to the red-eye problem is not always an obvious one. Chapter 3 has discussed the gap between 'generic' and 'specific' and recommended strategies for filling the gap.

We will look now at a 3-stage strategy for generating solutions of making connections between solution trigger and the problem.

The first of the three stages proposed here involves identification of resources in the current system upon which the 'asymmetry' solution route might be applied. This means looking for things in and around the current system space that are symmetrical, but it also means looking for asymmetries that we could make either more or less asymmetrical. We conducted this search as a systematic brainstorming session structured around the camera plus flash plus photographer plus subject space system illustrated in Figure 10.15. Thinking about time issues, we defined 'past' as the time before the picture is taken, when the photographer is framing the picture and the camera is warming up; 'present' as the point of pressing the shutter; and 'future' as the time immediately after the picture has been taken.

Figure 10.17 illustrates the un-processed outcome of this first (ten minute) brainstorm session, done with three willing volunteers equipped with 'LVT-for-TRIZ' MagNotes (Reference 10.3). The brainstorm question was to 'find things that are symmetrical'. The volunteers wrote down their ideas – one per Magnote – on the yellow hexagons.

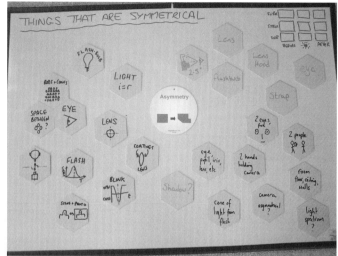

Figure 10.17: 'What Does Asymmetry Mean in the Red-Eye Problem?' Initial Brainstorm Output

The second stage is a relatively short one in which we seek to distill and re-enforce the ideas emerging from the first stage. This is most effectively done by asking the brainstorm participants to 'cluster' the ideas generated in the first stage into related groups. The outcome of this (2 minute) stage is illustrated in Figure 10.18.

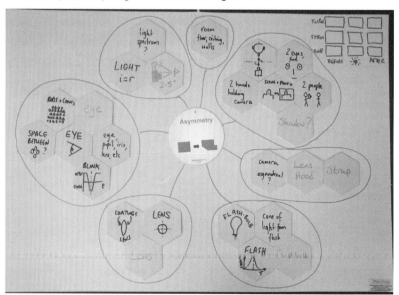

Figure 10.18: Clustered Brainstorm Output

The third stage of the solution process then involves taking these outputs – actually now 'resources' – i.e. they all represent opportunities to deploy the 'asymmetry solution – identified in the first stage in order to examine how the 'Asymmetry' Inventive Principle can

be used to produce useful solutions. A partial picture of the output from this session – which was allowed to run for around 30 minutes and generated a new board of ideas for each of the clusters identified in Figure 10.17 – is reproduced in Figure 10.19. The figure is 'partial' because we think we generated some useful and patentable solutions on the other boards and thought it best not to include them here (readers are encouraged to see if they can find them too!). The excluded parts composed the output from attempts to link 'asymmetry' to the other opportunity clusters from Figure 10.18. The incompleteness shouldn't be allowed to detract from the method being demonstrated – which, after all, is the main point of this example.

If we were doing this for real of course, we would also be looking to distill good ideas being generated by different generic solutions. For example, we might make a connection between the use of an asymmetrical flash illumination profile and the earlier double-flash concept; for again there is a largely untapped resource in tailoring the flash time history to the problem.

As it was, we ended up with a total of over a hundred Magnote-recorded ideas from the session on just the Asymmetry trigger.

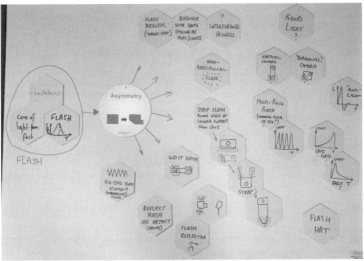

Figure 10.19: Partial Picture of 'Asymmetry' Solution Generation Session

This case study example has attempted to describe a reproducible process – or series of mini-processes – to help use the contradictions part of the TRIZ method. In it, we have seen that the Contradiction Matrix is a pretty good start point for the red-eye problem; allowing us to quickly re-generate good solutions to the problem.

More specifically, we have introduced the concept of a 'solution map', and hopefully demonstrated its importance in helping us to ensure we see that there are several solution routes to any problem and that there are times when we may be travelling down a route that is a cul-de-sac rather than a highway to increased system ideality.

We have also demonstrated a three-stage (resource identification, distillation and application) strategy for ensuring the most effective use of the Inventive Principles

(although the same strategy will be effective with other TRIZ tools too) in filling the gap between 'generic' and 'specific' solutions

Related to this, we have again seen the importance of recognising the existence of 'contradiction chains' (i.e. pre-flash is a good solution to the red-eye problem, but it comes at the expense of introducing other contradictions), and that the road to ideality involves challenging a succession of contradictions. This is the subject covered in more detail in the next but one section – which is intended to act as a summary to the whole concepts of contradiction and contradiction elimination

5) A Better Wind-Turbine

A final example of technical contradictions in action comes in the form of a look at a real problem associated with the design of wind-turbines. As well as showing TRIZ in action on a problem that has not yet been solved, the example seeks to offer an additional learning point as we transition from conceptual to specific solutions, linking in to other parts of the problem solving toolkit.

The problem under consideration concerns an issue affecting all wind-turbines, but especially the large-scale (500-750kW) machines – a typical example of which is illustrated in Figure 10.20

Figure 10.20: Typical Large-Scale Wind Turbine

The basic problem concerns what happens to the turbines in high winds, where – perhaps surprisingly – as wind speed rises above a certain level, the turbine wants to rotate too quickly, the centrifugal forces from which then cause the blades to want to fly off. The current strategy for solving this problem is to stop rotation altogether when the wind is too

high. Paradoxically, therefore, when the wind contains the most energy, the wind-turbine captures the least. It is desirable to not have to stop the turbine during high wind conditions.

The problem very definitely contains a contradiction; the basic thing we would like to improve in this situation is the ability to operate in high winds; the thing that stops us is that the blade falls off. Relating these two sides of the contradiction to the Matrix, it appears clear that the improving parameter connects best to SPEED. More difficult is the worsening parameter. From 'the blade falls off', we might make connections to Harmful Side Effects, Force, Stress, Area, Reliability or Strength. Maybe even Loss of Substance if we're thinking very laterally. Now, we could chose to look up the conflicting pairs for each of these possibilities – in which case we would end up with the rather high number of 19 different Inventive Principle suggestions, with only three appearing more than once. There is nothing wrong with this approach of course, but it would be rather time consuming and difficult to maintain level of effort at an acceptable level across all of the Principles. The alternative is to think a little more specifically about the problem and try to focus in on exactly what the problem is using a form of '**root contradiction**' analysis.

The logic for this goes something like:

> The blades fall off. (Matrix parameter = Loss of Substance, Reliability)
> Why?
> The loads are too high. (Matrix parameter = Force, Stress, Area)
> Why?
> Insufficient strength of material. (Matrix parameter = Strength)
> Why?
> Limits of science.

At which point we reach the end of the line. So, what we learn from this 'ask why five times' route (apart from the fact we ran out of why's after three), is that the root contradiction is the one involving Strength. What we mean by 'root' is that if we solve the contradiction at this level we automatically solve the other problems (whereas if we solve the contradiction at the 'blades fall off' level, we could still have a strength problem).

Generally speaking, if we have a situation like this where the list of possible contradictions and the resulting list of Inventive Principles is unworkably high, then it is a good idea to focus in at root level.

So what happens when we do that, and focus this wind-turbine problem on the speed versus strength contradiction?

For a start, the Matrix recommends the following Inventive Principles:

8	-	Counterweight
3	-	Local Quality
26	-	Copying
14	-	Curvature

Rather than repeat the mechanics of connecting these triggers to possible solutions as we have done in previous examples (if we were doing this for real, we would of course do exactly what we have suggested previously), it is perhaps useful to examine another strategy. In this case, the strategy involves a link with the knowledge/effects part of the TRIZ problem solving toolkit, or rather with the patent-search element thereof.

The basic idea is to see if anyone else has already made the connection between the Inventive Principles being suggested and something like the system under evaluation.

The easiest of the four Inventive Principles recommended from the root contradiction to do this with is 'Curvature'. The question we pose through an on-line patent search engine is, ' has anyone developed a blade with a curve?' To answer the question requires us to investigate searches of 'blade' (and synonyms) and 'curve' (and synonyms). Simply combining the two words should, irrespective of anything we find on the patent database, suggest to us the idea of a curved blade. The key point of finding other solutions where this connection has already been made is in helping us to pin down exactly what sort of curvature others have applied, and whether, when they have applied it, it has solved a speed versus strength contradiction. Very quickly using the 'blade' plus 'curve' search idea reveals that quite a few people have already combined the two ideas to precisely help solve a speed-v-strength contradiction. These include:-

- propeller design
- jet-engine fan blade design – 'sword-fan'
- a centrifugal compressor
- high speed wing design
- a boomerang-like toy

Not only do these findings confirm the validity of the 'curvature' direction, they give us some pretty good steers on exactly what sort of curvature to use – in this case to curve the blades away from the wind, and also swept back from the direction of rotation.

Applying a similar search idea to 'blade-and-counter-weight' and 'blade-and-copy' also reveals some promising ideas. 'Blade-and-local quality' is a more difficult search to conduct as 'local quality' is a rather generic and unlikely to be described in such terms within an invention disclosure. Here we need to be a little bit more creative in our search strategy. Local Quality – as detailed in the list of Principles at the end of the chapter – is about turning uniform things into non-uniform things; making parts of a system function in conditions most suitable to their operation, changing the local environment. These suggestions might encourage us to search for patents featuring blades with special tip, root, leading edge, or trailing edge geometries, local protrusions or depressions, roughened profiles, different length segments, and so on. The general point being that here we're making hopefully useful connections between problem component and solution trigger and using the patent database to validate those connections. As it happens, several of the above have been used in a variety of industries to solve precisely the contradiction we are tackling.

Contradiction Chains

We often hear talk about 'design without compromise' and 'contradiction elimination' in many TRIZ texts apart from this one. Both terms carry the implication that TRIZ offers some kind of a panacea to the ills of the engineering and design worlds. While this is clearly not the case in practice, the Contradictions tools and methods contained in the TRIZ schema are nevertheless still very important paradigm changing tools that offer much to help design better products, processes and services.

This brief section examines some of the underlying truths behind the Contradictions methods in order to perhaps begin to establish what we really mean when we talk about 'elimination' of contradictions.

Two Contradiction Scenarios

Generally speaking, technical contradictions fall into two categories; discrete and continuous. The two types are similar in that they may both be represented by the hyperbolic curve previously illustrated in Figure 10.2. The red line on the graph may be seen as a 'line of constant design capability', or the current design paradigm. For example, referring back to the first case study example concerned with the design of flange joints, we saw Parameter A as 'leakage performance' of the flange, and Parameter B as the number of bolts around the flange joint. Traditional flange design – where, incidentally, the designer may only be sub-consciously aware of the Figure 10.2 graph characteristic – sees the designer trying to find a balance between adequate leakage performance and minimum number of bolts. This generally means the flange is designed such that it 'just' doesn't leak (which, in turn probably explains why most flange joints leak). Or, with reference to Figure 10.2, the designer finds the point on the red line where the 'best' compromise is obtained.

So there lies the main *similarity* between 'discrete' and 'continuous' contradictions. The main *difference* is best examined through a pair of examples:

Discrete

A good example of a 'discrete' contradiction scenario is the bicycle seat case discussed in the second case study example. In this case, we could draw a figure like the Figure 10.2 hyperbolic curve in which the width of the current saddle is drawn along the x-axis, and a parameter like 'shape' is drawn up the y-axis.

In the saddle case study, the contradiction was stated to be 'eliminated'. In 'eliminating' the width-shape contradiction, the Figure 10.2 graph is no longer relevant – i.e. the axes of the figure no longer make sense because the two parameters width and shape are no longer in conflict with one another. This is a discrete contradiction scenario. It is discrete because the **particular** technical contradiction under consideration **has** literally been eliminated; we had a contradiction, and then we didn't. (This isn't to say, of course, that we haven't introduced other new contradictions – as we will see very shortly.)

Continuous

Continuous contradiction scenarios are generally more common. The above flange joint example is a continuous contradiction in that while we managed to halve the number of bolts around the joint, the contradiction between leakage performance and number of bolts still exists. Likewise, we might see the well-known contradiction between physical size and the fuel burn efficiency of the internal combustion engine – Figure 10.21 – as another example of a continuous contradiction scenario. The correlation between size and efficiency is very well established for most if not all internal combustion engine types, and in selecting a particular engine for a given application, when constrained to work within a traditional design approach, the designer has little scope for improving on the red-line characteristic. I.e. selecting engine size more or less simultaneously fixes engine efficiency for a given engine configuration.

The exception to this rule occurs when the designer is able to change the design paradigm. Using the Contradictions tools in TRIZ is a good means of changing the design paradigm. For example, the size-efficiency relationship is changed – i.e. a new red-line is

drawn – if the design paradigm shifts from, say, a conventional eight-valve to a sixteen valve porting configuration.

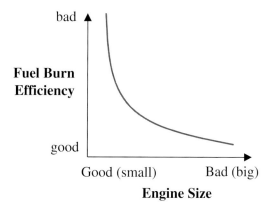

Figure 10.21: Typical Size versus Efficiency Contradiction for an Internal Combustion Engine

The size-efficiency relationship may be seen as a continuous contradiction because even if the designer is able to employ TRIZ to change the design paradigm in this way – 'to eliminate the contradiction' to use the incorrect terminology – the size-efficiency conflict still exists. The only difference now is that it exists on a new (hopefully better) red-line – as shown in Figure 10.22.

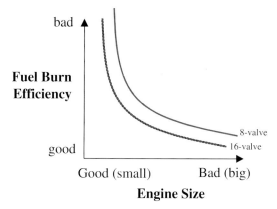

Figure 10.22: Design Paradigm Change Shifts Contradiction Characteristic Position

The continuous contradiction scenario may be seen as a chain of contradictions. A chain in that successive paradigm shifts will gradually move the characteristic line closer and closer to the (Ideal Final Result) optimum – as illustrated conceptually earlier in Figure 10.3. Using Contradictions to assist in creating these paradigm shifts is one of the great strengths of the TRIZ methodology.

But then, what about the discrete contradiction scenario, what about those cases where we do actually achieve an elimination of the contradiction?

Again the bicycle seat case study holds a number of clues. In this example we see that a width-shape contradiction has been eliminated. This is not, however, the same thing as 'design without compromise'. This is evident because the new seat continues to contain other contradictions. More specifically, it contains new contradictions that weren't present in the original scenario as discussed in the case study.

In this context, the term 'contradiction chains' continues to be relevant. Elimination of one contradiction has created others. Hopefully, there has been a net benefit to the overall system – i.e. hopefully we have changed the overall design paradigm for the better – but as with the continuous contradictions scenario, there remain other possibilities to improve the design. A very useful image encapsulating the underlying philosophy behind both discrete and continuous contradictions reverts to the original fluid-filled bag analogy from the beginning of the chapter. In this analogy, the idea of contradiction chains – whether discrete or continuous – is about changing the size of the bag in the direction of reducing amount of fluid in the bag (think of the fluid as something bad we are trying to get rid of, and that we have achieved our ideal final result when all of the fluid has been removed. The concept of contradiction chains, then, is about successively reducing the content of the bag – Figure 10.23.

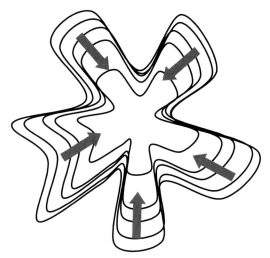

Figure 10.23: Contradictions and the Fluid Filled Bag

In most cases, the designer then has to make decisions on just how far to take the contradiction chain. Is it appropriate to launch the product in its current form, or would it be better to continue challenging the design paradigm by attempting to eliminate further design contradictions. This can only be done on a case-by-case basis, with due consideration of commercial and marketing issues. In the specific case of the bicycle seat, it now appears that it would perhaps have been more prudent to extend the contradiction chain to 'eliminate' more contradictions before product launch.

To summarise:-

1) The TRIZ 'Contradictions' tools and methods are extremely potent design paradigm changers.

2) Contradictions come in both 'discrete' and 'continuous' types.
3) TRIZ can literally eliminate contradictions of the discrete type (although, usually, elimination of one contradiction will give rise to another –hopefully lesser – contradiction).
4) TRIZ cannot literally 'eliminate' a contradiction of the continuous type. It can, however, be very successfully deployed to change the design paradigm for the better.
5) Contradictions – both discrete and continuous – come in chains. How far along a given chain a designer travels before a decision to launch a new product, process or service is made can only be reliably made on a case-by-case basis, taking due account of all commercial issues surrounding the basic technical design circumstances.

What Happens When The Contradiction Matrix Doesn't Work?

The classical Contradiction Matrix was never intended to be either infallible or comprehensive; merely a useful start point for solving a technical contradiction. The experience of users varies considerably; with a range of quoted 'success rate' of anywhere between 10 and 80%. A recent quantitative study suggested a figure slightly below 50% (Reference 10.4). Some TRIZ practitioners suggest trying all 40 Principles (after all, they are the only 40 ways of tackling a contradiction, right?) as a response to those situations where the Matrix does not provide useful directions. This is, of course, a perfectly valid course of action. A potential problem with it, however, is that there is a strong tendency to lose momentum when trying to investigate all 40 routes; and that consequently some will be given less than adequate consideration.

We present here three alternative routes to this 'try all 40' option, with the recommendation that they are, like the Matrix, by no means definitive. The three alternatives are:-
1) Basing Inventive Principle selection on improving parameter
2) Basing Inventive Principle selection on system complexity
3) Looking at the Principles from a completely different perspective.

1) Principle Selection Based on Improving Parameter

Some users find it difficult to formulate the contradictions present in the systems they are evaluating. The problem usually relates to identification of the worsening parameters – the things stopping the desired improvement from occurring. Most users, on the other hand, find it relatively simple to work out what it is they wish to improve.

Although we always recommend that people try to formulate contradictions – reason; because it is often profoundly important to understanding what is happening in a system – some will always wish to take a short-cut.

One method of doing precisely this is to look at rows across the Matrix and examine whether there is any correlation between the types of Inventive Principles being recommended and the type of improving feature being considered. In simple terms, this means counting up the number of times a Principle appears along each row and picking out those that appear most often.

Rather less crude than this, is to establish whether there is any other kind of correlation between the things we are trying to improve in a system and the Principles we might use

to help us. This is the basis of the analysis conducted during the process of assembling material for this book. The result of that analysis is presented in Figure 10.24.

Problem Type	Inventive Principles
All	1, 10, 13, 15, 19, 22, 25, 35
Improving Physical Attributes	2, 3, 4, 5, 7, 14 17, 28, 30, 37, 40
Improving Performance	9, 10, 16, 19, 21, 23
Improving 'Ilities	9, 11, 14, 18, 27, 40
...If a solution still hasn't emerged	6, 12, 20, 24 26, 29, 31, 32, 33, 34, 36, 38, 39

Segmentation
Preliminary Action
The Other Way Around
Dynamics
Periodic Action
Blessing in Disguise
Self-Service
Parameter Changes

Figure 10.24: Influence of Problem Type on Inventive Principle Selection

What the Figure shows is that there are a cluster of commonly used Inventive Principles that have no real correlation with problem type, and hence should be considered as possibly relevant to all types of problem. This 'top 8' is useful to keep in mind at all times if possible. After this cluster, there are three other clusters that group nicely around the three different improving feature types physical, performance and 'ilities (reliability, manufacturability, adaptability, repairability, etc). Thus if the parameter you are trying to improve in the system under evaluation falls into one of these categories, the Figure shows the Principles most likely to help solve these types of problems. Finally, there is another cluster of Principles which again don't really correlate to any particular problem type, which we suggest be used as 'fall-backs' if none of the other Principles from the other clusters have proved successful.

One group of problems where this kind of approach is particularly relevant appears to be those related to improving reliability. See Chapter 20 for a list of Inventive Principles most likely to solve this particular type of problem.

2) Principle Selection Based on System Complexity

One of the TRIZ identified trends of evolution (Chapter 13) highlights the manner in which systems evolve in a way that means their overall complexity (usually correlated at least in part to the number of components in a system) increases and then decreases over the span of a given s-curve. With this increasing-then-decreasing part count idea in mind,

examination of the Inventive Principles suggests that certain of the 40 involve inventive directions which also correlate to either increasing or decreasing part count:

Principles Associated With Increasing Part Count
(In numerical order)

Principle 1 – Segmentation – usually implies increased number of components (although, for non-technical systems may well mean a re-distribution or re-organization of existing resources rather than necessarily addition of new resources)

Principle 7 – Nested Doll

Principle 8 – Counterweight – implies addition of something to counter the downward tendency of the problem aspect.

Principle 9 – Preliminary Anti-Action – as 10 below

Principle 10 – Preliminary Action – implies supply of additional things to perform the preliminary action

Principle 11 – Beforehand Cushioning – addition of something to counter non-desirable affect in current system.

Principle 15 – Dynamics – transition from immobile to mobile system implies addition of components to permit relative movement of different sub-components

Principle 23 – Feedback – addition of components required to first sense and then relay feedback messages

Principle 24 – Intermediary

Principle 27 – Cheap Short-Living Objects ('replace an expensive object with a multiple of inexpensive objects, compromising certain qualities')

Principle 38 – Strong Oxidants ('Enriched Atmosphere') – addition of active elements plus possible need for additional elements to contain or control the active element.

Principle 39 – Inert Atmosphere – similar to Principle 38; addition of inert elements may also prompt addition of other elements to contain or control the inert elements.

Principles Associated With Decreasing Part Count
(In numerical order)

Principle 2 – Taking Out

Principle 3 – Local Quality – implies making existing components be modified to achieve the functions of several – particularly evident as a part-count reducer in casting operations especially since casting technology has evolved to permit casting of highly complex shapes

Principle 5 – Merging

Principle 6 – Universality ('make an object or structure perform multiple functions')

Principle 20 – Continuity of Useful Action ('B: eliminate all idle or intermittent actions or work')

Principle 25 – Self-Service

Principle 40 – Composite Materials – combining multiple structures/functions into a coherent composite structure.

Bringing the 'increasing' and 'decreasing' Principles together onto one picture (also showing the system complexity evolution trend) gives the reference image shown in Figure 10.25. It is hoped that this picture will be of some value to problem owners working in areas – particularly non-technical – where the Contradiction Matrix is not effective.

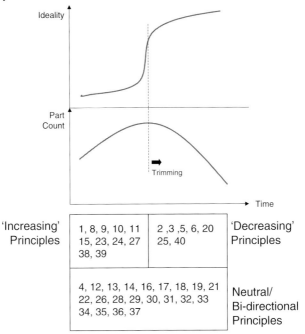

| 'Increasing' Principles | 1, 8, 9, 10, 11 15, 23, 24, 27 38, 39 | 2 ,3 ,5, 6, 20 25, 40 | 'Decreasing' Principles |
| | 4, 12, 13, 14, 16, 17, 18, 19, 21 22, 26, 28, 29, 30, 31, 32, 33 34, 35, 36, 37 | | Neutral/ Bi-directional Principles |

Figure 10.25: Influence of Problem Type on Inventive Principle Selection

Note that some of the Principles cannot be categorized into either 'increasing' or 'decreasing' part count usage because they are either part-count neutral ('Colour Changes') or may cause part count to change in either direction depending on the particular circumstances of the system.

These patterns can often be useful in reducing the number of Inventive Principles that might be relevant to a given problem type: There is little point in looking at Principles that will increase system complexity at a time in the evolution of a system where the trend indicates the need for a reducing strategy for example.

3) Different Perspectives

For many users, the 40 Inventive Principles are a very effective series of solution triggers. Used at this fairly basic level, they may be seen as a more comprehensive version of the SCAMMPERR model developed by Osborn (Reference 10.5). The problem with the 40

Principles for many newcomers, however is that 40 is a lot of triggers to remember. Most people keep a list with them, but there is the bigger issue that our brains are wired with a short term memory store capable of storing only around about 7 different pieces of information. Actually 7 ± 2. We wondered, therefore whether it would be possible to re-configure the 40 Principles into a structure that would ease our ability to remember them. As we progressed, incorporating NLP thinking and the SCAMMPERR model (see also Savransky (Reference 10.6)), we believe that it has been possible to not only achieve this, but also enrich the overall quality of the Principles.

In the first instance, we saw the space-time-interface dimensional thinking concept discussed in Chapter 2 as an important start point. Many will notice how some of the Principles can be related to all three dimensions – Segmentation for example can be applied as a contradiction breaking strategy with respect to physical segmentation, segmentation of time (see also 'Periodic Action' – which might specifically be seen as 'segmentation of time') and segmentation of the interfaces between things. We also noted that some Principles had analogues that reversed the Principle – e.g. 'Segmentation' and 'Merging' are often interpreted as two opposites. Some on the other hand didn't – Asymmetry being one such example. When asking the question 'would it be possible to challenge a contradiction by making something symmetrical instead of asymmetrical, we answered with a definitive yes. The opposite can also occur, balance and proportion then becoming important factors. The same happened with many other Principles.

Next we looked at our space-time-and interface entities and saw that within each category, all of the Principles grouped into just five different strategies for modifying a system :-

1) segment or merge (i.e. change the number of entities)
2) make the entities bigger or smaller
3) change the external geometry
4) change the internal structure
5) substitute the existing structure for something else.

We then found that the existing Principles fitted very neatly into a 5x3 matrix as illustrated below:-

	Space	Time	Interface	
Segment	1	18, 19	2 / 5, 6, 7, 33	**Number**
Magnify		20, 21	38 / 39	**Size**
Re-shape	3, 4, 14, 17	15	12, 16	**External Shape**
Modify	30, 31, 32, 36, 40	9, 10, 11	8, 37	**Internal Structure**
Substitute	26, 28, 29, 35a	27, 34	23, 24	**Content**

Figure 10.26: Revised Inventive Principles Structure

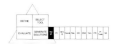

The figure diagonally divides each box to illustrate that every one has both its positive and negative sense. It also illustrates the relative position of each of the 40 Principles within the structure. Thus Principle 13 – the other way around – now features implicitly in each element of the Principle Matrix.

Actually, we found two other special case Principles that did not fit into the Matrix, but fitted instead into the higher order philosophical level. These were:-

> 25 Self-Service – This is a Principle which is highly connected to the Ideality concept. We note that the Principle does not appear in the classical Matrix nearly as often as an ideality-driven thought process would lead.

> 22 Blessing in Disguise – in a similar vein, this Principle encourages users to think about the resources element of the TRIZ philosophy. Again it does not feature in the classic Contradiction Matrix nearly as often as its use in a bigger context would demand.

In examining the SCAMMPERR model in more detail, we found that while 8 of the 9 strategies in the model were covered by the Inventive Principles and by the 5x3 matrix framework above, the 'P' – 'put to another use' was not. In SCAMMPERR, this trigger encourages users to solve problems by changing function. This is not normal TRIZ practice, but, again, when we asked the question 'would it be possible to challenge a contradiction by changing function, the answer was an unqualified 'yes'. Taken together with the above Principles 22 and 25, we believe this 'change function' Principle forms a useful third entry in a trio of special Principles linked directly to the five philosophical strands of TRIZ. I.e.

Functionality	-	Change Function
Resources	-	Blessing in Disguise
Ideality	-	Self-Service
Space/Time	-	New 5x3 Matrix
Contradictions	-	New 5x3 Matrix

So, we found it was not possible to quite achieve the 7±2 model – having 3 special Principles plus 8 labels for the Matrix. But what we did have was a system that featured significantly greater richness than the 40 Principles. The 40 Principles for example do not explicitly suggest that making a thing physically bigger or smaller is a way of solving a contradiction (although Principle 21 – Hurrying does do in the time dimension – see figure). Similarly, some of the 40 Principles (e.g. Local Quality and Asymmetry) are traditionally directed towards physical things – whereas in each case there are very definite time and interface analogies of the Principle.

Thus (SPACE-TIME-INTERFACE) + (SEGMENT, SIZE, SHAPE, STRUCTURE, SUBSTITUTE) + (FUNCTION-IDEALITY-RESOURCES) – SIT-5S-FIR – provides a means of remembering a richer, more structured version of the 40 Principles.

Or (more closely related to a start-point at the 5 main philosophical elements):

FUNCTIONALITY-IDEALITY-RESOURCES-(SPACE-TIME-INTERFACE)-CONTRADICTIONS

|
5S

What Do I Do?

The technical contradictions part of TRIZ is often the first thing that many newcomers will be exposed to (the Matrix having strangely magnetic properties to some). Often unfortunately, the concept of contradiction elimination is often more difficult to achieve than the method would imply – contradiction elimination is very closely related to invention; being almost a definition of a strong invention.

That being said, the Contradictions tools are a very important part of TRIZ. In the first instance, we therefore suggest that users familiarise themselves with the form and content of the Contradiction Matrix contained in the fold-out sheet. Specifically, it is a good idea to become familiar with the parameters contained in the Matrix.

As stated earlier, 'if a system exists, it contains contradictions'. The next stage of the process of using this part of TRIZ then requires that we are able to identify some of the contradictions in a system. If we have entered this chapter following a recommendation from Chapter 9, it probably means that we have already identified good contradictions to solve from either an FAA analysis or from an s-curve analysis.

How we actually use the Contradictions tool depends largely on preferred ways of working. Some people prefer to just use the Inventive Principles; others like the idea that the Matrix will reduce the number of possible Principles to be evaluated, while still others will prefer some of the alternative strategies related in the latter part of the chapter. The main message here, is to find strategies that best suit your way of doing things.

The Inventive Principles suggested by the method are quite generic in nature. Effective use demands familiarity with the way in which the human brain works as an effective connector of ideas. In this regard, we recommend that you examine the content of Chapter 3.

References

1) www.creax.com.
2) Mann, D.L., 'Case Studies in TRIZ: A Better Wrench' TRIZ Journal, September 1999.
3) Blake, A., Mann, D.L., 'Making Knowledge Tangible', TRIZ Journal, November 2000.
4) Mann, D.L., 'Assessing the', TRIZ Journal, February 2002.
5) Osborn, A.F., 'Applied Imagination: Principles and Procedures of Creative Problem-Solving', Scribners, 1963.
6) Savransky, S., 'Engineering of Creativity', CRC Press, 2000.

Inventive Principles

This final section of the chapter provides a reference of the 40 Inventive Principles currently contained within TRIZ, complete with descriptions of the detailed solution triggers contained within each Principle, and a few examples of how other problem solvers have used a particular Principle to tackle a given contradiction situation.

The more you become familiar with the Principles, the more you will see them in action everywhere around us, in business situations, in biology, in architecture (where, incidentally, it is also established that the same Principles apply). Readers may like to keep a record of their own examples of Principles as they observe them.

Principle 1. Segmentation

A. Divide a system into separate parts or sections.
- Have a range of different focal length lenses for a camera
- Gator-grip socket spanner
- Multi-pin connectors
- Bubble-wrap
- Multiple pistons in an internal combustion engine
- Multi-engined aircraft
- Pocket-spring mattress
- Stratification of different constituents inside a chemical process vessel

B. Make a system easy to put together and take apart.
- Rapid-release bicycle saddle/wheel/etc fasteners
- Quick disconnect joints in plumbing and hydraulic systems
- Single fastener V-band clamps on flange joints
- Loose-leaf paper in a ring-binder

C. Increase the amount of segmentation.
- Use of multiple control surfaces on aerodynamic structures
- 16 and 24 valve versus 8 valve internal combustion engines
- Multi-blade cartridge razors
- Multi-zone combustion systems
- Build up a component from layers (e.g. stereo-lithography, welds, etc)

Principle 2. Taking out

A. Where a system provides several functions of which one or more are not required (and may be harmful) at certain conditions, design the system so that they are or can be taken out.
- Inflatable car passenger
- Use the sound of a barking dog, without the dog, as a burglar alarm.
- Scarecrow
- Non-smoking areas in restaurants or in railway carriages

Principle 3. Local quality

A. Where an object or system is uniform or homogenous, make it non-uniform
- Reduce drag on aerodynamic surfaces by adding riblets or 'shark-skin' protrusions

- Moulded hand grips on tools
- Single-sided sellotape
- Drink cans shaped to facilitate stable stacking
- Material surface treatments/coatings - plating, erosion/corrosion protection, non-stick, etc

B. *Change things around the system (e.g. the environment)) from uniform to non-uniform.*
- Use a temperature, density, or pressure gradient instead of constant temperature, density or pressure. E.g. glider
- Pilot-operated valve
- MIG or TIG welding

C. *Enable each part of a system to function in locally optimised conditions.*
- Freezer compartment in refrigerator
- Different zones in the combustion system of an engine
- Night-time adjustment on a rear-view mirror
- Lunch box with special compartments for hot and cold solid foods and for liquids

D. *Enable each part of a system or object to carry out different (possibly directly opposite) useful functions.*
- Swiss-Army knife
- Combined can and bottle opener
- Sharp and blunt end of a drawing pin
- Eraser on the end of a pencil
- Hammer with nail puller

Principle 4. Asymmetry

A. *Where an object or system is symmetrical or contains lines of symmetry, introduce asymmetries.*
- Introduce a geometric feature which prevents incorrect usage/assembly of a component (e.g. earth pin on electric plug)
- Asymmetrical funnel allows higher flow-rate than normal funnel
- Put a flat spot on a cylindrical shaft to attach a locking feature
- Oval and complex shaped O-rings
- Coated glass or paper
- Introduction of angled or scarfed geometry features on component edges
- Cutaway on a guitar improves access to high notes
- Spout of a jug
- Cam
- Ratchet
- Aerofoil – asymmetry generates lift.
- Eccentric drive
- Keys

B. *Change the shape of an object or system to suit external asymmetries (e.g. ergonomic features)*
- Human shaped seating, etc
- Take account of differences between left and right handed users
- Finger and thumb grip features on objects
- Spectacles
- Car steering system compensates for camber in road
- Wing design compensated for asymmetric flow produced by propeller

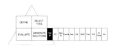

C. If an object or system is already asymmetrical, increase the degree of asymmetry.
- Use of variable control surfaces to alter lift properties of an aircraft wing
- Special connectors with complex shape/pin configurations to ensure correct assembly
- Introduction of several different measurement scales on a ruler

Principle 5. Merging

A. Physically join or merge identical or related objects, operations or functions.
- Automatic rifle/machine gun
- Multi-colour ink cartridges
- Multi-blade razors
- Bo-focal lens spectacles
- Double/triple glazing
- Strips of staples
- Catarmaran/trimaran

B. Join or merge objects, operations or functions so that they act together in time.
- Combine harvester
- Manufacture cells
- Grass collector on a lawn-mower
- Mixer taps

Principle 6. Universality

A. Make an object or system able to perform multiple functions; eliminating the need for other systems.
- Child's car safety seat converts to a stroller
- Home entertainment centre
- Grill in a microwave oven
- Radio-alarm clock
- Swiss Army knife
- Work-mate
- Universal joint
- Electrically conducting clothing enables many new functions to be delivered
- Use of Standards in e.g. data exchange
- Cleaning strip at beginning of a cassette tape cleans tape heads

Principle 7. "Nested doll"

A. Put one object or system inside another
- Place a safe inside a wall or under floorboards
- Retractable aircraft under-carriage
- Introduce voids into 3D structures
- Injected cavity-wall insulation
- Paint-brush attached to inside of lid of nail-varnish, etc
- Lining inside a coat

B. Put several objects or systems inside others.
- Nested tables

- Telescope
- Measuring cups or spoons
- Stacking chairs
- Multi-layer erosion/corrosion coatings

C. *Allow one object or system to pass through an appropriate hole in another.*
- Telescopic car aerial
- Retractable power-lead in vacuum cleaner
- Seat belt retraction mechanism

Principle 8. Anti-weight

A. *Where the weight of an object or system causes problems, combine it with something that provides lift.*
- Inject foaming agent into a bundle of logs, to make it float better.
- Aerostatic aeroplane contains lighter-than-air pockets
- Hot air balloon.
- Swim-bladder inside a fish

B. *Where the weight of an object or system causes problems, use aerodynamic, hydrodynamic, buoyancy and other forces to provide lift.*
- Vortex generators improve lift of aircraft wings.
- Wing-in-ground effect aircraft
- Hydrofoils lift ship out of the water to reduce drag.
- Make use of centrifugal forces in rotating systems (e.g .Watt governor)

Principle 9. Preliminary anti-action

A. *Where an action contains both harmful and useful effects, precede the action with opposite or anti-actions to reduce or eliminate the harmful effects.*
- Buffer a solution to prevent harm from extremes of pH.
- Make clay pigeons out of ice or dung in order that they do not have to be collected afterwards.
- Use masking tape when painting difficult edges
- Masking objects before harmful exposure: Use a lead apron on parts of the body not being exposed to X-rays.

B. *Introduce stresses in an object to oppose known harmful working stresses later on.*
- Pre-stress rebar before pouring concrete.
- Pre-stressed bolts
- Pre-shrunk jeans

Principle 10. Preliminary action

A. *Introduce a useful action into an object or system (either fully or partially before it is needed.*
- Pre-pasted wall paper
- Sterilize all instruments needed for a surgical procedure.
- Self-adhesive stamps
- Self-tapping screws

B. Pre-arrange objects or systems such that they can come into action at the most convenient time and place.
- Manufacture flow-lines
- Assembly lines using pre-assembled sub-assemblies.
- Pre-deposited blade in a surgery cast facilitates removal.

Principle 11. Beforehand cushioning

A. introduce emergency backups to compensate for the potentially low reliability of an object ('belt and braces')
- Magnetic strip on photographic film that directs the developer to compensate for poor exposure
- Back-up parachute
- Dual channel control system
- Air-bag in a car
- Spare wheel
- Relief valve
- Emergency lighting circuit
- Battery back-up
- Automatic save operations performed by computer programs
- Zip-files
- Mask borders of objects to be painted, use stencils
- Crash barriers on motorways

Principle 12. Equipotentiality

A. If an object or system requires or is exposed to tension or compression forces, redesign the object's environment so the forces are eliminated or are balanced by the surrounding environment
- Canal locks
- Spring loaded parts delivery system in a factory
- Mechanic's pit in a garage means car does not have to be lifted.
- Place a heavy object on ice, and let ice melt in order to lower it.

Principle 13. 'The other way round'

A. Use an opposite action(s) used to solve the problem (e.g. instead of cooling an object, heat it).
- To loosen stuck parts, cool the inner part instead of heating the outer part.
- Vacuum casting
- Improve damage resistance of a component by shot-peening

B. Make movable objects fixed, and fixed objects movable.
- Hamster wheel
- Rotary engines
- Rotate the part instead of the tool.
- Wind tunnels
- Moving sidewalk with standing people
- Drive through restaurant or bank

C. *Turn the object, system or process 'upside down'.*
- Clean bottles by inverting and injecting water from below; the water then drains by itself.
- Turn an assembly upside down to insert fasteners
- Open tinned beans from the bottom to get out beans that would otherwise have stuck to the bottom due to storage.

Principle 14. Spheroidality - Curvature

A. *Turn straight edges or flat surfaces into curves.*
- Use arches and domes for strength in architecture.
- Introduce fillet radii between surfaces at different angles
- Introduce stress relieving holes at the ends of slots
- Curved hair-brush

B. *Use rollers, balls, spirals, domes.*
- Spiral gear (Nautilus) produces continuous resistance for weight lifting.
- Ball point and roller point pens for smooth ink distribution
- Use spherical casters instead of cylindrical wheels to move furniture
- Archimedes screw

C. *Switch between linear and rotary motion*
- Rotary actuators in hydraulic system.
- Push/pull versus rotary switches (e.g. lighting dimmer switch)
- Linear motors
- Linear versus rotating tracking arm on a record turntable ensures constant angle of stylus relative to groove
- Screw-top versus push-in bottle stopper.
- Screw-thread versus nail.

D. *Introduce or make use of centrifugal forces.*
- Centrifugal casting for even wall thickness structures
- Spin components after painting to remove excess paint
- Replace wringing clothes to remove water with spinning clothes in a washing machine.
- Separate chemicals with different density properties using a centrifuge.
- Watt governor
- Vortex/cyclone separates different density objects

Principle 15. Dynamics

A. *Allow a system or object to change to achieve optimal operation under different conditions.*
- Adjustable steering wheel (or seat, or back support, or mirror position...)
- Loose (sand) particles inside a tyre give it self-balancing properties
- Gel fillings inside root allow it to adapt to user
- Shape memory alloys/polymers.

B. *Split an object or system into parts capable of moving relative to each other.*
- Bi-furcated bicycle saddle
- Articulated lorry
- Folding chair/mobile phone/laptop/etc

- Collapsible
- Brush seals

C. If an object or system is rigid or inflexible, make it movable or adaptable.
- Bendy drinking straw
- Flexible joint
- Collapsible hose is flexible in use, and has additional flexibility of cross-section to make it easier to store.

D. Increase the amount of free motion
- Place sand inside tyre to produce self-balancing properties
- Flexible drive allows motion around bends
- Use different stiffness fibres in toothbrush

Principle 16. Partial or excessive actions

A. If exactly the right amount of an action is hard to achieve, use 'slightly less' or 'slightly more' of the action, to reduce or eliminate the problem.
- Over spray when painting, then remove excess.
- Fill, then "top off" when pouring a pint of Guinness.
- Shrink wrapping process uses plastic deformation of wrapping to accommodate variations in vacuum pressure.
- 'Roughing' and 'Finish' machining operations.
- Over-fill holes with plaster and then rub back to smooth.
- (Use of Pareto analysis to prioritise actions when not all can be achieved with the available resources.)

Principle 17. Another dimension

A. If an object contains or moves in a straight line, consider use of dimensions or movement outside the line.
- Serrated or scalloped edges on a knife blade or hole punch
- Application of fade or draw to the affect the trajectory of a golf ball
- Paper edges clipped or made bigger in order to facilitate ease of location of entries in an address book, or for file dividers
- Curved bristles on a brush
- Coiled telephone cable

B. If an object contains or moves in a plane, consider use of dimensions or movement outside the current plane.
- Pizza-box with ribbed (as opposed to flat) base
- Spiral staircase uses less floor area
- Introduction of down and up slopes between stations on railway reduces train acceleration and deceleration power requirements
- Black keys higher than white keys on a piano to facilitate ease of location when playing
- Conical instead of plain flange joint
- Paper clip works by being deflected out of plane

C. Use a stacking arrangement of objects instead of a single level arrangement.
- Cassette with 6 CD's to increase music time and variety
- Electronic chips on both sides of a printed circuit board
- Multi-storey office blocks or car-parks

D. Re-orient the object or system, lay it on its side.
- Heels on a shoe alter height and leg-shape of wearer
- Hang a mirror with corners (rather than edges) top and bottom to cater for greater variety of user heights
- Take a door off its hinges to plane top and bottom surfaces to size

E. Use 'another side' of a given object or system.
- Press a groove onto both sides of a record
- Mount computer chip components on both sides of a silicon card
- Print text around the rim of a coin
- Fix a leaking car radiator or pipe by adding fluid sealant to the inside rather than trying to seal from outside.

Principle 18. Mechanical vibration

A. Cause an object to oscillate or vibrate.
- Electric carving knife with vibrating blades
- Shake/stir paint to mix before applying
- Hammer drill
- Vibration exciter removes voids from poured concrete.
- Vibrate during sieving operations to improve throughput.
- Musical instrument

B. Increase the vibration frequency (possibly up to ultrasonic).
- Dog-whistle (transmit sound outside human range)
- Ultrasonic cleaning
- Non-destructive crack detection using ultrasound.

C. Make use of an object or system's resonant frequency.
- Destroy gallstones or kidney stones using ultrasonic resonance.
- Ease bottle cleaning by pulsing washing action at resonant frequency of bottles
- Tuning fork
- Increase action of a catalyst by vibrating it at it's resonant frequency

D. Use piezoelectric vibrators..
- Quartz crystal oscillations drive high accuracy clocks.
- Piezoelectric vibrators improve fluid atomisation from a spray nozzle

E. Use combined field oscillations.
- Mixing alloys in an induction furnace
- Sono-chemistry
- Combined ultrasonic and heating in drying operations

Principle 19. Periodic action

A. Replace continuous actions with periodic or pulsating actions.
- Hitting something repeatedly with a hammer
- Replace a continuous siren with a pulsed sound.
- Pulsed bicycle lights make cyclist more noticeable to drivers
- Pulsed vacuum cleaner suction improves collection performance
- Pulsed water jet cutting

B. If an action is already periodic, change the periodic magnitude or frequency to suit external requirements.
- Replace a pulsed siren with sound that changes amplitude and frequency.

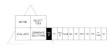

- Washing machine/dish-washer water injection operates uses different cycles for different load types.
- Dots and dashes in Morse Code transmissions

C. Use gaps between actions to perform different useful actions.
- Clean barrier filters by back-flowing them when not in use.
- Brush between suction pulses in vacuum cleaner.
- Multiple conversations taking place along the same telephone transmission line.
- Use of energy storage means – e.g. batteries, fly-wheels, etc

Principle 20. Continuity of useful action

A. Make all parts of an object or system work at full load or optimum efficiency, all the time.
- Flywheel stores energy when a vehicle stops, so the motor can keep running at optimum power.
- Constant output gas turbine in hybrid car, or APU in aircraft, runs at highest efficiency all the time it is switched on.
- Constant speed/variable pitch propeller
- Self-tuning engine – constantly tunes itself to ensure maximum efficiency
- Heart pacemaker
- Improve composting process by continuously turning material to be composted.
- Continuous glass or steel production

B. Eliminate all idle or non-productive actions or work.
- Self-cleaning/self-emptying filter eliminates down-time
- Print during the return of a printer carriage--dot matrix printer, daisy wheel printers, inkjet printers.
- Digital storage media allow 'instant' information access (as opposed to tapes which require to be rewound)
- Rapid-drying paint

Principle 21. Skipping

A. Conduct an action at very high speed to eliminate harmful side effects.
- Use a high-speed dentist's drill to avoid heating tissue.
- Cut plastic faster than heat can propagate in the material, to avoid deforming the shape.
- Break toffee with an impulsive blow from a hammer
- Drop forge
- Flash photography
- Super-critical shaft – run through resonant modes quickly

Principle 22. "Blessing in disguise" or "Turn Lemons into Lemonade"

A. Transform harmful objects or actions (particularly, the environment or surroundings) so that the deliver a positive effect.
- Use waste heat to generate electric power.
- Recycle waste (scrap) material from one process as raw materials for another.
- Vaccinations
- Lower body temperature in order to slow metabolism during medical operations.

- Composting

B. Add a second harmful object or action to neutralize or eliminate the effects of an existing harmful object or action..
- Add a buffering material to a corrosive solution.
- Use a helium-oxygen mix for diving, to eliminate both nitrogen narcosis and oxygen poisoning from air and other nitrox mixes.
- Gamma rays detect positron emissions from explosives.

C. Increase a harmful factor to such a level that it is no longer causes harm.
- Use a backfire to eliminate the fuel from a forest fire.
- Use explosives to blow out an oil-well fire.
- Laser knife cauterises skin/blood vessels as it cuts

Principle 23. Feedback

A. Introduce feedback to improve a process or action.
- Automatic volume control in audio circuits
- Signal from gyrocompass is used to control simple aircraft autopilots
- Thermostat controls temperature
- Engine management system regulates timing according to emission measurements.
- Statistical Process Control
- Monitor speakers assist singer during amplified performance

B. If feedback is already used, make it adaptable to variations in operating requirements or conditions.
- Change sensitivity of an autopilot when within 5 miles of an airport.
- Change sensitivity of a thermostat when cooling vs. heating, since it uses energy less efficiently when cooling.
- Use proportional, integral and/or differential control algorithm combinations

Principle 24. 'Intermediary'

A. Introduce an intermediary between two objects, systems or actions.
- Play a guitar with a plectrum
- Use a chisel to control rock breaking/sculpting process
- Drink coasters
- Dwell period during a manufacture process operation

B. Introduce a temporary intermediary which disappears or can be easily removed after it has completed its function.
- Gloves to get hot dishes out of an oven
- Joining papers with a paper clip
- Introduction of catalysts into chemical reaction
- Abrasive particles enhance water jet cutting

Principle 25. Self-service

A. Enable an object or system to perform functions or organise itself.
- A soda fountain pump that runs on the pressure of the carbon dioxide that is used to "fizz" the drinks. This assures that drinks will not be flat, and eliminates the need for sensors.

- Halogen lamps regenerate the filament during use--evaporated material is redeposited.
- Self-locking nut
- Self-cleaning oven
- Self-balancing wheel.

B. *Make use of waste resources, energy, or substances.*
- Use heat from a process to generate electricity: "Co-generation".
- Use animal waste as fertilizer.
- Use food and lawn waste to create compost.

Principle 26. Copying

A. *Use simple and inexpensive copies in place of expensive, possibly vulnerable objects or systems.*
- Virtual reality
- Virtual mock-ups/electronic pre-assembly modelling
- Imitation jewellery.
- Astroturf
- Pilot-operated valve in hydraulics

B. *Replace an object, or action with an optical copy.*
- Do surveying from space photographs instead of on the ground.
- Measure an object by measuring the photograph.
- Shadowgraph.

C. *If optical copies are already being used, make use of infrared or ultraviolet wavelengths.*
- Make images in infrared to detect heat sources, such as diseases in crops, or intruders in a security system.
- Use UV as a non-destructive crack detection method
- UV light used to attract insects into trap

Principle 27. Cheap short-living objects

A. *Replace an expensive object or system with a multitude of inexpensive, short-life objects.*
- Disposable nappies/paper-cups/plates/cameras/torches/etc
- Matches versus lighters
- Throw-away cigarette lighters
- Industrial diamonds used in cutting tools

Principle 28 Mechanics substitution/Another Sense

A. *Replace an existing means with a means making use of another sense (optical, acoustic, taste, touch or smell).*
- Replace a physical fence to confine a dog or cat with an acoustic "fence" (signal audible to the animal).
- Use a bad smelling compound in natural gas to alert users to leakage, instead of a mechanical or electrical sensor.
- Fingerprint/retina scan instead of a key

B. *Introduce electric, magnetic or electromagnetic fields to interact with an object or system.*
- To mix 2 powders, electro statically charge one positive and the other negative.
- Magnetic bearings
- Field-activated switches

C. *Change from static to movable, fixed to variable, and/or from unstructured to structured fields.*
- Early communications used omni-directional broadcasting. We now use antennas with very detailed structure of the pattern of radiation.
- MRI scanners
- Magneto-optic stress sensors

D. *Use fields in conjunction with field-activated (e.g. ferromagnetic) objects or systems.*
- Heat a substance containing ferromagnetic material by using varying magnetic field. When the temperature exceeds the Curie point, the material becomes paramagnetic, and no longer absorbs heat.
- Ferro-magnetic catalysts
- Ferro-fluids
- Electro-theological fluids
- Photochromic glass

Principle 29. Pneumatics and hydraulics

A. *Use gases and liquids instead of solid parts or systems*
- Transition from mechanical to hydraulic or pneumatic systems
- Fluid clock
- Inflatable furniture/mattress/etc
- Gel filled shoe insole adapts to user
- Hovercraft
- Gas bearings

Principle 30. Flexible shells and thin films

A. *Incorporate flexible shells and thin films instead of solid structures*
- Use inflatable (thin film) structures.
- Webbed structures
- Stored energy in flexible bags – e.g. accumulators in a hydraulic system.
- Sails/para-sails/etc

B. *Isolate an object or system from a potentially harmful environment using flexible shells and thin films.*
- Bubble-wrap
- Egg-box
- Tea bag
- Hydrodynamic bearings

Principle 31. Porous materials

A. *Make an object porous or add porous elements*
- Drill holes in a structure to reduce the weight.

- Cavity wall insulation
- Transpiration film cooled structures
- Foam metals
- Use sponge-like structures as fluid absorption media.

B. *If an object is already porous, add something useful into the pores.*
- Use a porous metal mesh to wick excess solder away from a joint.
- Store hydrogen in the pores of a palladium sponge. (Fuel "tank" for the hydrogen car--much safer than storing hydrogen gas)
- Desiccant in polystyrene packing materials
- Medicated swabs/dressings

Principle 32. Colour changes

A. *Change the colour of an object or its surroundings.*
- Use safe lights in a photographic darkroom.
- Use colour-changing thermal paint to measure temperature
- Thermo-chromic plastic spoon
- Temperature-sensitive dyes used on food product labels to indicate when desired serving temperature has been achieved.
- Electro-chromic glass
- Light-sensitive glasses
- Camouflage
- Dazzle camouflage used on World War 1 ships
- Employ interference fringes on surface structures to change colour (as in butterfly wings, etc)

B. *Change the transparency of an object or its surroundings.*
- Use photolithography to change transparent material to a solid mask for semiconductor processing.
- Light-sensitive glass
- Smoke-screen

C. *In order to change the visibility of things, use coloured additives or luminescent elements*
- Fluorescent additives used during UV spectroscopy
- UV marker pens used to help identify stolen goods
- Use opposing colours to increase visibility – e.g. butchers use green decoration to make the red in meat look redder.

D. *Change the emissivity properties of an object subject to radiant heating*
- Use of black and white coloured panels to assist thermal management on space vehicles.
- Use of parabolic reflectors in solar panels to increase energy capture.
- Paint object with high emissivity paint in order to be able to measure it's temperature with a calibrated thermal imager.

Principle 33. Homogeneity

A. *Make interacting objects from the same material (or material with matching properties).*
- Make the container out of the same material as the contents, to reduce chemical reactions.

- Friction welding requires no intermediary material between the two surfaces to be joined.
- Temporary plant-pots made out of compostable material
- Make ice-cubes out of the drink they will go in

Principle 34. Discarding and recovering

A. *Make elements of an object or system that have fulfilled their functions disappear (by dissolving, evaporating, etc.) or appear to disappear.*
- Use a dissolving capsule for medication.
- Ice structures: use water ice or carbon dioxide (dry ice) to make a template for a rammed earth structure, such as a temporary dam. Fill with earth, then, let the ice melt or sublime to leave the final structure.
- Bio-degradable containers
- Lost-wax casting process

B. *Restore consumable or degradable parts of an object or system during operation.*
- Self-sharpening blades – knives/lawn-mowers/etc
- Automobile engines that give themselves a "tune up" while running
- Self-loading rifle

Principle 35. Parameter changes

A. *Change an object's physical state (e.g. to a gas, liquid, or solid).*
- Transition from mechanical to fluid or electrical drives
- Freeze the liquid centres of filled candies, then dip in melted chocolate, instead of handling the messy, gooey, hot liquid.
- Transport oxygen or nitrogen or petroleum gas as a liquid, instead of a gas, to reduce volume.
- Dry ice
- Ice cubes.
- Jelly

B. *Change concentration or consistency.*
- Liquid versus bar or powder detergents.
- Concentrated or de-hydrated orange juice makes transportation easier.
- Abradable linings used in seal design

C. *Change the degree of flexibility.*
- Use adjustable dampers to reduce the noise of parts falling into a container by restricting the motion of the walls of the container.
- Vulcanise rubber to change its flexibility and durability.
- Compliant brush seals rather than labyrinth or other fixed geometry seals.

D. *Change the temperature.*
- Raise the temperature above the Curie point to change a ferromagnetic substance to a paramagnetic substance.
- Cooking/baking/etc.
- Lower the temperature of medical specimens to preserve them for later analysis.

E. *Change the pressure.*
- Pressure cooker cooks more quickly and without losing flavours.
- Electron beam welding in a vacuum.
- Vacuum packing of perishable goods.

F. *Change other parameters*
- Shape memory alloys/polymers
- Use Curie point to alter magnetic properties
- Thixotropic paints
- Rheopexic fluids

Principle 36. Phase transitions

A. *Make use of phenomena taking place during phase transitions (e.g. volume changes, loss or absorption of heat, etc.).*
- Latent heat effects in melting/boiling
- Water expands when frozen, unlike most other liquids.
- Heat pumps use the heat of vaporization and heat of condensation of a closed thermodynamic cycle to do useful work.
- Volume expansion during water-to-steam transition
- Superconductivity

Principle 37. Thermal expansion

A. *Use thermal expansion (or contraction) of materials to achieve a useful effect.*
- Fit a tight joint together by cooling the inner part to contract, heating the outer part to expand, putting the joint together, and returning to equilibrium.
- Shape memory alloys/polymers.
- Shrink-wrapping
- Metal tie-bars used to straighten buckling walls in old buildings

B. *Use multiple materials with different coefficients of thermal expansion to achieve different useful effects.*
- Bi-metallic strips used for thermostats, etc
- Two-way shape memory alloys.
- Passive blade-tip clearance control in jet-engines
- Combine materials with positive and negative thermal expansion coefficients to obtain alloys with zero (or specifically tailored) expansion properties - e.g. cerro-tru alloy used in the mounting and location of fragile turbine blade components during manufacture operations

Principle 38. Strong oxidants

A. *Replace atmospheric air with oxygen-enriched air.*
- Scuba diving with Nitrox or other non-air mixtures for extended endurance
- Place patients inside oxygen tent
- Use nitrous oxide injection to improve engine performance

B. *Use pure oxygen.*
- Cut at a higher temperature using an oxy-acetylene torch.
- Treat wounds in a high-pressure oxygen environment to kill anaerobic bacteria and aid healing.

C. *Use ionising radiation.*
- Irradiation of food to improve preservative qualities.
- Ionise air to reduce aerodynamic resistance

- Use ionised air to sterilise food

D. *Use ionised oxygen.*
- Speed up chemical reactions by ionizing the gas before use.
- Separate oxygen from gas by ionising oxygen component

E. *Use ozone.*
- Use ozone to destroy micro-organisms in corn
- Ozone dissolved in water used to remove organic contaminants from ship hulls

Principle 39. Inert atmosphere

A. *Replace a normal environment with an inert one.*
- Prevent degradation of a hot metal filament by using an argon atmosphere.
- MIG/TIG welding
- Electron-beam welding performed in a vacuum
- Zero-gravity manufacture operations
- Vacuum packaging
- CO_2 fire extinguisher

B. *Add neutral parts, or inert elements to an object or system.*
- Naval aviation fuel contains additives to alter flash point.
- Dampers
- Sound absorbing panels/structures
- Add fire retardants to titanium to prevent fire in challenging environments

Principle 40. Composite materials

A. *Change from uniform to composite (multiple) materials where each material is optimised to a particular functional requirement.*
- Aircraft structures where low weight and high strength are required. (With fibres aligned according to loading conditions – including multiple layers of fibres aligned in different directions.)
- Composite golf club shaft aligns structures to give low weight, high shaft-wise flexibility and high torsional stiffness.
- Concrete aggregate.
- Glass-re-enforced plastic
- Fibre-re-enforced ceramics
- Hard/soft/hard multi-layer coatings to improve erosion, etc properties.
- Non-stick coatings on cooking pans.

11.
Problem Solving Tools
Physical Contradictions

Jack can't see he can't see
and can't see
Jill can't see Jill can't see it.
and vice versa
R.D.Laing, Knots

Physical contradictions involve those situations in which we desire different properties of a certain parameter. This definition includes situations where, for example, I want an object to be 'big and small', 'present and absent', 'hot and cold', 'heavy and light', and so on. In each of these situations, the Matrix from the previous chapter is not going to help us to solve the contradiction – the boxes in the diagonal from top left to bottom right is full of blanks. On the other hand, what we will see here is that challenging a physical contradiction will use exactly the same 40 Inventive Principles as used for technical contradictions; the only difference now is that we will require a different strategy to determine which of the Principles are more likely than others to help us to solve our problem.

The basis of this strategy is separation, and the search for different times, places or conditions at which we might want the different properties laying at the heart of the contradiction. In a coffee cup, for example, we might identify a 'hot and cold' contradiction – we want the cup to be hot on the inside in order to keep the coffee hot, but we would also like the coffee cup to be cold on the outside so that we don't burn our hands when we try and pick it up. This represents an example of a physical contradiction separate-able in space; in that there are physically different places where we want the two different attributes hot and cold. If we can find a means of 'separating' the contradiction like this, then we have the basis for both a better understanding of the problem, and also a means of tapping into the successful strategies of others who have successfully 'eliminated' the contradiction. (Note; we will use the term 'eliminate' in this chapter in the same way we used it in the last one – that is, as a direction and long term destination.)

There are four basic strategies for solving a physical contradiction problem. We will examine all four, and then look at a number of case study examples of the strategies in action on some real problems.

Four Separation Strategies

The four basic methods of 'separating' physical contradictions are:-
1) In Space
2) In Time
3) On Condition
4) By transition to an alternative system

Generally speaking, this list should be viewed as a hierarchy of strategies, which we would generally look to explore in a top-to-bottom sequence. The first three strategies are associated with a pair of questions related to 'where', 'when' and 'if' respectively. The

fourth is a category of solution routes we might explore if we have no success with the preceding strategies. So, a typical physical contradiction solution strategy would involve asking the questions:-

1) Where do I want condition A? and Where do I want condition –A?
2) When do I want condition A? and When do I want condition –A?
3) I want condition A if? and I want condition –A if?

Where –A represents the opposite of any attribute A.

Obtaining a difference between the answers of any of the question pairs, means that the contradiction is amenable to solution by the separation strategy in question.

So, to follow up the 'hot and cold' coffee cup contradiction from above, our three pairs of questions become:-

1) Where do I want the coffee cup to be hot? Answer – on the inside
   Where do I want the coffee cup to be cold? Answer – on the outside
2) When do I want the coffee cup to be hot? Answer – when I'm drinking
   When do I want the coffee cup to be cold? Answer – when I'm drinking
3) I want the coffee cup to be hot if? Answer – I like hot coffee to stay hot
   I want the coffee cup to be cold if? Answer – I like cold coffee

Thus, we see from that this problem is amenable to solution by separation by space and on condition – because these are the question pairs that give us a difference in answer between the two sides of the separation. Actually, unless I do like cold coffee, this is probably not a valid solution route to the problem; but this is a choice we have to make on a case-by-case basis. In this instance, we will assume that we cannot solve this problem by separation on condition. This leaves us with he option of solving by separating in space; in that we require different attributes (hot and cold) at different physical locations.

Having established that the separate in space solution route is a good one, we would now like to access the inventive solutions adopted by other problem solvers who have tackled the same generic 'separate in space' problem we are facing. We do this using the data found in Table 11.1. This table is our equivalent of the Matrix used to help solve technical contradictions. The first thing to note about this table is that the solution suggestions it contains are exactly the same Inventive Principles as are used to tackle technical contradictions. The second is that the table usually presents us with a rather larger list of Inventive Principle suggestions than are found on the Contradiction Matrix. The advantage of this is that we have more solution options; the disadvantage is that our systematic brainstorm through each possible solution will take longer.

In the case of our coffee cup problem and the separation in space problem type, we have 11 possible solution routes. (Plus, it is worth noting, if we don't find a solution among these 11 options, we will drop down the table into the fourth 'alternative ways' box and see if we can achieve any success with these Principles.)

While it is our intention to demonstrate the mechanics of the physical contradiction solving process rather than actually solving the coffee cup problem, some readers may wish to take a moment to investigate how the 11 separate in space solution triggers can be applied to help us design a coffee cup that does actually achieve the desired 'hot and cold' characteristics.

Regarding the process, Table 11.1 represents an important TRIZ tool; offering for physical contradiction problems the equivalent to what the Contradiction Matrix does for technical contradictions. As such, you may wish to use keep this table to hand as you would if you like the Contradiction Matrix.

Contradiction Solution Route	Inventive Principles Used To Tackle This Type of Contradiction
Separation in Space	1. Segmentation 2. Taking out 3. Local Quality 17. Another Dimension 13. Other Way Around 14. Curvature 7. Nested Doll 30. Flexible Shells/Thin Films 4. Asymmetry 24. Intermediary 26. Copying
Separation in Time	15. Dynamics 10. Prior Action 19. Periodic Action 11. Beforehand Cushioning 16. Partial or Excessive Action 21. Skipping 26. Copying 18. Mechanical Vibration 37. Thermal Expansion 34. Discarding & Recovering 9. Prior Counter-Action 20. Continuity of Useful Action
Separation on Condition	35. Parameter Changes 32. Colour Changes 36. Phase Transition 31. Porous Materials 38. Strong Oxidants 39. Inert Atmosphere 28. Mechanics Substitution 29. Pneumatics & Hydraulics
Transition to Alternative System 1. Transition to Sub-System	 1. Segmentation 25. Self-Service 40. Composite Materials 33. Homogeneity 12. Equi-Potentiality
2. Transition to Super-System	5. Merging 6. Universality 23. Feedback 22. Blessing In Disguise
3. Transition to Alternative System	27. Cheap/Short Living
4. Transition to Inverse System	13. Other Way Around 8. Counter-Weight

Table 11.1: Physical Contradiction Solution Strategies
(work from top-down when looking for solutions)

The list of Principles given for each separation category is in order of descending frequency of use by other problem solvers. Thus 'segmentation' has been used as a contradiction elimination strategy by the greatest number of investigated cases of 'separate in space' contradictions. As with the Contradiction Matrix, the data contained in the Table is intended to be used as a 'good start' rather than as in any way an exclusive list; at the end of the day, any of the 40 Principles may possibly be capable of tackling any contradiction in an inventive way.

One final point about the data contained in Table 11.1; the contents differ slightly in terms of form and more significantly in terms of content relative to other versions of this table to be found in other TRIZ texts. The content change – i.e. the Inventive Principles recommended for any given separation strategy – is based on a recent and ongoing analysis of solutions from the global patent database in which inventors have successfully challenged physical contradictions. The list of Principles is somewhat longer than those found in previously published lists.

The best way to understand the Table and the physical contradiction solving part of TRIZ is to see it in action. The rest of this chapter, therefore, describes a number of case study examples of the tool in action. As with case studies elsewhere in the book, despite the tendency of our brains to focus on the specific solutions obtained, the real aim is that we should focus on the process:

1) Car Wheel Covers

The roots of this case study lay in the book 'The Principles of Design' by Suh (Reference 11.1). In that book, the case is used as a means of demonstrating the Axiomatic Design method (something we will return to in Chapter 21 – Solution Evaluation – which is the area Axiomatic Design will help to the greatest effect), here we will use it as a way of both seeing the physical contradiction tool in action, and as an example of how eliminating contradictions can help get us out of the psychological inertia associated with optimising existing solutions that refuse to be optimised any more, and into better ways of thinking about problems.

The case study involves the design of wheel trims for car wheels. Drive a few kilometers anywhere in the world and chances are you will find someone's lost wheel cover. The start point of this case study is recognising that the design of most wheel covers – where the cover is held onto a wheel by an arrangement of spring clips – is inherently going to result in this situation. The graph illustrated in Figure 11.1 is the result of a comprehensive (and no doubt expensive) study carried out by one major car manufacturer aimed at trying to optimise the design of these wheel covers.

The problem the designers faced was that, if spring force was too small, the wheel covers fell off, and, if the spring force was too high, vehicle owners found it difficult to remove the cover when a wheel change was required. As shown in the Figure, the designers conducted a series of sophisticated customer trials using wheel covers with different spring forces and systematically measured how satisfied the customers were with each of the different cases. Very simply, they found that 100% of customers were satisfied if the force required to remove the cover was 30N or less, and that 100% of customers were happy that their wheel-covers hadn't fallen off if the retention force was 35N or more.

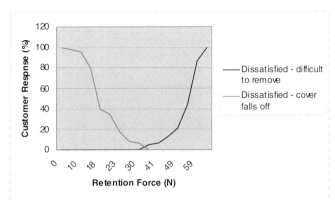

Figure 11.1: Trying To Optimise The Design of Wheel Cover Spring Clips

As well as being both customer focused and rigorous optimisers, the designers in this case can also seen in the non-TRIZ 'design is a trade-off' mind-set. Given the customer data, the 'design-is-a-trade-off' mindset says that the 'optimum' spring retention force needed to be somewhere between 30 and 35N. Being scientists, they also recognised that mass-production would mean some statistical variation in the achievable spring force. The functional requirement for the wheel cover spring design, therefore, became '*Provide a retention force of 34±4N*'.

In non-TRIZ 'optimising' terms, they had done the best they could. In effect they had come up with a solution which was 'optimum' because it dis-satisfied the minimum number of customers. In fact, their data had shown that a 34±4N solution would dis-satisfy somewhere between 2 and 6% of their customers. Or, put another way, probably somewhere around 100,000 per year.

The contradiction present in the wheel cover case is a Physical Contradiction. It is a physical contradiction because the wheel cover retention force is required to be HIGH (to retain the cover) AND LOW (to make it easy to remove). Identifying the presence of this contradiction is the first step in deriving stronger solutions.

The next step requires us to examine whether it is possible to separate the contradictory 'high' and 'low' retention force requirements. Our list of start-point questions thus become:
1) Where do I want the retention force to be high?
   Where do I want the retention force to be low?
2) When do I want the retention force to be high?
   When do I want the retention force to be low?
3) I want the retention force to be high if?
   I want the retention force to be low if?

In the case of the first pair of questions, the answer both times is 'at the interface between cover and wheel', and so this problem is not one amenable to solution by separation in space. When we ask the second pair of questions on the other hand, we get two different answers:
2) When do I want the retention force to be high? Answer – when I'm not making a wheel change
   When do I want the retention force to be low? Answer – when I am making a wheel change

223

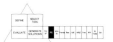

And so, because we have two different answers, we know that the high-and-low contradiction is in this case amenable to elimination by separation in time. The 'separation in time' strategies contained in Table 11.1 then give us a host of possible solution strategies for the problem:

- 'Preliminary Action' (e.g. push-and-twist type wheel covers)
- 'Skipping' (e.g. eliminate the spring and use some other means of holding the wheel cover – e.g. Peugeot sometimes use the wheel-nuts to hold the cover as well as the wheel)
- 'Discarding and Recovering' (e.g. eliminate the spring altogether – e.g. alloy wheels (the wheel is the wheel-cover))
- etc

If we don't achieve a good enough solution from this separate in time strategy, we should try the third 'separate on condition' category question. It turns out we can give the same answers to this question as we did for the separate in time category, and so we have established that the contradiction is also amenable to solution using the strategies contained in the 'separate on condition' box in Table 11.1.

As stated at it's beginning, this case has looked at a specific wheel-cover problem. A more complete analysis (see Chapter 2) would have encouraged a much more thorough examination of the functionality contained in the wheel-cover and its surrounding components. In the situation where we decide the only useful function of the wheel-cover is an aesthetic one, for example, we may well look to other parts of TRIZ – trimming for example in this case - to provide a more complete solution. It is worth noting, however, that TRIZ tries in several places to provide us with hints that encourage us to re-cast the problem we are tackling. The fourth set of strategies for solving physical contradictions – one that the method recommends us to always look at - for example, in which there is the 'transition to super-system' option would first give us a specific prompt to think about the problem in the context of the bigger picture, and second, give us the useful Principle 5 'Merging' solution trigger.

2) Bicycle Saddle

The bicycle saddle example from the previous chapter is amenable to analysis as a physical contradiction as well as technical. Some people – particularly in their early experience with TRIZ find themselves instinctively happier with one or other of physical and technical contradictions. We show here that different parts of TRIZ can get us to the same end point.

As far as the saddle design is concerned, a good physical contradiction to solve would be 'I want the saddle to be wide AND narrow'. Given this definition, the next part of the process, requires us to think about how we might separate the contradiction. Again, the three key words are when, where and if;

where do we want the saddle to be wide?
where do we want the saddle to be narrow?

when do we want the saddle to be wide?
when do we want the saddle to be narrow?

we want the saddle to be wide if?
we want the saddle to be narrow if?

In this case, answering these pairs of questions gives an immediate difference in answer at the first question pair; we want the saddle to be wide at the position where our pelvic bone structure rests on the saddle, and we want the saddle to be narrow where our legs are. This difference in answer then tells us that the contradiction is amenable to solution by the strategies contained in the 'separate in space' category. Table 11.1 then gives us triggers like 'Segmentation', 'the Other Way Around' and 'Another Dimension' – each of which are pointing us in the direction of the design achieved through tackling the problem as a technical contradiction. These suggestions are further re-enforced when we also ask the 'when' question and recognize a difference in requirements for the saddle shape depending on when our leg is in the pedal-up position and when it is in the pedal-down position – and we get the 'Dynamics' suggestion.

Combinations of Separations and Principles

Instances like this bicycle saddle where we find it possible to separate a given contradiction by more than one of the four strategies are quite common. Particularly common are cases where we find it possible to separate in terms of both time and space. We will explore this space and time separation possibility option as the basis for examining how best to tackle this kind of problem. Other combinations of contradiction separation possibilities will use exactly the same techniques as those described for this particular case. The two most important two-part questions associated with establishing whether a physical contradiction problem is amenable to solution by separation in space or time strategies are:-

1) WHERE do I want characteristic A and where do I want characteristic –A

2) WHEN do I want characteristic A, and when do I want characteristic –A

(where –A is the opposite of A – e.g. 'big' versus 'small')

Anytime we obtain a difference between our answers between A and –A, we have then established that the problem is amenable to solutions separated by both time AND space.

A good example comes from an extension of the wrench case study discussed in the previous chapter. A good physical contradiction here is represented in Figure 11.2.

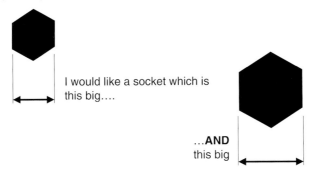

I would like a socket which is this big….

…**AND** this big

Figure 11.2: Socket Spanner Physical Contradiction

Asking the two questions, we then get:-

Q. Where do I want a big socket   A. Around a big nut
Q. Where do I want a small socket   A. Around a small nut

Q. When do I want a big socket   A. When fastening a big nut
Q. When do I want a small socket   A. When fastening a small nut

I.e. different answers in each case.

The main point of this section is to suggest that in these situations, it is a very good idea to look at Inventive Principles from both the space and time categories in Table 11.1, selecting at least one from each list, and looking to use them in combination.

An interesting solution for the socket wrench problem is the GatorGrip™ universal wrench illustrated in Figure 11.3. This solution combines 'Segmentation' from the separate in space category plus 'Dynamics' from the separate in time category.

1) Separating Contradictory Requirements

a) in Space
   Segmentation.....

b) in Time
   Dynamics......

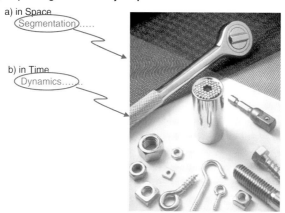

Figure 11.3: GatorGrip™ Universal Socket Wrench

3) Sleeping Policeman

A similar, but perhaps less well-known physical contradiction problem can be derived from the 'sleeping policeman' speed-bumps found on many modern urban roads. Most devices are either asphalt or concrete humps, although more 'sophisticated' designs use a solid rubber hump design. To any driver intent on driving above the speed limit, sleeping policemen are an excellent deterrent. To anyone driving below the speed limit or to emergency vehicles, however, they are an annoying and potentially life-threatening nuisance.

Looked at from a physical contradiction perspective, a far better solution would come if it were possible to develop a system which contained a speed hump AND didn't contain a speed hump;

Q. Where do I want a speed hump   A. Under speeding cars
Q. Where do I not want a speed hump   A. Under cars driving below the speed limit

Q. When do I want a speed hump   A. When a car is driving too fast
Q. When do I not want a small socket   A. When a car is driving legally

Again, we see a very good solution appearing in the design shown in Figure 11.4. This system makes use of principles from both SPACE and TIME Principle lists in a manner very similar to the earlier wrench example.

1) Separating Contradictory Requirements

a) in Space
(Segmentation).....

b) in Time
(Dynamics.....).

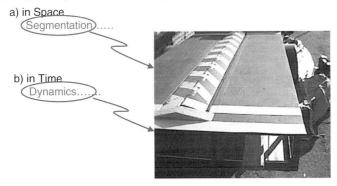

Figure 11.4: Motorised Retractable Speed Bump

Both of these cases offer examples of combined use of Inventive Principles from different physical contradiction 'separation' solution strategies. The combination of 'segmentation' and 'dynamics' in fact may be seen to be very common across a range of other similar contradiction problems.

Although both solutions 'solve' physical contradictions and as such improve the main useful function of either system, it may well be argued they have done this at the expense of a more complicated system. Anyone trying to use a GatorGrip™, for example, will soon discover several other problems emerging from solution of the 'big and small' problem – not least of which are accessibility of a fundamentally bigger device, and sticking of the pins when the socket becomes exposed to dirt and grime.

For both problems, the Table 11.1 physical contradiction solution scheme offers solutions that are usually 'stronger' than the separation solutions if the third 'on condition' category is used. The 'Parameter Changes' 'increase the degree of flexibility' trigger, for example, is not too far away from a recent, much more simple, inflatable solution to the sleeping policeman problem – Figure 11.5 – currently under test in London.

(Incidentally, those happier using the Trends part of the TRIZ toolkit (Chapter 13) may notice a useful connection between these solutions and the 'Dynamization' trend – another example of different tools getting us to similar end-points.)

Figure 11.5: Norgren/Dunlop Pneumatic Deflatable Speed Hump

Graphical Representation of Physical Contradictions

In the previous chapter we saw that a technical contradiction could be presented graphically as a hyperbolic curve (see Figure 10.2 for example). Figure 11.1 offers clues to the equivalent graph for a physical contradiction. A more general physical contradiction graph is drawn in Figure 11.6.

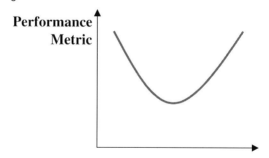

Performance Metric

Parameter A

Figure 11.6: Graphical Representation of a Physical Contradiction.

This graphical approach is often a very good way of identifying a physical contradiction. The parabolic shape graph is extremely common. It is particularly prominent in optimisation processes – where the aim is to find the minimum 'optimum' point (or maximum if the parabola is drawn the other way up – also a representation of a physical contradiction).

Anywhere, in fact, where we find ourselves searching for an 'optimum' value of some parameter – like the search for an optimum spring retention force in the wheel-cover example – this physical contradiction part of TRIZ is encouraging us to think about re-

defining the problem to derive a much stronger solution than the ones achievable through optimisation. Typical examples of this kind of scenario include:-

1) the blade angle in a safety razor is known to possess an optimum cutting angle. Similarly, for a multi-blade design, there is a different optimum angle to achieve ready clearance of cut hairs through and out of the between-blade passages. The designers currently seek the 'optimum' compromise between these two conflicting angle requirements. TRIZ would define a better solution as one capable of achieving *both* optimum angles.

2) Also regarding the razor, or more generally anything that we require to cut with, are parallel desires to have a cutting edge that is both very fine (so that it cuts easily) and blunt (so that it has a long life). The usual response in this situation is to find an 'optimum' compromise thickness. Defining and solving the physical contradiction 'I want the blade to be sharp and blunt' would allow both conditions to be achieved simultaneously.

3) Internal combustion engines possess an optimum fuel-air ratio for the most efficient combustion of the fuel; Unfortunately, this 'optimum' value is different at different conditions (e.g. cold start versus high speed cruise), and for different requirements (e.g. I will get lowest NOx emissions at one ratio, and lowest CO emissions at another. While some modern designs are beginning to address these conflicting optimum ratio values, most designs still try and achieve an overall best 'average' value.

4) Reference 11.2 describes a physical contradiction case study concerning the design of particle separators in which considerable amounts of money were spent (wasted?) trying to achieve an acceptable compromise optimum solution, when a far stronger contradiction-eliminating solution was waiting to be found.

5) In production processes, you will still find many organisations try and calculate an 'optimum' batch size during multiple operation manufacture. This optimum is typically actually the best compromise between conflicting requirements to have a high batch size (equals low set-up costs) and a low batch size (equals low inventory). A far better solution would achieve both low set-up cost and low inventory.

6) Design of transmission gearing systems represents a whole series of local optimisations to identify the best compromise gear ratios to suit an infinite variety of actual operating conditions. Each gear ratio design choice is a compromise between conflicting requirements.

7) In certain food engineering processes involving preparation of fried foods, there is a parallel requirement to employ some kind of oil as a cooking medium, but also to avoid the use of oil because of mess and disposal issues. A smart solution would be one achieving 'oil and no oil'.

8) In chemical processes it is common to try and optimise the size of a catalyst, between two physically conflicting desires. The catalyst is required to be small in order to achieve the highest possible surface area to volume ratio, but the catalyst is also required to be big in order to make it easier to retrieve at the end of the reaction. Compromise approaches to this problem inevitably lead to non-optimum reaction speed and loss of some catalyst. Solving the physical contradiction 'I want a catalyst that is big AND small' would allow optimum reaction speed and no loss of catalyst.

And so on. Physical contradictions are everywhere around us. Sometimes optimisation strategies will offer adequate solutions; TRIZ, on the other hand, is trying to encourage successive challenge of the contradictions as part of a desire to achieve ideality – Figure 11.7.

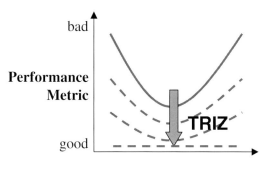

Parameter A

Figure 11.7: Graphical Representation of Physical Contradiction 'Elimination' Process .

The graph illustrates a parallel desire to not only move the optimum towards 'good', but to also remove relationship between changing values of the Parameter and the performance achieved – i.e. we wish to remove the parabolic correlation between parameter and performance.

Of course, the graphical approach is not the only way of recognising a physical contradiction. There are a host of situations where the contradiction is discrete rather than the continuous nature implied by a parabolic graph. Some of these are more obvious than others. A child's crayon that 'writes AND doesn't write' is an example of a non-obvious discrete contradiction. Identification of contradictions like this one are a very good way of innovating – in fact finding a good unresolved contradiction presents one of the best innovation opportunities of any of the systematic creativity tools – in that almost as soon as the contradiction is defined it becomes possible to identify new opportunities. For the crayon that writes and doesn't write, for example, the 'separate on condition' questions should quickly get us to the concept of a crayon that writes on a special paper given to the child by a parent, but isn't able to mark walls, carpets, etc.

What Do I Do?

The identification and elimination of physical contradictions represents an important part of TRIZ and systematic creativity. In order to use the tool to best effect, the following general strategy is recommended (ultimately, of course, you should consider adapting these elements to best suit the way your individual brain likes to operate):

1) Identify a physical contradiction – this may happen via a number of routes, perhaps most commonly when you find yourself struggling to achieve adequate performance by optimising a given design parameter, or by seeing a parabolic profile graph, or by thinking about what the **ideal** attributes of a parameter might be.
2) Having identified a good contradiction, work through the three pairs of separation questions – where, when and if – in order to identify possible solution strategies.

3) Where a problem is amenable to solution by more than one of the separation strategies, think about using the Inventive Principle solutions triggers in combination.

4) If none of the separation strategies are possible, or if you wish to explore other solution routes, examine the strategies contained in the fourth 'alternative ways' box in Table 11.1.

5) Use the Inventive Principle suggestions to connect your problem to possible solutions – see the list of Principles with examples at the end of Chapter 10.

References

1) Suh, N., 'The Principles of Design', Oxford University Press, 1990.
2) Mann, D.L., 'Case Studies In TRIZ: A Helicopter Particle Separator', TRIZ Journal, February 1999.

12.
Problem Solving Tools -
S-Field Analysis/Inventive Standards

It's life, Jim, but not as we know it'
Scottie to Captain Kirk, Star Trek

The S-Field (substance-field, su-field) part of the TRIZ toolkit seems to be the one that polarises people more than any other. Some TRIZ devotees will base all of their analyses around the construction and analysis of s-field models, while others will use the tool only as a point of last resort. The approach taken within this book is that Chapter 9 will recommend the use of s-fields when they are the most appropriate tool for the task at hand.

The essence of the tool is simple and yet, for many, highly non-instinctive. The foundation on which the tool is constructed derives from the uncovering of a test of what makes a system viable – and therefore, able to successfully perform a function. The test (which we won't go into the detail of justifying here – interested readers should seek further information from References 12.1 or 12.2) simply states that in order to successfully deliver a function a minimum of two substances and a field are required. By convention, these three things are labelled S_1, S_2 and F respectively. By convention also, the three things are typically drawn together in a triangular pattern as illustrated in Figure 12.1.

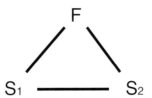

Figure 12.1: Basic S-Field Model

The word 'substance' is probably one of the weaker translations from Russian to English. 'Substance' has a fairly specific meaning, or rather conjures a rather specific mental image of 'something with substance', whereas what is intended is a 'thing' in its most general form. Unfortunately 'thing-field analysis' sounds less scientific, and so we currently have to live with 'substance-field'. There are moves to resort back to the original Russian and call s-field models 'vepoles', but for the purposes of this book, we'll stick to s-fields, and keep the generic 'thing' word at the forefront of our mind.

The other word 'field' is a rather better translation, and is taken to mean any form of energy present in a system. We will provide a definitive list of such fields shortly. First, however, it is necessary to explore a little bit more about what s-fields do and how they can help to solve problems.

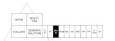

The next thing, then that we need to examine are the lines that join the two substances and the field in the s-field model. The lines are there to represent the type of interaction taking place between the different pairs of substances and field. There is a convention used in the defining of these lines as detailed in Figure 12.2.

TYPES OF INTERACTION

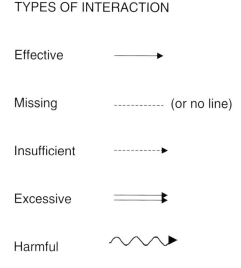

Figure 12.2: Types of S-Field Model Connecting Lines

Hence, the s-field model drawn in Figure 12.1 represents the ideal situation in which the system contains effective relationships between each of the substances and the field. The above table of other possible relationships should suggest that this ideal is not always achieved, and that there are in fact a wide variety of different combinations of lines that could be present in the s-field model. These combinations include the possibility that there are more than one relations between the different constituents – for example there may be an effective and a harmful interaction between any pair in the triangle.

In large part, the basis of the s-field model as a problem solving tool then stems from the classification of problems using the various combinations of substances, fields and interactions that are possible. This is the TRIZ concept of mapping specific problems into generic ones again. Provided we can transform our problem situation into an s-field model, what the original TRIZ researchers have then given us is a means of seeing how others who have faced the same type of model have gone about resolving the problem. These resolution strategies have been collected together as a list of Inventive Standards. A comprehensive list of these Standards, along with a series of examples of them in action is provided at the reference section at the end of the chapter.

Apart from a special class of problems (measurement problems), all of the Inventive Standards used by other problems solvers in tackling a particular form of s-field model fall into four types. These are:-
1) Solve the problem by **completing** an incomplete s-field model
2) solve the problem by **modifying** one or more of the existing substances or field
3) solve the problem by **adding** new substances, fields or combinations thereof, or
4) solve the problem by **transitioning** it to a higher or lower hierarchical level.

The original method of classifying the Inventive Standards (one still used by the majority working with TRIZ) is somewhat different from this classification method. We will use the above system because we believe it offers a more logical method of segmenting the picture in order to best get to a solution. For those that are used to the original classification convention, we have listed the original classification numbers alongside each Standard in the reference section. For everyone else, the main decision you are required to make once you have defined your s-field model is whether you would prefer to solve it by completion, modification, addition or transition. In some instances, it may be that all three will have to be evaluated, but at least now we have the choice.

The Inventive Standards themselves are used in a manner very similar to that used for the Inventive Principles and the Trends of Evolution. They each represent problem solution routes in a generic sense. It is our job to translate those generic solutions into the specifics of our particular problem situation.

The rest of this chapter now describes the mechanics of actually using the Inventive Standards once we have drawn an s-field model, followed by a series of case study examples to hopefully illustrate some common s-field model problem scenarios.

S-Field Model/Inventive Standards – Sequence of Events

Having defined what the function the system under evaluation is required to achieve is and have drawn the s-field model (if we have entered this chapter after having completed an FAA model, we will find that it has done a lot of the hard work of defining the relationships between substances for us – indeed, any pair of components with a connecting functional relationship can be extracted from the overall FAA model and re-drawn as an s-field model), we need to ask and answer a series of questions in this recommended sequence:

<u>1) Are the minimum two substances and a field present?</u>

If the answer is, no they are not, then according to the test underpinning the s-field model concept it is not possible that the system is viable. The only option available to rectify this situation is to go to the section of Inventive Standards concerned with completing an **incomplete** s-field. The only solution suggestion in this section says 'if you don't have two substances and a field; go and get them'. In classical TRIZ terms, this is Inventive Standard 1.1.1.

Until you are able to find the missing substances and fields, there will be no point in travelling any further. It is surprising just how many problems there are where this is the case. This is particularly so when we find ourselves wishing to add new functions to a system.

If the answer to this first question is yes, the next question is:

<u>2) Is this a measurement problem?</u>

If it is, then we are into the special class of exceptions to the modify, add or transition options described above. The classical Inventive Standards already contain a special classification for measurement problems. If the answer to this first question has been yes,

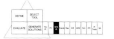

we can go straight to the reference section at the end of the chapter and start looking at the Inventive Standards for measurement problems.

If it's not a measurement problem, the next question is:

3) Are there any harmful relationships in the system?

This includes situations where the s-field model might also include insufficient or excessive relationships. Generally speaking, harmful interactions should be dealt with as a higher priority (note however, that if you are entering the s-field tool from diagnosing a broader perspective FAA model – e.g. via the recommendations contained in Chapter 9, then it will have given some prior guidelines on which problems are more important than others).

If the answer to this third question is yes, go to the category of Inventive Standards especially formulated for situations containing harmful functions. Within this category, are the three generic types of solution type modify, add or transition. They are presented in a sequence that starts with solution suggestions offering minimum disruption to the system and works through to solutions that involve more profound changes. Some people prefer to work through the available solutions in a more random order. Both approaches are valid, and the choice between them depends largely on personal preference.

If the answer to this question is no, then this means the s-field model contains insufficient, excessive or both types of interaction. If this is the case, go to the class of Inventive Standards for 'Insufficient/Excessive Interactions' and work through the equivalent list of solution suggestions in the modify, add and transition categories, either adopting the sequence contained in the reference section or a more random approach again as per personal preference.

Fields

Before we look at a series of case study examples, it is worth spending a few seconds recording the sorts of things that are classified as 'fields' in the s-field tool. As stated at the beginning of the chapter, a 'field' is defined as any source of energy within a system. The following table provides a list of the known available types of field.

Type of Field	Sub-categories
Mechanical	Gravitational, Frictional, Inertial, Centrifugal, Coriolis, Tension, Compression, Elasticity, Reaction, Vibration
Hydraulic/Pneumatic	Hydrostatic, Hydrodynamic, Aerostatic, Aerodynamic, Surface Tension
Thermal	Conduction, Convection, Radiation, Static Temperature Gradient, Total Temperature Gradient, Expansion, Insulation
Pressure	Static Pressure, Total Pressure, Static Pressure Gradient, Total Pressure Gradient, Buoyancy, Lift, Magnus, Vacuum, Supersonic Shock Wave

Electrical	Electrostatic, Electrodynamic, Electrophoretic, Alternating, Inductive, Electromagnetic, Capacitative, Piezo-electric, Rectification, Transformation
Chemical	Oxidation, Reduction, Diffusion, Combustion, Dissolution, Combination, Transformation, Electrolytic, Endothermic, Exothermic
Biological	Enzyme, Photosynthesis, Catabolic, Anabolic, Osmotic, Reproductive, Decay, Fermentation
Magnetic	Static, Alternating, Ferro-magnetic, Electro-magnetic
Weak Nuclear Attraction	
Strong Nuclear Attraction	
Optical	Reflection, Refraction, Diffraction, Interference, Polarisation, IR, visible, UV
Acoustic	Sound, Ultrasound
Olfactory	

Table 12.1: Types of Field

This table is a useful reference throughout our application of s-fields, and in many situations can act as an additional list of triggers to help us to think about solving problems. After all, if every system needs at least one field to be present in order to achieve a function, it is a good idea to keep a track of the possible options.

Case Study Examples

Baboons, Mandarins and Ship Propellers

We start this section with two problems that to the untrained eye appear to be about as dis-similar as two problems could appear to be. The first involves a story first recorded in the newspaper Sotsialisticheskaya industriya, and found in Reference 17.3 involving a problem of baboon herds eating crops of mandarins in the Transvaal province of South Africa. No traditional method of scaring away the baboons (dogs, guards, sirens, etc) was found to work, and the farmers were at a loss as to what to do. The second problem concerns a problem associated with the erosion of a ship's propeller by cavitation. Essentially, the high speed of the propeller caused areas of low pressure in which dissolved air in the water was able to expand and re-collapse at a very high rate of change – thus creating local very high temperature mini-explosions adjacent to the surface of the propeller. Propellers were wearing out at a very rapid rate.

The common link between these apparently disconnected problems is one of the things that demonstrates the immense knowledge distillation powers of the s-field part of TRIZ. The common link, if you haven't seen it, is that both problems feature two substances with a harmful interaction between them. In the case of the first problem, the baboon has a harmful effect on the mandarins; and in the second water has a harmful effect on the propeller. In terms of s-field models, the two situations may be represented as:

237

$$S_1 \rightsquigarrow S_2$$

Once this common link has been established, the s-field model tool enables us to see how other people have successfully tackled this generic type of 'harmful effect between two substances' problem. Hence, if we go to the list of Inventive Standards to the category concerning problems with harmful interactions and begin reading, the first suggestion we obtain is one to modify the existing substances:

* *Remove the harmful effect by introducing a substance which is a modification of the existing substances (Reference 1.2.2)*

This apparently innocuous solution trigger is written in such a way as to promote creative thinking. The first part of this process involves examining the two substances and seeing which would be the most appropriate to introduce the required 'modification of'.

In the case of the propeller problem, the instinctive answer is probably the propeller as this is the substance we have some design control over. In this scenario a modification of the propeller might involve a change of material to something with a harder surface, or heat-treatment or a shot-peening operation. While these strategies would all probably help to improve the situation, they are by no means the only possibilities. Specifically, the Inventive Standard suggests we could modify either of the substances. What could we modify about the water? There is an awful lot of water in the ocean, so that sounds expensive, but what about if it were possible to modify the water local to the propeller? At this point, we might want to jump to the chapter on resources (14) and see if that provides any ideas on possible modifications to water. One of the ideas featured in the list of low-cost/easily available resources involves freezing – which in fact turned out to offer an extremely elegant solution to the problem – chill the propeller such that a thin layer of ice forms over the surface (without altering the aerodynamic properties). Then as the cavitation explosions wear the ice away, another layer forms.

Okay, so what about the baboons and the mandarins? Which of those is the easier to modify? Well, we could modify the baboons by capturing them all, or by injecting them with something that means they don't like the taste of mandarins anymore, but this all sounds rather difficult. The mandarins sound like they would be easier to modify, but we don't really want to have to do things like paint them or poison them because this would make them inedible or require the use of additional resources to clean them. In this case we need to think a little bit harder about what we could add to this system that counts as a 'modification of a mandarin'? Again the Inventive Standard is there to act as a thought provoker – what is a mandarin? A fruit, an orange thing, a citrus fruit? How could we modify it? A different fruit? A different colour?

A good answer to the problem, and the one successfully adopted by the Transvaal farmers was to plant rows of lemon trees surrounding the mandarin trees. The result? The baboons approached the fruit groves, saw lemons, perhaps tasted lemons, didn't like the taste and left in disgust. The farmer? Received an additional income from the sale of lemons.

Catalysts

A common problem with the catalysts used to speed chemical reactions in industrial sized plants is described in Figure 12.3 below:

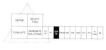

Figure 12.3: The Catalyst Problem in Chemical Reactions

We have alreadyy seen this problem in the previous chapter as the physical contradiction 'I want the catalyst to be big and small'. The problem of recovering (or rather failing to recover) small particles of catalyst is one that is also amenable to solution by use of s-fields.

As per the previous details of how the s-field tool works, the first thing we need to do with this problem is defined the function required to be performed. We will describe this as 'separate catalyst'. Then we need to construct an s-field model to represent the situation. This in turn requires us to define what substances and fields are present. In terms of the former, clearly, we have at least two substances present – there is the catalyst, and the constituents of the chemicals we are reacting. The essence of the problem (being the thing the s-field model is trying to focus on) is that the soup of chemicals is preventing the catalysts from being separated.

What about fields? The list of possible options shown in Table 12.1 suggests several that may be present – any number of possible chemical reactions for example – but in terms of fields that are helping (or preventing) the delivery of the required 'separate' function, there are probably none. Gravity is likely to be present, as it is in most engineering systems, but for the moment let us assume that its effect is neutral in this instance. In which case, the current s-field model for our 'separate catalyst' system is:

Given this initial situation, our first question in determining which solution path to take is 'do you have two substances and a field? Answer; no. Solution; get the missing element. In this case, we need to find such a field. Again the list of possible field options in Table 12.1 offers us a comprehensive list of options/solution triggers. If there is a solution to this problem, it must come from the successful harnessing of one of these fields.

We are more interested in process here than in solutions, but you may care to note that all of the known and emerging methods of separating catalysts from chemical mixtures (centrifuges, magnetic – wrapping or spraying a thin layer of the catalyst around a magnetic core, ultrasound, etc) can be traced back to this table.

It is also worth noting that if we do decide to include gravity in the initial model (e.g. we use gravity to allow the catalyst to oottle out of the working fluid), and then show that it's action is insufficient, we will end up with the same solution directions; if there is insufficient field action in the system, either enhance it or add another one.

This case study highlights one of the most useful applications of the s-field part of the systematic creativity toolkit; those situations where we are looking to deliver a function

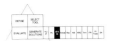

when the 'system' as it currently stands is fundamentally unable to deliver. 'Separate' is a very common such function. The next case study illustrates a related example:

Pistons and Oil
Start an internal combustion engine after having let it stand idle for a week or two and the initial noise can be somewhat disconcerting to the owner. What is being heard is metal-on-metal contact between piston and cylinder. The reason? All of the oil that is supposed to form a protective intermediary layer between the two has fallen to the sump of the engine under the action of gravity. The initial s-field diagram for this situation is:

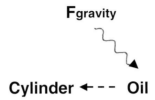

What this model says is that gravity has a harmful effect on the oil, and that the oil then has an insufficient relationship with the cylinder. In actual fact, this model is incomplete. A more complete description would recognise that there is actually a second field involved in this system – a surface tension between cylinder and oil. This model would look like:

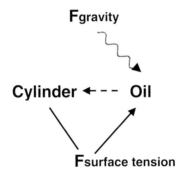

The aim with all s-field problems is to transition the initial situation to the ideal situation of two substances and a field with effective interactions between each pair of substance and field (i.e. to achieve the s-field model in Figure 12.1).

Some people are happier leaving the effects of gravity off this type of model (in that a) it is always present, and b) as it is acting in a wholly negative way and thus cannot be contributing to the system 'cylinder holds oil', there is no point including it). If we chose to make this omission, the s-field model would then look like:-

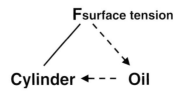

The overall point of showing these different pictures is that there are several ways of representing the same situation. The general learning points we can draw from the different figures are

a) if there is only a harmful field, there can be no hope of achieving a useful function
b) in order to achieve the state whereby we do achieve a useful function, the net sum of all the fields present must equate to a single composite field acting effectively.

What this last point means is that we need to conduct some kind of field summation operation. In the case of this problem, such a summation equates to the fact that, in its current state, the system does not have a net sufficient field effect. Our only recourse in this situation is to add some more field effect somehow. This might involve enhancing the current surface tension field (the only one contributing to the delivery of the useful function) or the addition of a new field from the list of possibilities in Table 12.1.

(Two solutions to this problem are the Castrol GTX Magnatec oil – containing unique polarised synthetic ester molecules -'Unique Molecular Attraction(UMA)' - which enhance surface tension properties – and the emerging family of ferro-fluids – which add a new magnetic field to enhance the ability of the oil to stick to the cylinder wall.)

Coloured Pencils
Anyone who has used coloured pencils will know how difficult it is to erase any mistakes. In order to understand why this should be the case, we need to zoom-in to examine the pencil lead at the sub-micron scale. Most coloured pencils are formed from a complex combination of constituents providing different functions and attributes – colour, strength, evenness, flexibility, prevention of fragment formation, etc. Of particular relevance to the question of erasability is the use of waxes to provide the binding function. The waxes used are very good at achieving the function of keeping the lead together and releasing it onto the paper in a controlled manner, but they are a nuisance when it comes to erasing. This is because the heat generated by an eraser causes the waxes to melt and thus bind themselves into the surface of the paper.

From a TRIZ perspective, we might see this problem in one of three main ways; the first would be to look at it as a 'knowledge' problem; are there any ways of achieving the 'binding' function other than using wax? The second way would involve recognising the existence of a contradiction associated with the wax. As shown in the figure – an extract from a rather more complex function and attribute analysis picture – the wax provides a useful 'bind' function, and also a harmful 'marks' function.

This contradiction is one in which we wished to improve erasability ('adaptability or versatility' or 'convenience of use' on the Matrix), and that loss of the 'binding' function ('stability of the object's composition') was the thing that prevented the improvement.

The problem can also be represented as an s-field problem if we zoom in to look at the harmful 'marks' relationship that exists between the wax and paper. In this problem, in encouraging us to think about the 'field' present in this system, we are offered an additional perspective on the problem: the field present is a mechanical one, and, because the wax is sticking to the paper, it counts as an 'excessive' one. The s-field model for the system thus looks like:-

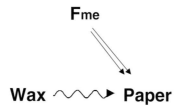

The harmful interaction between the two substances should be resolved by examining the inventive standards for 'harmful' interactions. Because the harmful interaction exists between the substances (rather than from the field), we should look to the standards relating to first modification of substances. Similarly, the excessive field part of the problem should cause us to first look to inventive standards associated with modification of fields.
Both in fact point to a replacement of the wax with some other form and method of binding to the paper (incidentally, solving the contradiction also gives the suggestion 'Parameter Changes').

Incidentally, a very elegant solution to this problem may be found in US patent 6,271,286 granted to Binney and Smith in August 2001. In the invention, the inventors, have successfully replaced the wax with the use of tiny PTFE or similar fibres to perform the binding function.

This kind of re-enforcement of solution direction from different parts of the TRIZ toolkit is often useful in confirming the validity and prudence of a given solution route; if every tool is pointing you in the same direction, you can be pretty confident that that direction is an appropriate one.

Final Thoughts

As outlined in Chapter 9, the s-field tool plays its biggest role in the creative problem-solving arena in areas where the current 'system' either doesn't exist or it is still at a relatively immature stage in its evolutionary development. In a related fashion, it is also of great use when we decide to add a new function to a system. The missing key for many in these situations is failure to recognise the importance of FIELDS in systems.

What Do I Do?

The most effective use of the s-field tool will emerge from the following basic deployment strategy:

1) Define in simple terms the function the system under consideration is expected to deliver. For example 'separate waste', 'measure height', 'move particle'.

2) Any such system, if it is to deliver the function must satisfy the 'two substances plus a field' viability test that lies at the heart of the s-field tool. Define the substances and fields that exist in the system, trying at all times to focus on just those things that form the heart of the function delivery.

3) Draw the s-field diagram for the system as it currently stands, detailing the interactions between the substances and fields using the line conventions described in Figure 12.2.

4) Work through the questions in the above section describing sequence of events, and be guided to the relevant Inventive Standards that have helped others to solve similar generic types of problem.

5) Use the Inventive Standards as solution triggers to help generate specific solutions to the problem. This may require examination of all of the suggestions in a particular category of Standards, although generally speaking, the ones at the top of a given list are more commonly successful than those at the bottom of a given list.

The s-field part of TRIZ is one of its most abstract for many newcomers. Practice defining s-field models for systems around you in order to build familiarity.

References

1) Altshuller, G. ,'Creativity As An Exact Science', Gordon & Breach, 1984.
2) Salamatov, Y., 'TRIZ: The Right Solution At The Right Time', Insytec, The Netherlands, 1999.
3) Timokhov, V.I., 'Collection of Creative Tasks In Biology, Ecology and TRIZ', TRIZ-SHANS, System of Professional Designers, Consultants and Teachers, St Petersburg, 1996.

List Of Inventive Standards With Examples

The following list of standards is categorised into four main classifications. These are 'incomplete', 'measurement', 'harmful interactions' and 'insufficient/excessive interactions'. Within the third and fourth of these categories are additional sub-categories for 'modifying existing constituents of the s-field model', 'adding new constituents' and 'transitioning' to a higher or lower hierarchical level.

The sequence of questions described earlier in the chapter will dictate which of the three main categories to use. The choice over 'modify', 'add' or 'transition' sub-categories is more open to personal preference, although there is a general progression from low to high amount of change to the existing system as you pass through the three different sub-categories.

Note that, in addition to the 76 Inventive Standards, this section features a small number of additional Standards not featured in the original list. These are given a reference number beginning with the letter D. The new Standards have emerged from research into s-field type problems which have not been solved by the original list. That research has been conducted specifically for this book.

INCOMPLETE S-FIELDS

* Add substances or fields in order to establish the two substance plus one field minimum requirement, first of all looking to use substances and fields already present in the environment. (Reference 1.1.1/5.2.1)

- To break a rock requires a hammer and a mechanical and/or gravitational field
- To measure a distance, an additional substance and field are required (e.g. tape measure plus optical field)
- To keep oil attached to a surface requires a field (e.g. ferrofluid)
- To separate particles from a fluid requires addition of a field in order to make one thing move relative to the other
- To clear water from a windscreen requires a field
- A prime mover only works if there is an energy conversion process (field)

MEASUREMENT/DETECTION PROBLEMS

* Modify the system so that there is no need to make the detection or measurement (Reference 4.1.1)
  - Self compensating/self-calibrating/self-balancing systems all eliminate the need for measurement
  - Pressure relief valves provide protection in hydraulic circuits by preventing over-pressure (i.e. no pressure measurement is required)
  - User-adjustable lenses eliminate need for measurements by optician

* Make the detection or measurement on a copy, image or replica of the object (Reference 4.1.2)
  - Shadow-graph inspection methods
  - X-ray inspection of welds
  - Calibrated thermal imager used to obtain temperature measurements
  - Measure size of a dangerous animal by taking its photograph next to a calibrated scale
  - Measure the temperature of an insect by measuring the temperature of a jar containing lots of insects

* Transform the problem into one involving successive measurement of changes (Reference 4.1.3)
  - Go/No-go gauges
  - Ticker-tape machine measures acceleration by measuring increasing gap between adjacent tick marks, where ticks are placed at constant time intervals
  - Optical probe measures changes in speed from changing frequency

* Enhance an existing or add a new field to provide an easily detectable parameter related to the parameter required to be measured or detected (Reference 4.2.1)
  - Electrostatic sensors detect particles carrying an inherent charge as they pass through a duct (e.g. detection of sand particles and other debris into and out of a gas turbine engine)
  - Electro-chromic rear-view mirror darkens on detection of bright lights
  - Raman spectroscopy – bouncing a laser light off a surface and recording scatter can reveal the exact chemical composition of the materials present (also known as inelastic light scattering)

* Include an easily detectable internal or external additive (and possibly a new field to assist the detection or measurement) (Reference 4.2.2)
  - Litmus paper
  - Steam whistle detects boiling kettle
  - Canaries used to be used to measure presence of poisonous gases in mines
  - Use a fluorescent dye in refrigerant fluid to enhance detection of leaks
  - Add odorous compound to non-smelling poison gases to enable human detection
  - Use a sieve to measure the size of small particles
  - Thermo-chromic plastics
  - Thermal paint

- Fluorescent additives used to sense presence of excessive glucose levels in subcutaneous skin tissue

*If it is not possible to modify the system, then introduce an easily detected additive or object to the external environment (and possibly add a new field to assist the detection or measurement) (Reference 4.2.3)
- Magnetic plugs detect metallic debris in oil
- A disclosing agent is often added to water to highlight presence of plaque on teeth
- Laser anemometry tracks small, low density particles which follow streamlines in a flow-field
- Introduce thin streams of smoke into a wind-tunnel in order to see the flow of air around objects being evaluated in the tunnel.
- Wool tufts assist flow visualisation in wind tunnels, etc

* If it is not possible to introduce an easily detectable additive into the environment, obtain them by changing something already in the environment (and possibly add a new field to assist the detection or measurement) (Reference 4.2.4)
- Cavitation bubbles appear (compressed/dissolved air comes out of solution) in a fluid which suddenly experiences a rapid pressure reduction.
- In bubble chambers liquid hydrogen is kept just below the boiling point of temperature and pressure. Energetic particles passing through cause local boiling, forming a path of bubbles that are photographed to study the particle dynamics.
- Combining hot and cold water on a flow visualisation table provides visible streamlines at the dividing line between hot and cold.
- Use dry ice (frozen CO_2) as a flow visualisation aid
- Flowing air creates static charges which can be used to enable flow measurement

* Make use of physical, chemical or biological effects present in the system to help make the measurement (Reference 4.3.1)
- Shape memory alloys/polymers change shape according to a set trigger temperature
- Exothermic reaction in bone cement informs surgeon that cement is set
- Bi-metallic strip acts as thermal switch
- Thermal expansion/contraction gives a measure of temperature

* Use resonance in all or part of the system such that a change in the resonant frequency helps to make the measurement (Reference 4.3.2)
- Tuning fork measures frequency of notes on a tuneable musical instrument
- Magnetic resonance detects presence of contaminants (e.g. sulphur, heavy metals) in an oil flow
- Change in resonant frequency of an object in a flow field can be used to detect the presence of particulate or fluid contaminants
- Change in resonant frequency of a rotating shaft provides indication of a change in operating characteristic (often used as a means of detecting health degradation in condition monitoring equipment)
- MRI scanner
- Use change in resonant frequency to detect when a receptacle has received the required amount of a fluid (e.g. filling bottles)

* Attach something (possibly already in the environment) to the system and use changes in it's resonant frequency to make the measurement (Reference 4.3.3)
  - Instead of directly measuring capacitance, insert the object of unknown capacitance into a circuit of known inductance, then vary the frequency of the applied voltage to find the resonant frequency of the combined circuit in order to calculate the capacitance of the added object.
  - A mass of boiling liquid can be measured by measuring the natural frequency of gas resulting from evaporation
  - Use a calibrated variable capacity Helmholtz resonator to measure flow

* Introduce a ferromagnetic substance (solid or particles) to the system or it's surroundings, and use a magnetic field to help make the measurement or detection (Reference 4.4)
  - Introduction of ferro-magnetic particles into ignition material of matches means defect materials (i.e. matches which contain no ignition material) can be detected because they will not be attracted by a magnetic field
  - Ferromagnetic markers on objects facilitates ease of counting by providing a change in magnetic field every time an object passes the sensor
  - Use changes in magnetic field to measure flow rate of a ferro-fluid

* Use physical effects associated with ferromagnetics (Curie Point, Hopkins, Barkhausen, etc) (Reference 4.4.5)
  - Use Curie effect as a thermal switch – magnetic contact between elements is maintained until a certain temperature is reached, above which, the Curie effect turns the magnetic properties off
  - Use Curie point hysteresis to provide damping in an on-off switching device
  - Use Barkhausen Effect to measure residual stresses in steel after heat treatment or grinding
  - Magnetic Barkhausen Emission (MBE) offers potential for accurate stress measurement as an alternative to strain gauging
  - Non-invasive measurement of kinematic and physical properties of conducting materials using magnetometry

HARMFUL EFFECTS

Modify Existing Substance

* Remove the harmful effect by introducing a substance which is a modification of the existing substances (Reference 1.2.2)
* Stress-thickening fluid inside bicycle saddle stiffens and conforms to the shape of the cyclist to remove discomfort
* Introduction of bevelled edge on a retaining ring reduces harmful movement between ring and part to be retained or housing
* Wing-flaps and/or vortex generators prevent stall on wings
* Add vents to an umbrella to equalise pressures and prevent gusts from causing damage
* Add bevelled edges to components – e.g. pistons, retaining rings, to eliminate wear problems

* Decompose one of the substances or the external environment (Reference 5.1.1.9/5.5.1/3)
* Bio-degradable oil removes long term environmental damage potential following a spill
* Soluble cores enable easy removal of otherwise harmful materials when casting complex internal geometries
* 'Lost-wax' casting process

* Combine elements from a lower structural level (Reference 5.5.2/3)
* Chain-link fencing
* Fly-eye lens in a security camera eliminates the need for complex pan and tilt mechanisms
* Honeycomb structural re-inforcement and impact absorption structures

* Employ a phase transition in one or both of the substances (Reference 5.3.1)
* Prevent cavitation damage on structures submerged in water by refrigerating them in order to form a localised ice layer which isolates the cavitation bubbles from the structure
* Use of ice as a binding agent for abrasive particles in a polishing system eliminates harmful heat generation by utilising latent heat effect
* Steam iron removes creases from clothes

Modify The Field

* Replace an uncontrolled or poorly controlled field with a more controllable one (Reference - 2.2.1)
* Double camera flash eliminates 'red-eye'
* Digital versus analogue signal transmission eliminates noise and interference effects
* Electrorheological suspensions – where changing electric field changes viscosity of fluid – eliminates problems associated with varying speed ratio clutches

- Controlled heating of cells (hyperthermia) kills cancerous cells while leaving normal cells unharmed

* Transition from a uniform or disordered field to non-uniform and/or ordered fields (which may be time variant, permanent or temporary) (Reference 2.2.5/2.4.9)
- Use a standing wave to position particles of fluids that otherwise are not under control
- Polarised light eliminates glare
- Control cooling rate during ice-cream manufacture to control texture
- Segmented induction heaters used to improve temperature homogeneity in super-plastically formed composites

* Vary the field to co-ordinate with a time varying element of the system (Reference 2.4.10)
- Material compositions can be more precisely identified by measuring the spectrum of the resonant frequency of electrons in response to changing frequencies of a magnetic field
- Varying magnetic field disintegrates droplets of fuel by varying amounts depending on power setting of prime-mover – allows optimisation of combustion efficiency across a wider range of operating conditions
- Electrochromic glass programmed to match light transmission to time of day

* Match (or mismatch) the frequency of the field to the natural frequency of the object substance (Reference 2.3.1)
- Microwave ovens heat food by acting at the resonant frequency of the water molecules
- Vibrate hopper at resonant frequency to enable removal of clogged or blacked contents
- Apply alternating magnetic field to a rigid body to produce variable resonance and thus an effective sound radiator

* If multiple fields exist, match (or mismatch) the frequencies of those fields (2.3.2)
- Harmful machine vibrations can be eliminated by generating a $180°$ out of phase vibration
- Multi-axis laser measurement systems build up a three-dimensional profile of an object by correlating multiple signals
- Acousto-optic weapon guidance systems correlate different signal types when acquiring and tracking target

* If a field is being used, use physical effects to turn the field on or off according to the conditions of the harmful action (Reference 1.2.5)
- Electrically switched electromagnets
- Permanent magnets incorporated into aircraft compasses to compensate for the errors created by the aircraft structure
- Use Curie effect to wipe unwanted data from magnetic recording media

Add A New Substance

* Remove the harmful effect by introducing a third substance (possibly temporarily) between the existing substances (Reference 1.2.1)
  * Use of anti-proliferative or anti-angiogenic anti-bodies to help inhibit spread of cancerous cells
  * Unpleasant tasting drugs encapsulated in gelatin capsules that delay release of the drug until it passes into the stomach
  * Polyurethane spray stops delicate paintings being damaged
  * Safety nets (2mm-mesh nylon) trap moisture particles to remove fog from roadsides (Japan Federal Highway Agency)
  * Car bumpers
  * Reduce noise, increase life of linear motion guide ball-bearings by including cage rings between adjacent balls
  * Jewel case protects CDs/DVDs
  * Anti-freeze lowers freezing temperature and protects engine from damage by (expanding) ice formation
  * Addition of copper in tungsten-halogen lamp reduces filament sag and corrosion

* If the field has a harmful effect on one of the substances, introduce a new substance which draws the harmful effect of the field away from the affected substance (Reference 1.2.3)
  * Sun-blocks stop UV-rays from harming the skin
  * Lead shield protects parts of the body not required to be viewed during x-ray
  * Sacrificial plates on ship hull re-direct corrosion effects
  * Heat sinks prevent overheating in electrical and other components

* Incorporate an external additive from the surrounding environment (which may be temporary) in either of the substances (Reference 1.1.4)
  * Put salted grit on roads to prevent icing
  * Use sea-water ballast to damp-out damaging movements in a marker buoy in rough seas
  * Add oil to expand leather seals when looking to remove leak

* Introduce new substances with special properties (Reference D2)
  * Brake ferns act as hyper-accumulators and remove arsenic from contaminated soil
  * Add dried rice to salt cellar to prevent clogging of salt (rice acts as a dessicant)
  * Shape memory alloy stent eliminates need for potentially hazardous angioplasty inflation method.
  * Rheopexic gels conform to a desired shape when placed under stress therefore spreading loads and preventing possible harmful stresses

* Introduce voids (Reference 5.1.1.1)
  * Underground cables are protected from frost damage caused by ground stresses by introducing a cavity around the cables beforehand
  * Inclusion of 'crumple zone' in a car

- Air-gap in bottled fluids accommodates expansion effects and prevents potential explosion or leakage damage
- Gap between railway rails prevents buckling damage when rails get hot
- Bubble air into a high-diving pool to prevent harmful effect on diver during entry into the water (also helps the diver to see where the surface of the water is during descent)

* If there are restrictions on the quantity of new substance allowed, use a small quantity of a very active one (Reference 5.1.1.4)
- (Poisonous) fluoride in drinking water supplies helps prevent tooth decay
- Vitamin and mineral dietary supplements
- Homeopathic medicines work on the basis that the more dilute the active ingredient (some of which would be toxic in larger quantities), the more effective the remedy

* If there are restrictions on the quantity of additive allowed, selectively concentrate the new substance into just those parts of the object that need it (Reference 5.1.1.5)
- Nasal de-congestants (and other localised medicines)
- Radiator sealant works only where a leak exists allowing the remainder to be flushed away
- Liquid paper in a pen – removes mistakes only where they have occurred
- Spotting weed-killers – placed only where they are required

* If there are restrictions on the quantity of new substance allowed, use foams or inflatable structures (Reference 5.1.4)
- Inflatable life jackets and rafts (take up less space on an aircraft)
- Include a foam matrix within a tank of rocket fuel acts to absorb explosions
- Air-bags inside cars

* If there are restrictions on the use of new substances, introduce a substance which can be decomposed later (Reference 5.1.1.8)
- Non-persistent, bio-degrading pesticides
- Bio-grade trigger materials – additives which promote decomposition of parent structure
- Add sludge and oxygen in hydrocarbon coking operations to prevent harmful reaction temperature variations

* Make the added substance by decomposing the external environment (5.1.1.9)
- Organic fertiliser promotes plant growth by replacing vital nutrients in soil
- Sterilisation using ozone
- Thermo-forming using superheated steam eliminates damage when moulding certain plastics

* Add a substance which will disappear (or become indistinguishable) after it has fulfilled its function (Reference 5.1.3)
- Use of bio-absorbable materials on hip replacement and other surgical implants gives initial structural support which then disappears when no longer required.

- Add small quantity of cooking oil to a scrambled egg pan when cleaning to remove otherwise difficult to lodge egg
- Make clay pigeons out of dung or manure prevents having to retrieve clays

Add A New Field

* Make use of a field that already exists in the environment around the system (Reference 5.2.2)
   - Barometer records drop in atmospheric pressure which in turn provides a rain or storm warning
- Cats eyes reflect the light back from car headlights to help highlight the road ahead at night.
- Use earth's magnetic field to aid navigation (alternatively navigate using the stars)
- Geothermal energy heats home without (apparent!) and eliminates consumption of non-renewable energy sources

* Introduce a new field (Reference 5.1.1.2)
- Traffic lights (optical field) prevent traffic accidents at road junctions
- Light lock prevents unauthorised access through a doorway
- Add odorous element to natural gas to enable detection

* Introduce a new field to neutralise the harmful effect of an existing field (Reference 1.2.4)
- Anti-noise
- Anti-acid indigestion tablets
- 'Daylight' filters on a camera compensate for the false yellow appearance of photographs taken in the presence of electric lights

* Introduce fields for which the substances present in the system or external environment can act as media or sources (Reference 5.2.3)
- Add a swirl component into aerodynamic flow fields to eliminate harmful effects – e.g. rear screen of some cars is 'self-cleaning' due to control of flow around the rear of the vehicle
- Reversible UV curable adhesive tapes don't mark sub-strait when removed
- Air curtain in doorway eliminates heat loss

* Replace an uncontrolled or poorly controlled field with a more controllable one (Reference - 2.2.1)
- Differential pressure on a composite during manufacture causes warpage on release, control of pressure drop and/or addition of new field (e.g. ultrasound) prevents warp
- Polarising light eliminates glare
- Use audio compression to eliminate (i.e. lower or raise) extreme loud and quiet (respectively) content during radio or similar broadcasts

Add A New Substance AND Field

* If there is a harmful (control) problem, add a second, more controllable S-Field
(Reference 2.1.2, 2.4.11, 2.4.12)
* Watt governor (rotating mass plus centrifugal field) prevents overspeed of a rotating
system
* Shift from simple to proportional, integral and/or differential control architectures to
prevent potentially damaging system responses to un-planned inputs
* Dental amalgam's are hardened and rapidly cured using IR light

* Introduce a new field to neutralise the harmful effect of existing field by acting on a new
substance added to the substance experiencing the harmful effect (Reference 1.2.4)
* Catalytic converter reduces harmful emissions from automotive engine
* Proximity sensor prevents car bumping into obstruction
* Vortex generators on aerodynamic surfaces delay onset of stall

* Use substances with special properties and add an associated field to use those
properties (Reference D2) – refer also to 'special properties' resources table in Chapter
14.
* Use activated carbon in filters to remove harmful elements
* Digesting bacteria remove harmful chemicals/waste products/etc
* High-powered UV light kills potentially harmful oocysts in drinking water

Transition To The Sub-System

* Transition from the macro to the micro level - look at S-Field at the micro level,
(Reference 3.2.1,)
* Reduce gear noise by modifying tooth geometry – e.g. involute spiral
* Rounded tip bristles on tooth-brush prevent damage
* Tread marks on tyres are designed to facilitate removal of water to improve grip in rainy
conditions
* Ribbed road markings warn driver when veering outside designated lanes
* 'High Friction' (textured) paint reduces likelihood of slipping on factory floor

* Obtain micro-level particles by decomposing elements at the macro-level, starting with
the nearest (Reference 5.5.1/5.5.3)
* Use of bio-remediating bacteria breaks down oil following a spill
* Use of enzymes in dishwasher detergent breaks down insoluble starch residues into
soluble sugars
* Anaerobic bacterial digestion of sewage sludge

* Obtain micro-level particles by combining particles from an even smaller scale, starting
with the nearest (Reference 5.5.2/5.5.3)
* Genetic manipulation to eliminate hereditary diseases (e.g. cystic fibrosis)
* Gene therapy
* Genetically modified bacteria used to manufacture human proteins – e.g. insulin

- Quorn™ (fungal meat substitute) is fermented using glucose, oxygen, and other nutrients

Transition To The Super-System

* Combine the system with another to form a bi- or poly- system (Reference 3.1.1)
- Fuel-cooled oil cooler – reduces harmful heating of oil in an engine by transferring heat to the fuel (which in turn benefits from an increase in temperature prior to combustion)
- Combined use of air-bag and seat-belt reduces likelihood of serious injury during a car crash
- Sound-proof covers, damping materials, etc reduce harmful noise from machinery
- Helmholz resonators reduce harmful noise from machinery
- (Multiple) cleaning heads stop contaminants from damaging video/audio tape
- Combine smoke detector into light fitting to eliminate view of un-attractive sensor and eliminate the need for additional wiring circuit

* Remove harmful effects in bi- or poly- systems by increasing the number and/or quality of the links between system elements (Reference 3.1.2)
- Multiple air-bags with inter-connected trigger mechanisms
- Float and ramp system at a marina. The docks rise and fall with the tides while the ramps automatically change the slope from land to dock.
- Geodesic architectural structures

* Remove harmful effects by increasing the differences between system components (Reference 3.1.3)
- Introduction of 'anti-noise' reduces harmful effect of noisy machinery
- Incorporate counter-rotating shafts in a jet engine to eliminate potentially harmful gyroscopic effects
- Prevent cracking of concrete by using large aggregate inclusions
- Hard/soft multi-layer armour prevents stab penetration while maintaining flexibility for wearer

* Integrate systems and reduce auxiliary components, and look to combine with other systems at a higher hierarchical level (Reference 3.1.4)
- Counter-rotating turbine stages eliminates the need for an intermediate nozzle stage
- Central-locking system for a house eliminates the need for many door and window locks
- Head-up displays in aircraft cockpit eliminates the need for pilot to physically move eye from physical instrument panel to canopy

* Distribute incompatible and/or 'opposite' properties among the system and its parts (Reference 3.1.5)
- Video recorder offering 'beginner' and 'expert' operating modes – eliminating operating frustration for different user groups
- Combine high and low emissivity surfaces in a structure to eliminate potentially harmful thermal effects when system is exposed to sunlight or other radiation sources

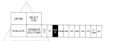

- Alternating attract-repel cycles in pulsed magnetic welding eliminates heated zone on work-piece

* If two actions are required, but they are incompatible, one action should be performed during pauses in the other (Reference 2.3.3)
- Conduct maintenance during scheduled down-time to remove harmful lost production time
- Ground-sharing by sports teams (possibly of different sports)
- Eliminate discontinuities from a fibre-glass spray nozzle by interspersing resin stream with control air jets

INSUFFICIENT/EXCESSIVE RELATIONSHIPS

Modify an Existing Substance

* Add an additive (which may be temporary) to one of the substances to enhance controllability or provide the required properties (Reference 1.1.2)
  * Addition of oil layer reduces friction between piston and cylinder
  * Solar collector focuses sunlight to enhance effectiveness of solar panel
  * Photo-chromic additives improve response of sunglasses to varying amounts of sunlight
  * Teflon makes food less likely to stick to a pan
  * PTFE coatings reduce bearing friction
  * Abrasive particles improve the cutting/polishing power of a water jet cutter
  * Baking powder enhances the effect of yeast

* If you are trying to achieve a minimum action and can't, apply a maximum action instead and remove the surplus (Reference 1.1.6)
  * Improve efficiency of paint-use by dipping the object to be painted into a container and then spinning the object to centrifuge excess paint back into the container
  * When patching a hole in plaster, overfill the hole and then sand back to flush when the plaster is set
  * Over-fill a glass of beer to ensure the customer receives a full measure of liquid rather than head
  * Flow control valve allows the working part of a hydraulic circuit to be controlled at a precise flow even with a constant (much higher) pump flow rate

* Increase the segmentation of one or both of the substances (Reference 2.2.2/5.1.2)
  * Multi-start screw-thread improves ease of assembly of a screw
  * Serrated blade improves cutting performance of knife for certain materials
  * Improve efficiency of combustion process by forming more, smaller fuel droplets
  * Improve surface area of catalyst by having more, smaller objects
  * Bifurcated bicycle seat improves comfort
  * Improve sealing using multi-tooth labyrinth seals or brush seals
  * High pressure water mist is more effective at putting out fires than a traditional sprinkler system

* Transition one or both of the substances from solid to hollow to multiple cavities to porous capillaries (Reference 2.2.3)
  * Improve strength/weight ratio of a structure by hollowing components
  * Hollowed turbine blade allows inclusion of cooling air, which in turn allows improvement of temperature capability
  * Increasing number of capillaries improves wicking capabilities of fabrics, etc
  * Hollow section o-rings improve sealing performance
  * Segmented air-mattresses are more comfortable than single cavity designs
  * Toilet-roll has a hole in the middle to facilitate attachment to bathroom fittings

* Make the system more flexible or adaptable (transition from no to one to several joints and on to completely flexible structures (Reference 2.2.4/2.4.8)

- Jointed or flexible stent improves the match between device and the (non-straight) arteries into which it is to be placed
- Flexible drive eases the design of mechanical drive systems by giving the designer more freedom to position what goes where
- Flexible vaulting pole stores energy during flexure which then allows greater height to be achieved
- Compliant brush seal improves sealing capability over a wider range of operating conditions than a non-compliant seal
- Flexible skis improve performance
- Piezoelectric 'paint'

* Make use of 'transformable' elements of substances (Reference D3) – refer also to 'transformable substances' resource table in Chapter 14
- Shape memory effect stent grows 'itself' and improves ease of fitting by surgeon
- Shape memory polymers used to improve dis-assembly properties of goods required to be re-cycled
- Heating magnets beyond Curie Point switches magnetic properties off – offering improved control of switching, movement, etc
- Rheopexic (stress thickening) gels improve comfort on a bicycle seat
- Electro-chromic glass changes colour in response to changing electrical signal
- Moving interference fringes enable objects to change apparent colour

* Transition from uniform or dis-ordered substances to ones which are non-uniform and/or ordered (and may be time variant) (Reference 2.2.6)
- Heat treatment homogenises surface
- Case-hardening
- Anti-backlash pinions
- Multi-string/multi-tension tennis racquets offer improved 'sweet spot' design
- Directionally solidified cast components offer improved strength properties over conventionally cast components
- Laser shock peening hardens material surface
- Controlled growth of crystals on a substrate in order to achieve required directional properties (e.g. erosion resistant coatings)
- Multi-layer erosion coatings use alternating hard and compliant layers

* Apply the action to a copy of one or both of the substances (Reference 5.1.1.7)
- Rear-view mirror improves visibility of objects behind a driver
- Dental technicians manufacture crowns/false teeth/etc to fit by using a plaster impression of the patient's mouth
- Surgeons practice on cadavers or simulated patients
- Test design changes on computer simulations – e.g. electronic mock-ups used to check for physical interference with mating components
- Video conferencing saves travelling time and expense

* Modify one of the substances to include voids (Reference 5.1.1.1)
- Foams used in fire extinguishers to maximise volume of minimum mass of extinguishing agent

- Foam metals – aero gel ('frozen smoke')
- Hollow ball ball-bearings – improved strength/weight ratio
- Hollow fibres improve heat insulation properties (e.g. bear fur)
- Chocolate bars made by introducing many tiny bubbles improves texture
- Vacuum-filled low-conductivity micro-balls improve heat insulation properties
- Air-filled cushion-sole shoes improve user comfort
- Drill holes in non-critical parts of girders, etc to reduce weight without detracting from strength properties

* Decompose one of the substances or the external environment (Reference 5.1.1.9/5.5.1/3)
- Bury garbage in the garden instead of using chemical fertilizers, to get the benefit of adding fertilizer without the side effects and wasted energy of the chemicals.
- If hydrogen is needed and not available in the system, but water is available, convert the water to hydrogen and oxygen by electrolysis.
- If atomic oxygen is needed, use ultraviolet light to dissociate ozone.
- Biodegradable oil reduces environmental impact of (e.g.) hydraulic oil spills

* Combine elements from a lower structural level (Reference 5.5.2/3)
- Velcro
- Polymer bonds
- Ozone (O_3) improves sterilisation process efficiency
- Black silicon has a surface material comprising many micron-scale spikes which serve to massively increase light absorption properties
- Intellikraft – nano-scale fibre composite surface treatments improves electrical storage capacity in piezo-electric materials
- Photosynthesis converts sunlight and CO_2 into complex structures

* Employ a phase transition in one or both of the substances (Reference 5.3.1)
- Use steam as a more effective cleaning agent than water
- Dry ice acts as a smoke screen
- Freezing gases, fluids eases bulk transport
- Making licqueur chocolates by freezing filling and dipping into chocolate improves efficiency
- Freeze chopped herbs into an ice-cube to improve storage convenience and maintain freshness
- Ice lollies offer a no-spill cooling drink

(Phase Transitions)

* Employ substances in which the phase transition occurs during the delivery of the useful function according to the operating conditions (Reference 5.3.2)
- In ice-skating, friction is reduced by using the phase change of ice to water under the blade pressure, which then changes back to ice and renews the surface of the area once the pressure reverts to normal.
- Rising steam used as mechanism for switching off a boiling kettle
- Expansion of water during boiling used in steam engines

- Plastic containers for drinks are stressed in two directions. First the plastic is injection moulded and cooled, then heated to just below the glass transition temperature and blow moulded, which orientates the plastic, making it clear and stronger than conventional blow moulding.

* Use the physical phenomena occurring during the phase transition (Reference 5.3.3)
- Use expansion of water during freezing to open up fissures in rocks to improve ability to break those rocks
- Use latent heat as a means of storing heat energy in certain fluids – e.g. sodium acetate used in hand-warmers
- Super-cooled water droplets remain in liquid state below 0°C
- Similar heat storage effects achievable using solid-solid phase change materials and a microwave oven
- Thermal fuse

* Replace a single phase state with a dual phase state (Reference 5.3.4)
- Dual-phase steels offer improved strength, formability, weldability, fatigue and corrosion properties over conventional steels
- Two-way shape memory alloys offer multiple shape change triggers from one structure
- Make a variable capacitance using a "dielectric-metal" phase transition material. When heated some of the layer becomes a conductor and when cooled it becomes a dielectric. Capacitance is thus controlled by temperature.
- Gaseous Si is more easily doped than the solid. The doped gas then can grow epitaxially on the solid substrate and make a better crystal structure with more uniform doping than a treated solid.

* Introduce physical or chemical interactions between the different phases of the system (Reference 5.3.5)
- Hydrogen gas can be stored in much higher densities than in its gaseous form by binding it in platinum and palladium sponges.
- Ice-filtering beer removes impurities – impurities act as seed points for phase change and thus solidify before the bulk of the fluid does and are hence easier to separate
- Use chemically reactive material as the working element of a heat cycle engine. The dissociation of the material under heating and the recombination when cooling improves the function of the engine (The dissociated material has lower molecular weight and therefore transfers heat faster.)

* Use reversible phase transitions (or use any reversibility hysteresis) to improve the functionality of the system (Reference 5.4.1)
- Ice anchor for ships
- Thermal switch (with damping if hysteresis is present)
- Altshuller's famous lightning rod that protects a radio telescope is a tube filled with low pressure gas. When the electrostatic potential in the area is high, as before a lightning discharge, the gas in the tube ionizes, making a preferred path for the lightning. When the lightning has discharged, the gas recombines, and the environment of the device being protected is neutral.
- Light-sensitive sunglasses maintain or reduce light transmission as brightness increases

* If a weak input needs to be turned into a large output, place the transforming substance at or close to its critical condition, such that the input acts as a trigger (Reference 5.4.2)
- Hair-trigger set close to breaking tension
- Cavitation erosion effect increased by operating equipment at reduced pressure close to object subjected to erosion effect
- Formation of bubbles in superheated liquid indicate very small ionization centers. The bubble chamber for detection of elementary particles works on this principle.
- Shape memory alloy with transition temperature at body temperature used in medical devices

Modify The Field

* If you are trying to achieve a minimum action and can't, apply the available action instead and remove the surplus (Reference 1.1.6)
- Apply paint and then remove excess by spinning (centrifugal field)
- Pressure-compensating valve in hydraulic circuit
- Limit switches
- Overflow – e.g. when pouring beer from a tap

* If you are trying to achieve a maximum action and can't, re-direct the field such that it acts on a substance attached to the relevant substance (Reference 1.1.7)
- Shallow frying food – heating and flavour sealing process speeded by presence of cooking oil
- Megaphone increases volume
- Uses mirrors to multiple light in a room

* Make an uncontrolled or poorly controlled field more controllable (Reference - 2.2.1)
- (Linear) motor uses switching sequence to move an object from one place to another
- Replace gravity-controlled systems with pressure-controlled system – e.g. water pump improves effectiveness of central heating system relative to passive system
- Contoured piston head improves flow of combustion products into and out of cylinder of IC engine
- Transition from mechanical to fluid to electrical drives

* Transition from a uniform or disordered field to non-uniform and/or ordered fields (which may be time variant, permanent or temporary) (Reference 2.2.5/2.4.9)
- Laser holography improves imaging of vibrating objects
- Use standing waves to move or position objects along a conveyor belt
- Polarising filter reduces glare
- Separate light into constituent colours (e.g. using a prism)
- Varying frequency siren improves attention attracting ability
- Flashing lights (for example on a bicycle) improve visibility – the human eye is highly attracted to changing signals
- Thermal paint changes colour according to surrounding temperature
- Scanning radar

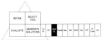

* Vary the field to co-ordinate with a time varying element of the system
  (Reference 2.4.10)
- Counter-current chromatography
- Sequence heaters/air-conditioners according to day/night temperature differences
- Traffic lights
- Optical communications

* Match (or mismatch) the frequency of the field to the natural frequency of the object
  substance (Reference 2.3.1)
- Improve bottle cleaning process by pulsing water-jet at the resonant frequency of the
  bottle
- Lithotripsy – break-up kidney stones using ultrasonic vibration tuned to the resonant
  frequency of the stone
- Improve rifle accuracy by matching barrel oscillation to bullet resonant frequency

* If multiple fields exist, match (or mismatch) the frequencies of those fields
  (Reference 2.3.2)
- Machine vibrations can be eliminated by generating a 180° out of phase vibration
- Anti-noise
- Light interference fringes used to measure small deflections in components being
  subjected to loading stresses

Add A New Substance

* Incorporate an internal additive (which may be temporary) into either of the substances
  (Reference 1.1.2/5.1.1.6)
- Sulphur, lead or nitrogen additives improve the lubricity of fuels and oils
- Strontium or lanthanum increase the super-conductivity of cuprates
- Chromium improves the ductility of titanium aluminides
- Oil decomposing bacteria
- Salt reduces freezing temperature and/or increases boiling point of water

* Incorporate an external additive (which may be temporary) into either of the substances
  (Reference 1.1.3/5.1.1.3)
- Catalysts
- Sodium gas slows down a pulse of laser light from light speed to, in extreme cases
  30m/s
- Adding salt to roads melts ice and improves safety
- Use polish to shine shoes
- Packaging improves transportability and life of perishable goods
- Washing-up liquid improves cleaning properties of water
- Polyorganosiloxane prevents insect debris from sticking to a surface
- Addition of grit improves cutting efficiency of water jet cutter
- Addition of helium improves hardness of metallic structures
- Damping foils silence noisy surfaces
- PMMA used to encourage bone growth on selective parts of prothesis

- Keronite is an electrolytically applied surface coating which markedly improves hardness and erosion resistance of aluminium and other lightweight metals

* Incorporate an external additive from the surrounding environment (which may be temporary) in either of the substances (Reference 1.1.4)
- Knead air into bread dough to improve rising properties
- Whisk air into cream to thicken it
- Dissolving oxygen in water improves speed/effectiveness of bio-culture growth
- Water causes wood to swell (permanently) – use this to form effective joints in, for example, dowel joints
- Add water to re-hydrate powders – e.g. instant coffee

* Incorporate an external additive which is a replacement, modification or decomposition of the current external environment (which may be temporary in either of the substances (Reference 1.1.5)
- Add ice particles to water jet to improve cutting/polishing properties (so do (cavitating) air bubbles for that matter)
- Air conditioning and/or de-humidifier makes the atmosphere in a room more pleasant
- De-ionising water improves its chemical purity
- Use of ozone improves sterilisation process
- Hot air balloon

* Introduce new substances with special properties (Reference D2) – refer also to the list of 'special properties' resources in the table in Chapter 14.
- Improve rapid prototyping hollow component moulding capability by including water-soluble cores which are easy to remove later
- Add a stress-thickening gel into a hollow section o-ring to improve sealing performance
- Lead zirconate titanate (PZT) is a piezoelectric material with markedly improved electricity generating properties, requiring compression by only a few microns to generate power
- Perfluorocarbons are very effective at dissolving oxygen and carbon dioxide gas, coupled with their low toxicity, this makes them suitable blood extenders or substitutes

* If you are trying to achieve a maximum action and can't, add a new substance to the relevant substance and re-direct the field such that it acts on the new substance (Reference 1.1.7)
- Melt chocolate by placing it in a bowl in a pan of water, and boil the water – this gives speedy melting without allowing overheating of the chocolate
- Coat foodstuffs in oil to improve cooking (e.g. sealing in flavours)
- Paint solar panel black in order to improve heat absorption properties
- Ditto by using a magnifying lens arrangement over the water-carrying pipes of a solar water heater

* If a selective action is required (e.g. maximum in one place, minimum in another), and the field is sometimes too high, add a substance to protect the system from the extremes (Reference 1.1.8.1)

- Use heat sinks during soldering operations to prevent overheating of sensitive components
- Use a radiation shield to protect patients from x-rays on parts of body not being examined
- Use a stencil to protect areas which are not required to be painted.
- Pressure relief valve
- Limit switches

* If a selective action is required, and the field is sometimes insufficient add a substance which interacts with the field to produce a localised effect to suit the selective requirements (Reference 1.1.8.2)
- Add electro or thermo chromic elements to inks, gels etc
- (Use thermochromic ink with different colour change trigger temperatures to obtain different effects)
- 'Canned bakery' smells used to 'direct' customers into and around a supermarket

 * Add 'voids' to one or both of the substances (Reference 5.1.1.1)
- Hollow ball ball-bearings – improved strength/weight ratio
- Hollow fibres improve heat insulation properties (e.g. bear fur)
- Chocolate bars made by introducing many tiny bubbles improves texture
- Vacuum-filled low-conductivity micro-balls improve heat insulation properties
- Air-filled cushion-sole shoes improve user comfort

* If there are restrictions on the quantity of additive allowed, use a small quantity of a very active one (Reference 5.1.1.4)
- Concentrates – acids, fruit drinks, food colourings, etc
- Use thermite explosive to weld aluminum to something else. Conventional welding for aluminum requires very high heat and corrosive chemical etchants..
- Parts per million of dopants in silicon can change its electronic properties enough to govern the properties of an integrated circuit. Doping the Si with the additive to get the right properties makes it possible to operate the circuit at much lower voltage, with much smaller circuit elements than older designs.
- Brimstone in match head

* If there are restrictions on the quantity of additive allowed, selectively concentrate the new substance into just those parts of the object that need it (Reference 5.1.1.5)
- Reduce car engine cold start emissions by distilling and partitioning the most volatile fuel elements during normal running and use them for subsequent cold starts.
- Spot location of spot removal chemicals. Sticks of detergents and sprays of enzymes are commercially available products for this purpose. This removes the spot, without subjecting the whole garment to the extra wear of the strong chemicals
- Therapeutic agents located at the exact location of the disease, tagged to release in a preferred organ. The use of iodine to carry other medication to the thyroid is an example. This avoids dosing healthy parts of the body with medications that have severe side effects.
- Concentrate fluoride at the site of beginning tooth decay, to re-mineralise the tooth and avoid destroying a large amount of the tooth with a conventional filling.

* If there are restrictions on the quantity of substance allowed, use foams or inflatable structures (Reference 5.1.4)
  * Inflatable mattress takes up little space when deflated
  * Ditto life-jacket
  * Foam fire extinguishers cover a large area from a small container
  * Use expanding foams to clean the inside of difficult to access pipes – foam expands to fill pipe, but quantity needs to be small to enable ease of flushing after insertion
  * Use inflatable bags to lift objects from the sea-bed

* If there are restrictions on the use of new substances, introduce a substance which can later be decomposed (Reference 5.1.1.8)
  * Bio-degradable additives speed break-down of oils upon disposal
  * People need sodium for metabolism, but metallic sodium is harmful. Ordinary salt is ingested, then converted to sodium and chlorine for use by the body.
  * Race cars use nitrous oxide instead of air for combustion to get higher power
  * Cavitation erosion – air bubbles released to atmosphere after erosion effect
  * Plant-pots made of hardened fertiliser

* Make the added substance by decomposing the external environment (5.1.1.9)
  * Bio-degradable oil removes long term environmental damage potential following a spill
  * Soluble cores enable easy removal of otherwise harmful materials when casting complex internal geometries
  * If atomic oxygen is needed, use ultraviolet light to dissociate ozone.
  * Obtain hydrogen from water using electrolysis.
  * 'Lost-wax' casting process

* Add a substance which will disappear (or become indistinguishable) after it has fulfilled its function (Reference 5.1.3)
  * A complex shape can be "sand" blasted with dry ice and have no residue to clean when the dry ice sublimes. Use of sand, artificial sapphire particles, etc., leaves residue and requires clean up.
  * Dissolvable sutures are absorbed by the body when the injury heals. Older style sutures require a separate medical procedure to remove the sutures, causing pain, inconvenience, and the possibility of infection.
  * Ditto other bio-sorbable materials.
  * Positron emission tomography uses short half-life radioactive materials to improve detection
  * Disappearing ink
  * Ether

Add A New Field

* Make use of a field that already exists in the environment around the system (Reference 5.2.2)
  * Sunlight heats water in a solar panel

- Wind turbine extracts energy from naturally moving air
- Increase lift on a glider by thermaling
- Clockwork radio (uses human power)
- Piezo-generator in shoe generates (small – phone powering?) electrical supply
- Thermal mass – stores heat accumulated during the day and releases it at night within large buildings

* Introduce a new field (Reference 5.1.1.2)
- Use a centrifuge to separate blood cells and plasma
- Add a centrifugal field to improve the performance of barrier and membrane filters
- Heat oil to reduce viscosity
- Stir a cup of tea to speed up dissolving of sugar
- Use thermal expansion to join two components with an interference fit between them
- Ultrasonic energy distorts fastener inserts to improve the ease with which they can be fitted
- Sono-chemistry

* Introduce fields for which the substances present in the system or external environment can act as media or sources (Reference 5.2.3)
- Hot air balloon
- Waste heat recovery systems – e.g. car heater, CHP schemes
- Sound transmission through a transmission medium
- Scented deodorants/air-fresheners, etc
- Thermal imaging
- UV activated 'cure-on-demand' adhesives improve glue performance

* Replace an uncontrolled or inadequately controlled field with a more controllable one (Reference - 2.2.1)
- Thermostatically controlled air-conditioning unit maintains user specified temperature inside a room/building
- Variable spin cycle on a washing machine
- Transition from hydraulic to electrical drive (analogue to digital – digital offering considerably more flexibility and adaptability)

Add A New Substance AND Field

* Improve the efficiency of a system by transforming one of the substances of the current system into an independently controllable S-Field (Reference 2.1.1)
- Introduce a chisel between a hammer and rock to improve the rock-breaking capability (the hammer mechanical field acts on the chisel; a mechanical field associated with the chisel then acts on the rock)
- Replace standard lubricating oils with ferro-fluid equivalents
- Light-activated switches replacing manual ones

* If there is a control problem, add a second, more controllable S-Field (Reference 2.1.2, 2.4.11, 2.4.12)

- Small amounts of mercury are delivered into a light bulb via a glass ampule. The ampule is broken to release the mercury after the lamp has been sealed by heating a wire loop around such that its expansion causes the ampule to break.
- TV remote switch uses IR signal
- Voice sensitive mobile phone (addition of microphone and audio field)
- Bluetooth
- Add a radiographically opaque material to bone cement in order to allow surgeons to x-ray during or after an operation to ensure that the cement has been correctly inserted.
- Ultrasound cavitation improves the cleaning action of a chemical dip
- Use an electronic current to generate a magnetic field

* Use substances with special properties and add an associated field to use those properties (Reference D2) – refer also to the 'special properties' resource table in Chapter 14.
- Electro-rheological fluids used in universal vice – position the part in the fluid, then apply the electric field to 'lock' the position
- Superconductors change magnetic properties as they pass through the superconducting transition temperature – this allows them to be used as switches or selective shields
- Electro-chromic or thermo-chromic glass changes colour/opacity according to user requirements
- Electro-luminescents produce (low levels) of light very efficiently

* Improve efficiency of a system by adding a ferro-magnetic substance and a magnetic field (Reference 2.4.1)
- Selectively magnetised structures can be made to be self-orienting to assist in assembly
- Magnetic bearings offer reduced frictional losses
- Magnetic screwdriver allows easier location/holding of screws
- Magnetic levitation transport systems

(Ferro-magnetics)

* Use ferro-magnetic particles (Reference 2.4.2)
- The rigidity of a rubber mold can be controlled by adding ferromagnetic material and then applying magnetic field.
- Inclusion of ferro-magnetic particles in match heads improves ability to count and direct during manufacture and packaging process
- Use ferro-magnetic particles and moving field to improve stirring of a fluid in which the particles are placed

* Use magnetic additives (Reference 2.4.5)
- Magnetic catalysts are easily separated from the surrounding chemical reaction using magnetism
- Addition of magnetic content to paper money improves control in vending machine and counting operations.

- In order to direct molecules of medication to the exact location where they are needed in the body, attach a magnetic molecule to the drug molecule and use an external array of magnets around the patient to guide the medication where it is needed.

* Use magnetic fluids (Reference 2.4.3)
- Ferro-fluids are used to make zero-leakage seals – fluid is prevented from leaking using a magnetic field
- Magnetic paints/glues/sprays/etc permit controllable application and directional orientation
- Elasticity of magnetic fluid film used in improved accelerometers
- Rheonetic magnetic fluids improve dynamic damping performance of shock absorbers by changes in viscosity caused by changes in surrounding magnetic field.

* Use ferromagnetic substances in conjunction with a segmented or porous structure (Reference 2.4.4)
- Porous magnetic networks improve coercivity and, in thin film applications (e.g. audio tape), reduce noise
- Construct a filter of ferromagnetic material between magnets. The alignment is controlled by the magnetic fields
- Ferro-magnetic sponge

* Add magnetic elements to the external environment (Reference 2.4.6)
- Add micron-scale magnetic particles to oil or water flow to aid flow visualisation using electromagnetic sensors
- Magnet white boards
- Fridge magnets

* Improve control by making use of physical effects associated with the magnetic substances (Reference 2.4.7)
- Heat ferro-magnetic particles above Curie point to turn magnetic field on and off as required
- Magnetic pulse welding does not produce a heated zone
- Barkhausen Effect used in the control of grain size in the manufacture of steel
- Barkhausen Effect used in multi-layer tamper-proof identification tagging
- Super paramagnetic fluids offer better thermal and oxidative stability than conventional ferro-fluids

* Move from uniform or disordered magnetic fields to non-uniform and/or ordered ones (Reference 2.4.9)
- Use selectively magnetised materials – isotropic or anisotropic, multi poles on one side, axially magnetised, axially magnetised with two poles, circumferential poles, etc in electric motor design
- Selectively magnetised objects ease (self-)assembly
- Selectively magnetised paper money improves identification properties in (e.g.) vending machines

* Use a time-varying magnetic field, matching natural rhythms in the system (Reference 2.4.10)
  • Pulsed electric motor offers improved performance over a normal electric motor (which in itself obviously makes use of a time-varying field)
  • Pulsed nuclear magnetic resonance spectroscopy improves measurement of solids in waxy crude oils
  • MRI scanner uses a tuned oscillating magnetic field to detect resonance of different particular nuclei

Transition To Sub-System

* Transition from the macro to the micro level - look at S-Field at the micro level, (Reference 3.2.1,)
  • Fly-eye lens contains lots of individual lens 'systems' which may be used in, for example, security cameras featuring no moving parts, or highly efficient solar collectors
  • In the Pilkington 'float-glass' process, rollers for moving glass have been replaced by molten tin.
  • Continuously variable transmissions (as opposed to geared/stepped designs)
  • Aerosol spray of charged particles
  • Hard/soft multi-layer erosion protection coatings
  • Primer, under and top coats when painting

* Obtain micro-level particles by decomposing elements at the macro-level, starting with the nearest (Reference 5.5.1/5.5.3)
  • Obtain hydrogen and oxygen using electrolysis
  • Shaved ice
  • Grated cheese
  • Use ultrasound to fragment water droplets into much smaller droplets (i.e. smaller than would be possible by passive means alone)
  • Grow salt crystals by processing sea-water

* Obtain micro-level particles by combining particles from an even smaller scale, starting with the nearest (Reference 5.5.2/5.5.3)
  • Nano-composites
  • Most chemical reactions
  • Growth of biological structures from DNA
  • Nano-belt sensors

Transition To The Super-System

* Combine the system with another to form a bi- or poly- system (Reference 3.1.1)
  • MMR vaccine
  • Combined magnetic and centrifugal action seals where both fields act on a ferro-fluid
  • Absorb heat from the sun inside double-glazing by circulating water through what would normally be the air gap. The water also improves the insulation properties of the window in cold weather

- Multi-sprocket gear set on a bicycle
- Computer software packages
- Music centre – CD plus tape plus radio, etc
- Multi-function watch – hours, minutes, seconds, date, alarm, illumination, etc
- Temperature and speed sensors integrated into cats-eyes improve functionality
- Dinner service/cutlery
- Truck and trailer

* Improve bi- or poly- system efficiency by increasing the number and/or quality of the links between system elements (Reference 3.1.2)
- 4-wheel drive vehicle
- Syncromesh gears
- Central locking system on car/house/office/etc
- Intranet/Internet
- Increase efficiency of public transport systems by adding under-road sensors so each vehicle (and passengers) know where other parts are.
- Jigsaw-slotted honeycomb structures give improved strength and offer option of repairability

* Improve efficiency by increasing the differences between system components (Reference 3.1.3)
- Bi-focal spectacle lens
- Combined pencil and eraser
- Claw-hammer
- Stapler/staple remover
- Solar-powered torch
- Day and night settings on a car rear-view mirror
- Combined positive and negative Poisson's ratio structures provide extreme damping capabilities

* Integrate systems and reduce auxiliary components, and look to combine with other systems at a higher hierarchical level (Reference 3.1.4)
- Fax machine with built-in photo-copying capability
- Vari-focus lens reduces number of lens elements required in, for example a camera
- Mobile phone includes clock/alarm etc
- Multi-vitamin tablets

* Distribute incompatible and/or 'opposite' properties among the system and its parts (Reference 3.1.5)
- Bicycle chain combines rigid links and flexible connections
- Hip replacement joint contains bioabsorbable and bone growth promoting coatings one above the other to first prevent and then promote bone growth in accordance with medical requirement
- Hard/soft multi-layer erosion protection coatings
- Structures knitted from meltable and non-meltable fibres offer the potential for easier forming into rigid and semi-rigid shapes
- Baked Alaska contains hot and cold elements

270

* If two actions are required, but they are incompatible, one action should be performed during pauses in the other (Reference 2.3.3)
- Conduct maintenance during scheduled down-time
- Work/play, weekday/weekend
- Defrost the refrigerator when contents have been consumed
- Valve timing in an internal combustion engine

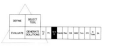

13.
Problem Solving Tools -
Trends Of Evolution

Warning; the future is always closer than it appears
Faith Popcorn

The trends part of TRIZ is for many emerging as one of the most powerful elements of the whole. The technology trends uncovered by the original TRIZ researchers, plus the new trends uncovered during the research underlying this text have two primary roles in their technical context (the second book in this series will discuss their relevance to business issues); the first as a strategic system evolution prediction tool, the second as a tool to help solve problems. This chapter examines both roles before ending with a collection of 35 technology trends to use as a reference, and a pair of short sections describing implications and uses of employing the trends in combination, and why sometimes the trends can appear to work in the opposite direction to normal. The five main sections are thus:-

1) System Evolution Strategy
2) Trends As A Problem Solving Tool
3) Trends in Combination
4) Trends in Apparent Reverse
5) Trends Reference.

Before starting with these topics, however, it will probably be instructive to introduce the generic trends, in order to obtain a grasp of what they look like, what information they contain, and how we might make best use of them.

Figure 13.1 illustrates an example of one of the trends. The trend is one known as 'space segmentation'. Like all of the other TRIZ trends, this space segmentation evolution pattern has been observed through analysis of how systems across a wide variety of industries have evolved. Like the other trends illustrated later, this trend works in a left-to-right fashion, with the direction of evolution generally seeing monolithic things evolving into hollow things, which then evolve into things with multiple hollows, which in turn evolve to things featuring capillary-type spaces, which then finally evolve such that the cavities are filled with some kind of active element.

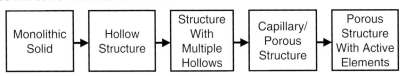

Figure 13.1: Example Evolution Trend: Space Segmentation

This relatively simple picture represents the distillation of a rather large amount of evolutionary data. It is worth examining some of the explicit and implicit data contained in this apparently simple picture:-

Firstly, we might ask why it is that systems evolve in this left-to-right direction (we will see later that there are predictable exceptions to this left-right rule, but generally we should

assume evolution happens in a left-to-right direction). The facts distilled from the patent and other knowledge databases provide a multitude of examples of systems evolving in this direction (think of house bricks, training shoes, insulation, chocolate, turbine blades, and so on) so certain systems clearly do evolve along this line. The reasoning behind why they do comes from the general message and single biggest key to using the trends effectively; *'somewhere there is a benefit from evolving from left to right along the trend'*. The reference section at the end of the chapter reproduces the space segmentation trend along with a list of benefits that others have found for making the jumps. We need to have a little faith (at least initially) that these benefits exist, but the evidence from use elsewhere is that if we look we will find those benefits.

The second point, then, related to this first one requires us to think again about the ideality equation, Ideality = (perceived benefits)/(costs + harm). If we accept that increasing ideality is the over-riding evolution trend, and that moving from left-to-right along the space segmentation gives increased benefits, then it should be possible to also achieve an increase in ideality. This correlation may not appear obvious. Indeed for the evolution from monolithic to hollow thing in the above space segmentation trend, although it might be easy to see a benefit in terms of weight reduction, it might also appear that the manufacture looks more complex, and hence cost may have gone up. In other words, there is often a conflict between the top half of the ideality equation (benefits) and the bottom half (usually cost). The experience gathered from all of the TRIZ research, however, firmly indicates that the evolutionary jumps do give a net benefit, even if cost or harm does go up initially (at least to certain customers), but that in the longer term, the top-versus-bottom conflict is solved – very often as manufacturing technology advances – and that ultimately customers will always achieve the benefits they want with negligible cost or harm penalty. This phenomenon, of course, depends on the truth of the supposition that customers want benefits. We could fill another book arguing this point. As an alternative, we suggest that you observe how many systems around you have followed the trend patterns, and then have a go at using the trends to evolve a system you are interested in.

One we often look at on courses is the humble toothbrush. A simple comparison between the toothbrush in Figure 13.2 and the space segmentation trend, should help us to at least begin to see the truth of the above benefits argument, but also – more importantly – give us a first look at how we can use the trends to help design better systems. The first thing we need to do in order to use the trend is to identify connections between our toothbrush and the trend stages. In terms of the generic TRIZ problem-solving model, what we are actually doing here is mapping our specific problem onto a generic problem. To make these connections effectively requires us to take due account of the 9-Windows concept from Chapter 4. To take two specific examples to illustrate this process in action, we might see that both the handle of the toothbrush (the system level view) and an individual bristle fibre (a sub-system view) are made from monolithic structures. In other words, they are right at the beginning of their possible evolution along the space segmentation trend.

Having made the connection between handle=monolithic and bristle=monolithic, the method of using the trend encourages us to accept that 'somewhere there is a (net) advantage in shifting to the right along the trend'. There is actually nothing to stop us (excepting possibly technical risk) from making several jumps if we like, but for the purposes of this exercise, we will just make a simple jump to the next stage 'hollow structure'. What this jump is telling us is that for both our handle and bristle there is an advantage in making both into hollow structures. If we can find such an advantage, then the trend may be seen to have given us one or more good evolutionary directions. A good

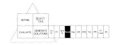

analogy here is that the trend is telling us what the solutions to our problem are; and it becomes our job to then work out *why* they are solutions.

Figure 13.2: Evolving The Toothbrush

Taking the handle first of all, the trend is suggesting a hollow design as a better one than our current solid design. Why might this be the case? Possible answers:-

- the brush will be lighter
- we could store one half of the brush inside the other half (as in a travel toothbrush)
- we could put toothpaste inside the body and possibly eliminate the need for a separate toothpaste dispenser
- a hollow handle could make it more flexible – and so more comfortable to hold
- on the other hand, we could use the hollowness to make the handle stiffer so that we have better control over the force we exert on our teeth during cleaning
- we could make the hollow feature a means of locating and storing the brush after use (super-system future!)
- we could make the end of the handle underneath the bristles hollow in order to make it easier to clean the debris that usually gets stuck there over time (system, future)
- and so on… you can probably think of many more ideas.

Hopefully with some if not all of those ideas, it is possible to at least see the potential for a benefit which also results (even if manufacture cost goes up by a small amount initially) in a net increase in ideality.

The bristles are a little bit more difficult. What might the advantages of a hollow bristle be? We will leave this one for you to think about, apart from a couple of ideas we hope some toothbrush manufacturer will give us before too long;

- a common problem with most conventional toothbrushes is that you put paste onto the brush, then put the brush onto your tooth and immediately the paste is forced down the side of the bristles, where it no longer has any beneficial effect. A hollow bristle (possibly combined with the hollow handle) would allow the end of the bristle to always have a layer of paste on it.

- A hollow bristle – or rather one with another (different colour) bristle inside it would enable the toothbrush to inform the user when the brush is worn out – i.e. the outside bristle wears to reveal the different coloured inside bristle.

(Incidentally, the toothbrush appears to be used as a case study on a number of TRIZ courses. You might like to try comparing your own toothbrush to the trends to speculate on some possible evolutionary advances, and then take a look at your local supermarket to see how many of them seem to be emerging onto the market these days. An example of TRIZ trends accelerating the evolution of toothbrushes? We hope so.)

The third general point about the trends before we look at their use in detail concerns another mental image that we think is useful when setting the trend lines in the context of problem solving. We make the suggestion to you that each trend picture of all of the trends we provide later represents a new evolutionary S-curve. The point is illustrated in Figure 13.3 below.

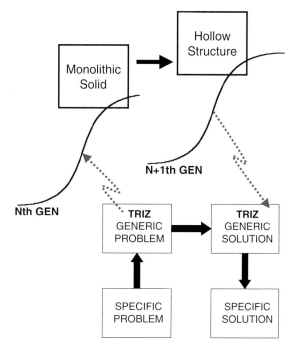

Figure 13.3: Each Stage of a Trend Represents a New S-Curve

This point might be a little difficult to accept – but remember from Chapter 7 that every individual component within a system has its own family of s-curves – and it is, when analysed in detail later, an over-simplification, but we nevertheless recommend it as a very useful image to keep in mind.

The final general point is intended to act as a summary of the preceding discussions. The point is illustrated in Figure 13.4 – which repeats the space segmentation trend line again, but this time adds the labels describing the dynamics of what makes systems evolve in the ay that they do. The absolute key to successful use of the trends in both strategic and problem solving contexts is the identification of the customer *benefits* that emerge as we speculate on *why* our system should jump to the right along the trend.

INCREASING BENEFITS

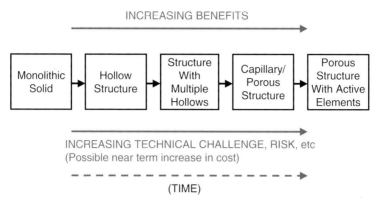

INCREASING TECHNICAL CHALLENGE, RISK, etc
(Possible near term increase in cost)

- - - - - - - - - - - - - - - - - ▶
(TIME)

Figure 13.4: General Rules About Trend Patterns

With two important exceptions, we will see that this picture applies to all of the 35 trends described in the reference section at the end of the chapter.

The two exceptions – the trends for Mono-Bi-Poly and Trimming – we will discuss now, before we start to actually use the trends in anger.

Mono-Bi-Poly

The Mono-Bi-Poly trend is essentially one that shows systems expanding from single entities, to double, triple and poly 'things'. As detailed in the reference section at the end of the chapter, the Mono-Bi-Poly trend has three main variants – firstly Mono-Bi-Poly(Similar) where the things that are increasing are all the same (e.g. blades on a propeller, teeth on a zipper, etc), secondly Mono-Bi-Poly(Various) where the things that are increasing are different from one another (classic example – Swiss Army knife), and the third Mono-Bi-Poly(Increasing Differences) in which we see systems inverting to deliver negative as well as positive functions (example – pencil with an eraser on the end). The left-to-right evolution trend exception applies to all three of these examples. The exception basically works like this:

As we add more things to a system in order to transform it into a bi-system and then a poly-system, the normal rule says that benefits are increasing. The exception with the Mono-Bi-Poly trend is that after we reach a certain number of things in the system, the benefits cease to appear any more and, if we persist in adding more, the overall ideality will actually drop. The phenomenon is illustrated in Figure 13.5 (and repeated in the reference section).

A simple example should serve to make the point: The humble fork is a system that has evolved along the Mono-Bi-Poly (Similar) trend from being a single-pointed device (a knife), to a device with two tines, to one with three, and nowadays four. At four tines, the fork has reached the point where adding more tines will produce no further benefit, and in fact, if we try and add a fifth or sixth tine, the only thing that would happen is that we would find it more difficult to stick the fork into whatever it is we want to hold with it.

Another point related to this reducing-benefits characteristic, meanwhile, is that adding more things to a system almost invariably increases cost – the bottom half of the ideality

equation. The usual consequence of this is that as the relative importance of benefits and cost varies, the 'optimum' number of things in the system will also tend to vary.

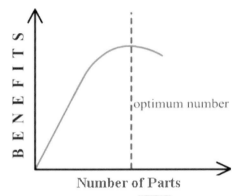

Figure 13.5: Exception to the Mono-Bi-Poly Trend – Benefits Cease After A Certain Level

A good example of this phenomenon in action can be seen in the shifting 'optimum' number of blades on a wind turbine – in which the balance between minimised first cost (low number of blades) versus power generated (higher number of blades has fluctuated over the years in line with the corresponding shifts between first and running costs. More on this case later in the chapter.

Trimming
The second exception to the 'benefits increase from left-to-right' rule comes with the trend known as trimming. This trend, as described in detail in the reference section, is one in which systems are shown to evolve to contain progressively fewer components as systems evolve. The basic mechanism of 'trimming' is that as designers get smarter in the ways they design a system – progressively making better and better use of resources, they learn to make components work harder. In other words, fewer components are used to deliver the same (or even improved) functionality.

The exception with this trend is that it does not always apply. One of the trend discoveries by the original TRIZ researchers was that as systems evolved along their s-curve they also followed through a characteristic path of, first increasing complexity, followed by decreasing complexity. This phenomenon is illustrated in Figure 13.6.

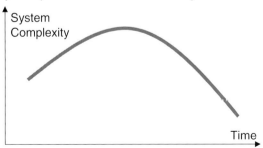

Figure 13.6: Evolution of Systems Through Increasing Followed by Decreasing Complexity
(time span is equal to duration of corresponding system s-curve)

For all but the very simplest of systems, there is a strong correlation between complexity and the number of parts within the system. This in turn means that the increasing-decreasing complexity characteristic also correlates to part count. The implications of this correlation, then, are that there are times during the evolution of a system when it is possible to reduce part count, and there are other times when trimming is not a viable option. The boundary between the two scenarios is what might be seen as a point of maximum viable complexity. This is a point at which something (usually customer, or often a reliability problem – for complex systems at least – Reference 13.1) triggers a shift towards reduced complexity, and when the focus of designers and engineers shifts to delivering benefits with reduced part count. Figure 13.7 thus shows when 'trimming' is and is not a valid trend of evolution.

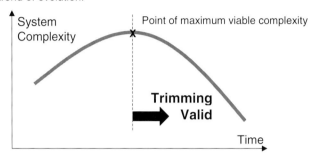

Figure 13.7: Where the Trimming Trend Applies

So there we have an outline of what the trends are, what the main exceptions are and how we should interpret them. Let us now examine their first practical application – assisting in the development of system evolution strategy:

1) System Evolution Strategy

Here we examine how we might deploy the trends in a strategic context. That is, in a setting where we are seeking to find out *where* a system (whether it be our own of one belonging to a competitor) might evolve, *how* it might get there, and perhaps most difficult *when* does it need to be at any particular level of maturity. We will examine the where's and how's first:

One of the main pillars in the TRIZ philosophy is the concept of systems evolving in the direction of increasing ideality (in fact, the original TRIZ research concluded that this evolutionary driver was the over-riding trend of technological evolution). The concept also includes the idea of the 'ideal final result (IFR)' – which, to remind ourselves from the text in Chapter 8, is defined as the evolutionary limit of a system in which all of the good things are delivered, and all of the bad things have disappeared. While this might sound somewhat fanciful on many levels, there are nevertheless many cases where such an IFR has been realised, this is particularly so when considering components within a bigger system.

The idea of a system in which the user achieves the useful function without the system actually existing is probably some distance into the future for many real-life systems. An important thought when comparing the exercise here with the idea of an IFR system, however, is that here we start with an existing system and use the trends to project its

evolutionary limits, rather than adopting the usual IFR practice of starting from IFR and working backwards. Thus it will be seen that in going forwards from the known it may well become apparent that the evolutionary limits of a given design style will fall short of the IFR. We illustrate this concept in Figure 13.8.

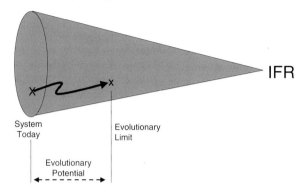

Figure 13.8: Ideal Final Result and 'Evolutionary Limit' Concepts

In actual fact, there are two important concepts relating to the use of the TRIZ trends in a strategic context: the first is that there is such a thing as an *'evolutionary limit'* for any current system. The second is that the difference between this limit and the current system is defined by how much unexploited potential exists in the current system. Taken together, the important image to keep in mind (and this might sound hard to believe at this stage if you are previously unfamiliar with TRIZ) is that we can take an existing system, compare it to the generic TRIZ trends, see how far along the trend line it is, and any evolutionary steps that haven't yet been exploited give us *'evolutionary potential'*. In the same way, another useful image to keep in mind is that an evolutionary limit is defined by what a current system could evolve to become if it advanced to the limits of each of the generic trend lines.

Evolutionary Potential Radar Plots

The concept of evolutionary potential and the related idea that we can use the trends of evolution contained within TRIZ to predict the evolutionary limits of a given system are both very important. The information contained within an analysis of the evolutionary potential of a given system may be expected to play a significant role in determining how best to spend R&D funds – there being little point investing in directions where the system is already at or approaching the fundamental limits of its potential, for example, and, conversely, there will be a lot of point investing in development of parts of the system right at the beginning of their evolutionary potential as likely benefit per unit of funds invested will be at its highest.

We present now a simple tool – the 'evolutionary potential radar plot' – for helping to structure and present evolutionary potential thinking. The example evolutionary potential plot illustrated in Figure 13.9 is used as a way of describing how far along each of the TRIZ trends a given system has evolved. Each spoke in the plot represents one of the TRIZ trends relevant to a given component under investigation. The outside perimeter of the plot represents evolutionary limit, and the shaded area represents how far along each

trend the current system has evolved. Thus the area difference between shaded area and perimeter is a measure of evolutionary potential.

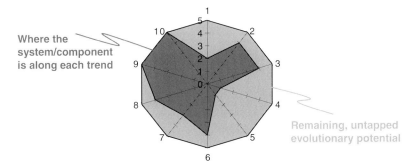

Figure 13.9: Evolutionary Potential Radar Plot

The construction of an actual evolutionary potential plot is best observed through consideration of a real example. We start below with a state of the art rolling contact element bearing:

The start point for defining the evolutionary potential of hydraulic system bearings has been to select a recent granted patent. US patent 6,296,395, granted in October 2001 to FAG in Germany has been chosen as a suitable starting point. The self-aligning bearing concept is illustrated in Figure 13.10 below.

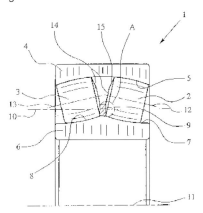

Figure 13.10: Exemplar State Of The Art Bearing System

The evolutionary potential assessment task involves comparing the bearing design with each of the TRIZ trends in order to find a point along the trend that best describes the current evolutionary state of the design. By way of example, Figure 13.1 earlier described the TRIZ trend known as 'space segmentation'. The trend shows a progression observed in other systems from solid to hollow to multi-hollow to capillary to active designs. As in all the other trends being presented, TRIZ depicts an evolutionary progression from left to right across each trend, in which benefits increase as a design travels further to the right.

For the US6,296,395 design, it may thus be observed that the design uses solid roller structures. As such the roller components have evolved along only one out of the possible five evolution stages (NB obviously the idea of hollow ball construction predicted by the trend has been achieved elsewhere and hence the equivalent evolutionary potential plot for that system would denote two out of the possible five stages of evolution). The space segmentation spoke on the radar plot the shaded area boundary for the chosen invention however will be drawn one-fifth of the way along a spoke with five graduation marks.

In terms of the current design, the task of the designer is now to work out what benefits may be accrued by tapping into the unexploited evolutionary potential. In other words, how would a hollow or multi-hollow or capillary structure offer benefits over the current hollow design? Possible examples, as detailed in the 'reasons for jumps' section in the trend references at the end of the chapter, might include increased strength/weight ratio, increased lubrication carrying capability and so on. The identification of such benefits often results in the opportunity to generate significant new intellectual property. For obvious reasons, this book does not seek to travel in that direction.

Instead, the process of comparing the exemplar design to the TRIZ trends continues with the geometric evolution trend shown in Figure 13.11.

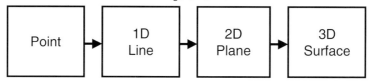

Figure 13.11: Geometric Evolution Trend

This is perhaps one of the more obvious trends; one in which benefits increase as a design exploits all of the available degrees of freedom. This is a particularly important trend in the context of many manufactured products; especially in examining the potential for evolution from the 2D to fully 3D stage, where, historically, it has been easier to manufacture things using 2D machining operations and consequently one of the available degrees of freedom has not been exploited. The increasing availability of machining capabilities where the difference in cost between 2D and 3D is zero means that the untapped benefits to be had by utilising the third dimension can be accrued without increased cost (i.e. the cost-benefit contradiction has been resolved by better manufacturing technology).

In the case of the exemplar bearing, although the roller profile has taken advantage of some degree of three-dimensionality, the invention disclosure talks specifically about symmetrical designs and hence in terms of the geometric evolution trend, the third dimension has not been fully exploited. Several other areas where the third dimension has not been fully used may be seen – for example the profile of the inner and outer races, and the end planes of the bearing – and as such, the evolutionary potential plot should show that only three out of the four evolution stages have been exploited. This can be drawn onto the evolutionary potential radar plot as a point three-quarters along a line with four points. If you are going to use a spreadsheet with some graph plotting capability, you may have to non-dimensionalise all of the trend line lengths to be the same and then scale the point marking the current evolutionary position accordingly.

A close relative of the space segmentation and geometric evolution trends is the surface segmentation trend illustrated in Figure 13.12. This trend defines increasing benefits to be gained by evolving smooth surfaces into 2D and 3D surfaces. As with the space

segmentation trend, the bearing under evaluation does not make use of any of the predicted evolutionary steps beyond the first; it thus has significant untapped surface segmentation evolutionary potential.

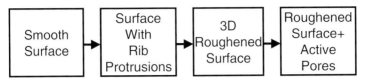

Figure 13.12: Surface Segmentation Trend

The controllability trend illustrated in the trend reference section is highly relevant in a bearing design context. The trend is specifically interesting here in terms of the use or otherwise of feedback in a system. It suggests the questions 'does the bearing design contain feedback, and what might the potential benefits of incorporating feedback be?' In answer to the first question, the exemplar bearing (and most other bearing designs) do not feature any form of feedback. Possible advantages of integrating some form of feedback into the system might then include various options for monitoring the health of the bearing, for measuring loads, or for allowing optimisation of the operation of the bearing based on varying operating conditions.

While all of these potential benefits are speculative, it is clear that the 6,296,395 bearing design – like the majority of other mechanical designs has significant untapped evolutionary potential in this area. Most likely this is due to some of the difficulties and likely complexity of achieving feedback in mechanical systems (TRIZ would encourage designers to identify existing resources within the system to help deliver the required function without complicating the system). It may be observed that magnetic or other 'field-based' bearings do not carry such difficulties – and in fact 'controllability' is one of the main benefits offered by evolution to such bearing design paradigms.

Lack of space and the need to focus on the mechanics of the tool dictates the absence of the details of the evolutionary potential analysis for the other trends in the TRIZ set. Instead, Figure 13.13 illustrates the end result of the comparisons between the other relevant TRIZ trends and the 6,296,395 design. The figure thus acts as an example of the sort of analysis that can and increasingly is being conducted for other systems. For the design under evaluation, the plot clearly shows there to be considerable amounts of untapped potential in the design, and therefore that there are consequently significant improvements that we be developed.

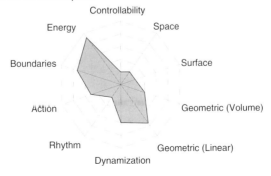

Figure 13.13: Bearing System Evolutionary Potential Radar Plot

It should be noted here that while this plot has been drawn for the bearing as a whole, it is often the case that the analysis is conducted at the level of individual components in order to define a series of evolutionary plots. Such plot families offer significant potential in terms of identifying areas to focus R&D efforts – for example there will be little point in devoting resources to developing a component with little remaining evolutionary potential when there are other components which are still at the un-evolved stages of several of the TRIZ trends. Figure 13.14 illustrates a typical evolutionary potential radar plot family showing the hierarchical structure of individual components feeding into a higher-level radar plot illustrating the evolutionary potential of the resulting assembly.

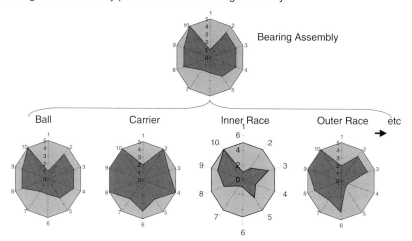

Figure 13.14: Bearing System Evolutionary Potential Radar Plot
(NB: all plots have been show with the same number of spokes for convenience – in practice, each radar plot will probably have a different number of relevant trends, and hence a different number of spokes)

This hierarchical structure is important as some of the trends that will not be relevant to a particular individual component – for example the 'action co-ordination' trend has little relevance to the design of an individual ball within the bearing – but does have relevance when those individual balls begin to interact in the context of the overall system.

We should also note that the plots are intended to be flexible – allowing the user to include just those trends that are relevant to a given system (the recommendation is that all trends are examined as being *possibly* relevant however). Figure 13.28 at the start of the trends reference section illustrates the possible trend options. In order to develop some order and commonality of approach when drawing evolutionary potential plots, you may find it useful to maintain the structure and sequence of trends presented in this example, especially with respect to the space, time and interface categorisations – in that way, any plot you see will always have, for example, 'interface' based trends at the top of the picture.

Lubrication Systems
The same basic evolutionary potential idea can be used for other systems. Sticking with the theme of hydraulic systems, Figure 13.15 reproduces a summary evolutionary potential radar plot for a typical lubrication system – a Finnish patent from April 2001 describing a flow control arrangement in a generic circulation lubrication system.

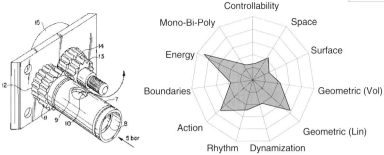

Figure 13.15: US patent 6,217,004 Lubrication System Evolutionary Potential Radar Plot

As with the preceding bearing example, the point of the figure is to illustrate the principles of the evolutionary potential concept and to examine the evolutionary state of a specific design. As with the bearing example, Figure 13.15 suggests that yet another state of the art design still offers the potential for significant evolution, and thus greater customer (and for that matter, manufacturer) benefit.

Filtration Systems

Figure 13.16 repeats the message of significant untapped potential for a typical hydraulic system barrier filter design.

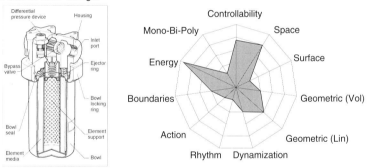

Figure 13.16: Filtration System Evolutionary Potential Radar Plot

Based on work elsewhere, examining alternative means of delivering the function (function and functionality represents another vital aspect of TRIZ) 'separate contaminants', it remains to be seen whether filter manufacturers will be able to develop and exploit this potential for barriers before an alternative system – one much more likely to achieve a true Ideal Final Result of achieve the function without the system – emerges to displace the barrier. This, of course is the difference between traditional 'improve the current' and ideality based 'start from IFR and work back' thinking described in Chapter 8. Potential users of the evolutionary potential tool need to keep in mind the bigger picture presented by the ideality and Ideal Final Result philosophies.

Innovation Timing

The TRIZ trends offer a uniquely powerful means of identifying the where and how's of innovation. Innovation timing – the when's – on the other hand are somewhat less

amenable to systematic prediction. Many books have been written on the subject (most notably Reference 13.2), although none so far have made any connection with TRIZ. The information we present here is necessarily brief given our engineering focus; anyone wishing for more detail should look out for the management version of this book. We spend our time here examining the strategic implications of combining technology trends with customer and market evolution trends to provide organisations in the context of a systematic business concept innovation ('BCI' – Reference 13.3) methodology.

In this section, if we put aside all the human issues that prevent organisations from innovating effectively, we record that the predominant influencing factor in business evolution timing is determined by whether the prevailing technology evolution precedes or lags behind customer expectations. Where technology lags behind customer expectation (as in many service industries or the design of many household products), we show that the existing TRIZ technology trends can be expected to play a major role in bridging the gap. Where technology evolution exceeds the expectations of a significant number of customers – as may be seen in a large number of case studies by Christensen (the afore mentioned Reference 13.2) such as computer hard-drives, earth-moving equipment and accounting software – and the market becomes ripe for the emergence of 'disruptive' technology insertions, we show how modified definition and application of the TRIZ trends can also be used to develop potent BCI solutions.

Technology Lagging Behind Customer Expectation

The picture reproduced in Figure 13.17 serves to illustrate the frequently observed scenario in which the fundamental limitations of a given solution become overtaken by customer expectations. This situation results in an 'administrative contradiction' – the customer knows what they want, but the system is unable to deliver it. This inadequacy of the system relative to expectation is a vital innovation driver – and represents a significant element of the 'form follows failure' thesis found in Henry Petroski's excellent 'The Evolution of Useful Things' book (Reference 13.4).

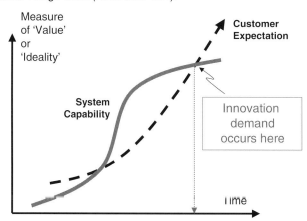

Figure 13.17: Common Innovation Driver I – Customer Need Exceeds Solution Capability

The characteristic of the customer expectation curve follows the trends suggested by the Kano diagram (Reference 13.5) and the inevitable shift of customer expectations as they

become more familiar with products. The Kano model tells us that while we used to be excited by the idea of air-conditioning in a car, for example, we now almost take it for granted that the car will have this facility. In a similar manner, the idea of in-car GPS is still seen as an 'exciter' – something that would actively delight us when we see it in the car. The rising characteristic of the customer expectation line in this scenario is in direct conflict with the inherent limitations created by the s-curve characteristics of a system.

The expectation curve and the system capability s-curve are of course plotted as averages. Particularly in the case of the customer expectation curve, this is a highly dangerous assumption. Certainly, one of the overriding messages from Chapter 7 on the dynamics of S-Curves should leave readers in no doubt that not only does every component within a system possess its own family of S-Curves, but that every individual customer may well also have a very different perception of the relative ideality of those different curves. Taking this into account will increasingly require us to plot these expectation pictures for every individual customer (leaving one or two important mass-customisation contradictions to be solved along the way!) if we are to truly understand the dynamics of when the innovation demand occurs.

The emergence of the administrative contradiction in this 'expectation exceeds technology' scenario meanwhile acts as the spur to innovation. The flattening of the top of the s-curve is symptomatic of the presence of a limiting contradiction in the system. The creation of a new or modified system that enables this s-curve to be lifted – i.e. presents the customer with sufficiently high new level of ideality or value – will only come about through resolution of a contradiction. This can be achieved through use of the Contradictions part of TRIZ, or, using the Trends of Evolution – where, although already stated elsewhere as over-simplistic – it is possible to say that each new step along the trend patterns is a new s-curve opportunity.

In this 'expectation exceeds capability' scenario, then, it is evident that the innovation-timing question is answered by a definite 'now'.

The real key to identification of this scenario is finding the administrative contradictions where the customer expectation is hidden from view. A good example of this is the recent emergence of pizza-boxes which are better able to keep delivery pizzas warm – this following probably close to 10 years of customers apparently 'accepting' the fact that the pizza that arrived on their doorstep was cold.

The two most useful tools to help identify these 'hidden' dis-satisfactions are QFD and a variant of subversion analysis in which we might use simple but powerful provocations of the form 'how could a customer be unhappy with this product?' or 'who doesn't buy our product, and why?'.

Technology Exceeds Customer Expectation

Our thrust in this section now shifts to look at a different scenario connecting customer expectation to solution capability – that of the case where solution capability exceeds customer expectation (Figure 13.18). This scenario is the basis for much of the work reported by Clayton Christensen in Reference 13.2.

The central thrust and paradox of the Innovator's Dilemma is that traditional 'good' management practice can lead organisations into big trouble when the solutions they offer **exceed** the needs of their customers. In Christensen's words, these situations lead to

287

opportunities for the entry into the market of 'disruptive' technologies. A disruptive technology is essentially one which changes the prevailing business model. Historically speaking, companies almost inherently fail to thrive (or often even survive) in situations where the market is expecting less of a product than it is capable of delivering.

One of the aims of this section is to encourage readers to think about possible disruptive technology opportunities or threats in their business, and, more importantly, to show how the TRIZ technology evolution trends are uniquely placed to help determine what the 'right' disruptive jumps might be.

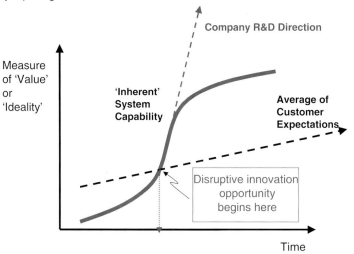

Figure 13.18: Common Innovation Driver II – Solution Capability Exceeds Customer Need

Case Study – Earth-Moving Equipment

In realising that probably not all of the readers of this book are interested in heavy earth-moving equipment, we hope that everyone can nevertheless extract some useful learning points from this discussion. Those that feel happier thinking about computer disc-drives or accounting software or retail shopping or electric cars might like to explore the details given for those cases given in Christensen's book and see the uncanny parallels to the earth-moving equipment case illustrated here.

Christensen details the evolution of earth-moving equipment from the original steam-driven mechanical devices of the type illustrated in Figure 13.19 to the hydraulic machines prevalent in today's earth moving environment. The introduction of hydraulic machines was indisputably 'disruptive' to the mechanical excavator business model.

To over-simplify grossly (and yet hopefully justifiably), the evolution of mechanical excavators was largely driven by the manufacturers (initially correct) belief that their markets were interested in moving ever greater amounts of earth per shovel load, and that this was particularly so for their most profitable customers. Consequently 'sound' management practice meant that the evolution of mechanical excavators was targeted at the earth-moving needs of the most profitable customers. As time went on, the industry found that it was possible to make bigger and bigger machines capable of moving more and more earth.

Figure 13.19: Mechanical Earth-Moving Equipment – Using Cables To Transmit Loads

Further evolution of the earth movers to increase shovel load size, however, although serving customers at the high end of the market began to exceed the requirements of other customers to whom shovel size increase was not worth the increase in cost and other down-sides that came attached to such big machines. These customers were becoming ripe for a disruptive technology insertion.

They got one when JCB introduced the first hydraulically powered earthmovers in 1947. The first hydraulic 'backhoes' were inferior to the cable-actuated mechanical machines in just about every traditional performance measure used by the existing customer base: to these (high profit generating) customers the new machine was not particularly attractive. On the other hand, the new machines did offer a considerable number of new advantages, not least of which was a whole new level of compactness, portability and flexibility of operation, and a marked improvement in safety if something went wrong (insert image of snapped cable moving at uncontrollably high speed here).

The new hydraulic machines thus carved themselves a whole new market of customers to whom the new advantages outweighed the deficiencies of a smaller load carrying capability. The new machines began to sell in large quantities, but principally to a newly created customer base.

As is so often then the case, the revenues from this new customer base (albeit they were still not sufficient to be of great interest to the established cable-activated machine manufacturers – hence 'good management practice' said to ignore them) funded the development of increasingly capable hydraulic systems. The hydraulic machine evolution entered a phase where it was able to rapidly catch-up with the performance capabilities of the mechanical machines. It did this whilst simultaneously preserving the advantages of compactness, portability, flexibility and safety. In another highly reproducible evolution pattern, the increasing capability of the hydraulic machines was happening at a rate greater than the changing requirements of the customers with the highest earth-moving requirements. Before too long the net value of the evolving hydraulic machines thus met and exceeded both the customer expectation and the fundamental ideality limits of the mechanical machines – Figure 13.20. As is so often the case, the disruptive technology eventually won the day – and today the mechanical, cable actuated earthmovers are restricted to very small niche applications.

The connection with TRIZ here is that it helps predict the evolution of systems, and in this case, specifically suggests the evolution from mechanical to fluid-based systems.

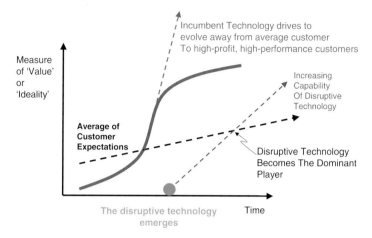

Figure 13.20: How The Disruptive Technology Overcomes The Established Technology

The TRIZ 'Dynamization' (see final section of this chapter) trend in other words, could have been used to predict the eventual dominance of the hydraulic systems over the mechanical. The trend, however, doesn't end with the hydraulic system; it suggests that these will eventually be overtaken by field-based systems;

Seeing as the hydraulic backhoe (Figure 13.21) is the currently dominant earth-mover, we might now switch from historical analysis to future prediction mode by using the TRIZ trend alongside Christensen's disruptive technology model to have a go at showing what both together would tell us about the future of earth-moving:

Figure 13.21: Present Day Backhoe Earth Mover

Field-Based Earth Movers

As described in the trend reference section, the reasons systems jump from fluid to field based solutions are various – increased reliability, increased design flexibility (positioning

of components), increased efficiency, increased controllability, increased safety, reduced harm from leaks, etc.

As far as load-carrying capability is concerned, however, an electrically actuated backhoe using the best of today's electrical actuation capability will not match the earth-moving performance of the hydraulic systems. The current customer base is thus unlikely to be attracted to an electrical machine.

According to the disruptive technology model, the new electrically based earth mover needs to find a new customer base to whom shovel load size performance is not as important as some of the inherent benefits of shifting away from hydraulics if it is to define a foundation from which to grow. Almost inherently, these customers don't exist today, or, if they do, they are highly unpredictable in terms of what they actually want. Hypothetically, for an electrical earth-mover, they might include a growing market of domestic users (see how the market for sit-on lawn-mowers evolved for example), or anyone requiring to dig lots of small holes with as little human labour as possible – e.g. cable companies – where the increased controllability and flexibility (i.e. the tool needs connecting to the power source by a simple wire only) of an electrically operated system would outweigh the reduced shovel-load performance. According to the model, these applications will in the short term be less profitable than the high performance hydraulic systems (which explains why the incumbent hydraulic companies are unlikely to be interested – at least based on historical evidence).

The next part of the prediction then goes something along the lines that because the electrical system is at the start of its evolutionary potential path, it doesn't need nearly so much investment to begin increasing the performance of the machines. Revenues from the new customer base fund development of higher shovel load systems; the electrical systems will then eventually become able to match the performance of the hydraulic systems, while retaining the other flexibility, controllability, reliability, etc advantages the hydraulic systems will never match – Figure 13.22.

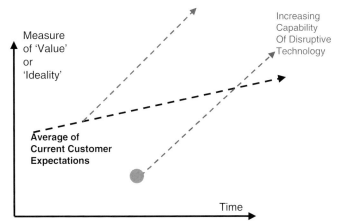

Figure 13.22: Disruptive Technology Wins Because Technology Evolution Commonly Exceeds Customer Expectation

Eventually, the electrical systems will achieve the performance capabilities of the hydraulic systems, after which point, the days of hydraulics will be numbered.

So what does this all mean?

Disruptive technologies usually 'win' because technology performance capability often rises more quickly than customer expectations.

The disruptive technology is highly likely to be initially inferior in terms of the traditional performance measures of the incumbent technology. The disruptive technology thus usually has to find a new customer base to sustain it in the initial development stages.

The new customer base is unlikely to match the profitability of the existing market in the short term. 'Good management practice' thus means the existing companies will not exploit the new technology (NB Christensen's book offers strategies to remedy this problem – albeit they are almost inherently painful and come attached to a short term drop in profit.)

The cycle repeats every time an established technology 'grows' away from the evolving customer requirement.

When a customer's appetite for 'performance' is sated, they will increasingly make purchase decisions based on reliability, convenience and price – in this regard, take particular note of the 'customer focus' trend in the trend reference section.

In the meantime, the major point of this section is to implant the vital connection between the disruptive technology business model and the TRIZ evolution trends. It is highly likely that the form of the disruptive technologies can and will be predicted by TRIZ. Almost the absolute key to successful business concept innovation in this 'technology exceeds expectation' scenario is the identification of the new markets (and new players) that will suit the apparently 'inferior' disruptive product.

The Christensen example of electric cars being more likely to emerge from the industries making golf-carts and milk-vans rather than any of the big car manufacturers is particularly apposite in this BCI scenario. The more organisations look outside their current self-imposed boundaries, the more likely it is that they will identify the threats, and (in the case of the golf cart manufacturers) opportunities awaiting those who can spot the discontinuities. Reference 13.2 discusses this side of the equation in more detail.

Relationship to TRIZ:
As a brief aside, it is perhaps interesting to examine TRIZ in the context of this 'disruptive technology' model. In many senses, in the West, TRIZ presents a richness that is considerably in advance of the expectations of most organisations. Whether this apparent 'over-capability' of TRIZ is genuine or due to the mis-selling and poor placement by the TRIZ community, it is not surprising to see the emergence of simplified versions like SIT.

2) Trends As A Problem Solving Tool

The above section described the use of the Trends part of TRIZ in a strategic role. This section examines their use in the nearer-term; as a means of solving problems. As may be seen by the number of times the 'select' part of the systematic creativity process (Chapter 9) references this chapter, the Trends tool has several diverse applications. Trends can be used to help us find new s-curves (one way of overcoming contradictions), for improving any actions we have determined to be insufficient or excessive, or simply as a way of improving any of the attributes of a component or process.

Many newcomers to TRIZ find the Trends part the most attractive and easy to use from a problem solving perspective. The reason for this is that they encourage us to think in a slightly different way to the normal TRIZ process. The difference is simple, but often profoundly important in its implications.

The Trends application process is similar to the general model of transforming a specific problem into a generic one, locating the general solution and then translating that general solution into a specific solution, albeit, as illustrated in Figure 13.23, the Trends process seems to by-pass parts of this process:-

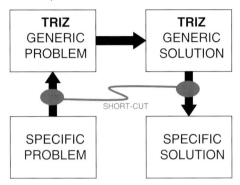

Figure 13.23: Trends in a Problem Solving Role

What the figure shows is that, although we still have to make the connections between the specific system under evaluation and the generic trends, once we have done that for an individual trend and have used that trend to identify the next evolutionary stage, we can use exactly the same connection we made to achieve the specific-to-generic jump in reverse to connect the generic solution back to a specific solution. In other words, the specific-generic transition only has to be done once. In many situations, the link from generic solution (i.e. the next stage in the trend to the right of the one the current system was connected to) back to the specific is so rapid that the user is often unaware that a transition has taken place at all.

A simple example should highlight the phenomenon, and demonstrate how we might use the trends in their problem-solving role. The system in question involves a typical lawn-mower featuring a single rotating metal blade. The problem is that the blade rapidly becomes blunt and then ceases to cut grass effectively.

Using the Trends to help us to solve this problem demands first that we compare the blade with each of the 35 trends in the reference section at the end of the chapter. In the case of each, the question we have to ask is 'where is the blade positioned on this trend?' We are thus looking for connections between the blade and one of the trend stages for each trend. Figure 13.24 illustrates one such case – where we have successfully made a connection between the blade and the 'immobile' stage on the Dynamization trend. (Note that we were able to make this connection despite the fact that the blade is rotating and hence obviously not 'immobile' in that sense – the point being that we are looking to make these connections in *any* sense – in this case, the fact that the blade is designed to be rigid qualifies it as immobile.)

As soon as we have made this connection, the trend pictures to the right of 'immobile' immediately suggest generic solutions to us and, because we have already made the connection between specific and generic, we are already picturing blades with joints, blades with multiple joints and fully flexible blades. We might also be thinking about water-jets replacing the blades, or even lasers (or other field-based solutions) carrying out the function of our troublesome rigid blade.

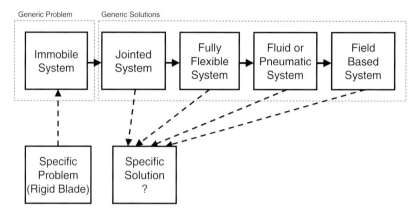

Figure 13.24: Trends in a Problem Solving Role – Lawn-mower Blade

Several of these in fact turn out to offer excellent solutions to the stated lawn-mower problem. We might also note how other industries requiring a 'cut' function have already been through similar evolution stages (which is of course partly where the trend emerged from) – perhaps most notably, the use of water-et cutters in the fish processing industry, and laser-knives and ultrasound cutters in several others.

At least part of the reason for picking this example is to highlight the fact that the solution directions suggested by this trend run counter to the 'common-sense' view of many people. 'Common-sense' appears to tell many that the right solution direction is to make the blade stronger; even more rigid. We see this in action in many other instances – if a structure tries to deflect under stress, then make it more rigid to fight the stress seems to be the prevailing logic in several industry sectors. The rigidity may, of course be necessary to some degree (see the Millennium Bridge in London for example), but the trend quite categorically suggests the 'right' evolutionary direction is one towards increasing flexibility, and using the stress rather than fighting it.

Again, the consistent message when using the trends is 'somewhere there is an advantage in moving to the right along the trend'.

In many instances, this means that our task when problem solving using the trends is not so much making the connections between trend and system, but working out *why* the answers emerging from the trends are answers.

3) Trends in Combination

As the Mono-Bi-Poly trend suggests, our deployment of the TRIZ trends can often be improved by considering interactions between multiple different trends as opposed to just

singly. (The same applies with respect to other tools as well – see the physical contradiction cases in Chapter 11 for example.)

This fact applies to all of the trends relevant to a system being evaluated which have some measure of untapped evolutionary potential. We will not discuss such cases any further than to merely mention that when examining unused potential, it is advisable to look for synergistic effects between different trend suggestions. In the above lawn-mower example, we can see this in action by combining the idea of a completely flexible blade with the space segmentation trend (making it a hollow or multiple hollow blade) and the geometric evolution trend – which would prompt us to make the flexible blade with a non-circular cross-section in order to tailor its cutting properties to the prevailing direction of rotation.

The trend we do want to talk about in a little more detail in this combination role, however, is the Mono-Bi-Poly trend. This trend too can be used in the same manner as described in the previous paragraph. To take an example, we might combine the idea of a water-jet based blade with the idea of including an additive into the water. This additive might be another liquid, or it might be small solid particles – both would be included to enhance the cutting action. If we were very smart, we would introduce solid particles that would perform another function as ell as 'enhance cutting' – e.g. we could make the solid particles out of fertiliser.

The reason for singling out the Mono-Bi-Poly trend for special attention in this 'trends in combination' section is only half hinted at by this fertiliser example. The bigger picture says that the number of options open to us when we use M-B-P to say 'add more stuff' – especially when it's more different stuff – is potentially quite large and often 'non-obvious'. The addition of fertiliser particles to the water jet will sound obvious to some and not others for example. (In the same way, the addition of salt particles (at a point where they have insufficient time to fully dissolve) into the water-jets used to cut fish to both enhance the efficiency of the cutting process and help preserve the fish might sound obvious following on directly from the lawn example, but isn't currently obvious to the fish-processing industry.)

Unfortunately, there does not appear to be any cast-iron rules regarding what sort of Mono-Bi-Poly action we might combine with other trends. On the other hand, someone, somewhere has already made a novel combination between the M-B-P and other improvements and we should take a note of these combinations. Figure 13.25 indicates some of the possibilities. They are intended to be used as a solution trigger list. In the same way, problem solvers may care to examine some of the resources trigger sheets in Chapter 14 to identify other things they might combine into the way they use the trends.

Type of M-B-P Application	Example
Internal Additives	- adding things into holes - molecular modifications - colour (smell, etc) change indicators - oil with added functions – anti-knock, etc - tranofor of functions from other sub-systems – electrically conducting clothing fibres for example
External Additives/ Additives Between Objects	- adding easily available substances to add new function - gases (e.g. inert gases in welding) - running shoes/golf shoes add spikes - lubricants

	- abrasives
	- additives to change friction properties
	- add something that will resonate when desired
Segmentation	- brush seals (also multi-stage)
	- different types of seals combined
	- different stiffness fibres at different locations/for different functions
	- different number of blades at different stages in a jet engine avoids resonant coupling effects
	- poke yoke – use of different segmentation patterns to make it impossible to connect things incorrectly (inc. asymmetry)
	- combined keep and throwaway systems
Actions	- periodic action combined with multiple different actions
	- chaotic/random periodicity
Co-Branding	- add someone else's branded product to yours to benefit both

Figure 13.25: Examples of M-B-P Combination Possibilities

For other examples of 'additives', see also the Inventive Standards section at the end of Chapter 12.

4) Trends In Reverse?

All of the trends plotted in this chapter show systems evolving in a left-to-right direction across the trend stages. This is done because this direction is the most common evolution direction. There are, however, a number of exceptions to this left-to-right rule, such that there are occasions when systems can be seen to evolve in the opposite direction. Fortunately these instances are predictable in nature. For the purposes of obtaining a complete understanding of the trends and the way we can deploy them most effectively, we need to examine these exceptions. They fall into two general categories; the first associated with an existing TRIZ discovery – The Law of Non-Uniform Evolution – and the second a more loosely connected series of rules we shall label 'market anomalies'. We will examine both in turn, starting with the Law of Non-uniform Evolution and its implications for trend deployment.

The Law of Non-Uniform Evolution
Previous statements describing increasing ideality as the over-riding trend are true, but over-simplified (they are nevertheless useful concepts to keep in mind – which is why the statements have been used repeatedly in the book). The over-simplification comes because, although the statement is true at the system level, it is not necessarily true as we zoom-in to look at the evolution of components within a system. Indeed, at the sub-system level, it is clear that sometimes a sub-system will travel in a direction of decreasing ideality in order to enable the overall system to achieve net increasing ideality. This sub-system exception to the increasing ideality rule emerges from the TRIZ Law of Non-Uniform Evolution. The Law states:

> The rate of evolution of different parts of a system
> and its associated sub-systems is not uniform

Evolution at the system level often causes a wave of consecutive changes in adjacent systems and sub-systems. The Law implies that sometimes some elements of a system need to get worse in order to serve the greater good of the overall system. The more

complex the system, the more non-uniform the evolution of the sub-system parts, and therefore the greater the likelihood that some elements will have to markedly decrease in ideality during the evolution of the overall system. It will be instructive to look at an example of the Law in action before discussing its implications on the TRIZ trends and our application of them:

Figure 13.26 illustrates key stages in the evolution of the system we know as 'bicycle'. The bicycle, despite being a relatively simple system, nevertheless exhibits several instances of the Law of Non-Uniform Evolution in action.

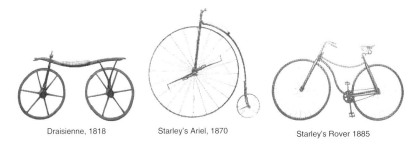

Draisienne, 1818   Starley's Ariel, 1870   Starley's Rover 1885

Figure 13.26: Partial Evolution History of the Bicycle

If we consider the main useful function, or the main benefit of the bicycle as being to transport a rider from A to B in the fastest time, with the minimum of effort, the maximum of comfort and safety, we can construct an evolution history consisting of various evolution stages. Each stage may be seen to represent a new generation (or new s-curve), with the maturing of one generation creating a limiting contradiction that required to be overcome (a shift to a new s-curve) before any further increase in ideality could be achieved. Table 13.1 below describes a partial history highlighting some of these evolutionary stages.

1818 - First bicycle; no pedals, transmission - Conflict - speed limited by leg movement
1840 - pedals introduced - Conflict - increased speed endangers rider
1845 - brakes appear, speed increased by - Conflict - speed limited by wheel durability
    increasing wheel diameter
1870 - wooden wheels replaced with metal, - Conflict - more effort required to turn wheel
    wheel diameter continues to increase   greater danger if rider falls off
1885 - Chain transmission eliminates need - Conflict - bicycle cannot be ridden at high
    for big wheel   speed over rough ground
1888 - pneumatic tyre introduced; speed - Conflict - pedals spin at high speed
1890 - free-wheeling clutch introduced

Table 13.1: Evolution of the Bicycle

The table shows how each generation was ended by the emergence of a conflict, which was then eliminated by the next generation. Thus, for example, the Draisienne bicycle of 1818 had no pedals, and so maximum speed (our main measure of Ideality in the above definition) was limited by the leg movement necessary to propel the bicycle. This speed limitation was then overcome by the incorporation of pedals. The next problem was that speed could now be increased to such a level that safety was compromised because the cyclist could not slow down with any degree of control. This safety issue then became the limiting contradiction in the system, and only when this was overcome (by the

incorporation of brakes in 1845) could designers contemplate measures to increase speed further.

The table highlights a whole series of emerging conflicts and resolving innovations. The main point of the table is to highlight the Law of Non-Uniform Evolution in action and the fact that although throughout the evolution of the system called 'bicycle' its overall ideality was increasing, the ideality of the various constituent parts was often doing anything but. Consider the wheels, for example, which have evolved from a simple wooden structure, to a much bigger thing with a metal rim, to a metal structure with gears, to a smaller hollow pneumatic tyre – only one step of which is consistent with the directions suggested by the TRIZ trends. Or look at the brakes – which started off not being present at all, and have since evolved through a number of stages again inconsistent with several of the trend directions.

Another simple example of the Law of Non-Uniform Evolution in action comes when we think about cutlery (Figure 13.27). This example is also instructive because it helps to highlight the fact that even though different sub-systems are independent of one another, the evolution to increasing ideality at the higher level – in this case the system 'eating food' – can drive the evolution of one independent part to influence that of another. The example comes from 'The Evolution of Useful Things' by Henry Petroski (Reference 13.4) and an article connecting the example to TRIZ (Reference 13.6).

The figure shows that we used to eat using two knives – one to stick into the thing we wanted to cut and the other to perform the cutting operation. Unfortunately, this method of holding meat (for example) was largely inadequate – the point allowing the meat to rotate when we tried to cut it. This failure was one of the drivers prompting the evolution of a two-tine fork (picture on the right). Suddenly now, there was a need to make a second, more complicated system element. But then, two tines meant that the meat no longer rotated

Figure 13.27: Influence of Fork Evolution on Knife Evolution

when we tried to cut it (it also meant we couldn't pick up small things like peas though – hence its eventual evolution to three and four tine designs). It also meant that the knife no longer needed to feature a point – notice, then, how the evolution of the fork prompted the evolution of the knife (think of the geometric evolution trend) from point to line to curve. The example highlights a common trend for the evolution of one part of a system to influence the evolution of another. It also, in keeping with the theme of Petroski's book illustrates his belief that the principle driver of evolution is 'form follows failure'. Or, 'technology lags customer expectation' from the earlier section of this chapter.

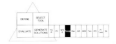

The main point emerging from the Law of Non-Uniform Evolution is that we need to be very careful when conducting a trend analysis of a system – particularly so when we are examining several hierarchical levels – that we take into account that the overall direction of evolution is driven by the increasing ideality of the highest level system being considered. Some of the sub-systems and components supporting the overall system – even if they are seemingly independent – may have to become 'worse' in order to support the greater good.

Market Anomalies

The effects of the market on the application and relevance of the TRIZ trends can be somewhat difficult to predict. Fortunately, their duration is often short-lived and so, although a market shift can cause a system to reverse direction along a trend for a while, the effect is usually transitory – being reversed again either by a return to 'normality' in the market dynamic, or the resolution of a contradiction.

By far the most difficult of the market anomalies to predict is one usually described as 'form follows fashion'. Examples of 'form follows fashion' include things like portable radios (for which increasing size was a distinct trend direction for a period), clothing (where we are to a large extent subject to the whims of a supposedly learned few designers from one season to the next), and assorted shifts towards 'retro' styling in things like motorcycles and a variety of consumer goods. Evolutionary shifts driven by such fashion considerations are very difficult to predict, despite the fact that there are often predictable cycles contained within the bigger picture (think of the cyclic nature of skirt lengths for example). Fortunately, the evidence from all examples of 'form follows fashion' is that eventually the allure of increased ideality eventually triumphs. The least predictable part of the whole story, is knowing *when* the shift will take place.

The most common market anomaly is a sudden increase in the dominance of the cost element of the ideality equation. This anomaly is often consistent with the overall drive to increasing ideality, but results in a shift in focus from the benefits or harms elements. If the increased emphasis on cost can only be achieved by a reduction in benefits, that is the time when we can see systems switching their trajectory across the trends from left-to-right to right-to-left.

By way of example, the economics of wind-turbines, as discussed earlier, are still quite precarious, with the balance between first cost and return obtained through power generated still one which is heavily influenced by government subsidy and other local effects. The economic balance between first cost and revenue for many early systems was that first cost was so dominant that machines with just one blade (plus a counter-weight for balance) were produced. Only when return rates improve did two- and three-bladed machines appear, and, even now, the economics are such that the increased power generating benefits of adding more blades or things like shrouds around blades, or increasing the complexity of the blade shape do not provide a sufficient return to warrant their incorporation.

This cost-focus shift in a market is often transitory. As such, it means that systems will be forced to evolve in the reverse (right-to-left) direction only until the prevailing economic situation reverts to emphasis on the benefits side of the equation. What happens in the longer term, of course (especially when we think of systems at the mature end of their s-curve and cost is the only thing left to focus on) is that the fight between top half and bottom half of the ideality equation is resolved by the elimination of a contradiction.

So, while the traditional economics of making a solid component versus making a hollow one (thinking about the space segmentation trend) or between a rigid system and a jointed one (thinking about dynamization) suggest that the solid, rigid thing must be cheaper, and the hollow jointed thing must be capable of delivering higher benefits, someone eventually works out how to produce the hollow, jointed thing at the same or lower cost than the solid, rigid thing. This type of top half/bottom half contradiction is very often resolved by improved manufacturing technology. The emergence of lost-wax casting techniques (or rather the re-emergence – several ancient civilisations knew the technique), for example, provided a means of resolving the solid versus hollow component manufacture cost/benefit contradiction. See the 'manufacture technology' resources list in Chapter 14 for a more comprehensive list of contradiction-breaking manufacture methods that may be able to help resolve a benefit/cost contradiction relevant to your situation.

In summary then for this discussion on 'trends in reverse', although market conditions can temporarily drive evolution the 'wrong way' along the trends, these aberrations are either halted by a reversal in the market or, if the drive towards lower cost remains, by the resolution of a contradiction between the top and bottom halves of the ideality equation.

5) Trends Reference

This final section presents a collection of 35 trend lines uncovered by TRIZ researchers and during the extensive additional research that has informed this book. The general format of presentation in each case involves the basic trend being presented across the top of the page. This trend image is then followed by, first a list of examples of the particular trend (note how some systems have not evolved all the way along a particular trend, or didn't start at the first stage, or have sometimes missed a stage out – all of these characteristics being relatively common), and then second, a list of reasons distilled from other solutions to suggest why the jumps might offer a benefit. These lists are not intended to be inclusive, and as such, if you find other reasons for the jumps, you might like to add them to the table for your future reference.

The sequencing of the trends is quite important. Whether you intend to use the trends as strategic tools or problem solving aids, it is important to try and connect each trend to your situation in the sequence presented. Some may not be relevant, but the point is that the question should at least be asked. We have tried to sequence the trends in accordance with a logical progression that makes the connective jumps our minds have to make a manageable size.

Some, of course, will prefer to use a more random approach. This is perfectly acceptable, although we recommend that you keep in mind the following important image: Figure 13.28 shows how the trends cluster into three broad (sometimes slightly blurred) categories covering space, time and interface situations. We have found this grouping useful in determining which of the trends are going to be relevant to a given situation; if, for example, the system being evaluated involves a static mechanical system, then the most likely matches to the trends will come through examination of the 'space' (i.e. physical space) trends rather than the 'time' based ones.

This space, time, interface clustering represents a recurring theme in systematic creativity – see also the Chapters on 9-Windows (4) and Contradictions (10) – particularly figures 4.14 and 10.26.

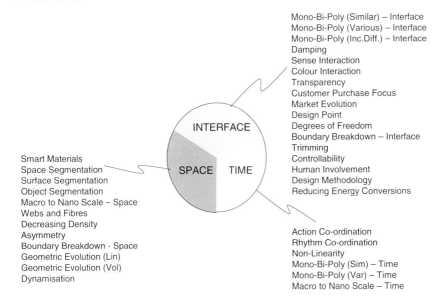

Mono-Bi-Poly (Similar) – Interface
Mono-Bi-Poly (Various) – Interface
Mono-Bi-Poly (Inc.Diff.) – Interface
Damping
Sense Interaction
Colour Interaction
Transparency
Customer Purchase Focus
Market Evolution
Design Point
Degrees of Freedom
Boundary Breakdown – Interface
Trimming
Controllability
Human Involvement
Design Methodology
Reducing Energy Conversions

INTERFACE

SPACE   TIME

Smart Materials
Space Segmentation
Surface Segmentation
Object Segmentation
Macro to Nano Scale – Space
Webs and Fibres
Decreasing Density
Asymmetry
Boundary Breakdown - Space
Geometric Evolution (Lin)
Geometric Evolution (Vol)
Dynamisation

Action Co-ordination
Rhythm Co-ordination
Non-Linearity
Mono-Bi-Poly (Sim) – Time
Mono-Bi-Poly (Var) – Time
Macro to Nano Scale – Time

Figure 13.28: Clustering of Technology Evolution Trends

(Note that some of the trends in this list have connections to more than one of the space, time and interface categories – there are 30 different trends, interpretable in a total of 35 ways. The Reference section contains one entry for each of the 30 individual trends.)

What Do I Do?

The Trends tool is one of the single largest parts of TRIZ and systematic creativity. It is also the tool that a high proportion of newcomers seem to obtain early success using. In this sense it appears to operate in a manner consistent with the way many people naturally think. Experience shows that an awful lot of problem situations can be tackled just by using the trends. There are two main application roles for the trend; one in a strategic context, the other in a problem-solving context. Both require that users are familiar with the trends illustrated in the following reference section, and are capable of connecting their situation to those trends. In the first instance, we recommend that you become familiar with this process.

Specific, then, to their role in a problem-solving context is the need to be able to work out *why* the solutions being suggested by trend patterns are in fact solutions to the problem under consideration.

In their strategic role, concepts like evolutionary potential (and the idea of the evolutionary potential radar plot) make a useful start point. This start then needs to be matched with a good understanding of market dynamics – for which, you should refer to the first section of

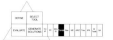

the chapter. This then needs to be backed up by some of the more detailed knowledge contained in the later sections of the chapter – in which we see some of the exceptions to the general trend directions and complications caused by combination effects coming in to play.

Finally, as with so many other parts of TRIZ, you may like to observe the Trends in action in the world around you and to keep a note of them in the spaces left in the reference section. This will serve to both extend your familiarity, and provide additional solution triggers for future reference.

References

1) Mann, D.L., 'Trimming Evolution Patterns for Complex Systems', TRIZ Journal, June 1999.
2) Christensen, C.M., 'The Innovator's Dilemma: When New Technologies Cause Great Firms To Fail', Harvard Business School Press, 1997.
3) Hamel, G., 'Leading The Revolution', Harvard Business School Press, 1999.
4) Petroski, H., 'The Evolution of Useful Things', Vintage Books, 1994.
5) Walden, D., 'Special Issue on Kano's Methods for Understanding Customer-Defined Quality', Center for Quality of Management Journal, Reprint RP02700, Fall 1993.
6) Mann, D.L., 'The (Predictable) Evolution of Useful Things', TRIZ Journal, August 1999.

SMART MATERIALS

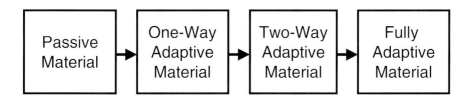

Examples

(Smart) gel-filled bicycle saddles, shoe-insoles, etc, self-disassembly polymers, shape-memory alloy fasteners, glass capable of transforming from transparent to opaque and degrees in-between.

Reasons For Jumps

Evolution Stage	Reasons for Jumps
Passive to One-Way	-solve a physical contradiction by creating two different states (big/small, viscous/non-viscous, etc) -create a 2-way switch -reduced control system complexity -opportunities for self-organising/self-serving systems - make simple measurements-
One Way to Two Way	-increased operational flexibility -three-way switching
Two-Way to Fully Adaptive	-system adaptable to multiple user requirements (mass customisation) -offers continuous variability -sophisticated measurement indicator

Notes:

A relatively new trend, following the discovery of certain smart material systems – rheopexic, thermochromic, electrochromic, shape-memory alloys, shape-memory polymers, etc.

The physical contradiction eliminating capability of smart materials means they will become increasingly important in the design of future systems.

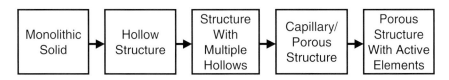

SPACE SEGMENTATION

| Monolithic Solid | → | Hollow Structure | → | Structure With Multiple Hollows | → | Capillary/ Porous Structure | → | Porous Structure With Active Elements |

Examples

Bricks, chocolate bars, turbine blades, toothbrush handles (!), double-glazing, radiators, spectacle lens (monolithic to hollow), shoe-soles, clothing, armour, tyres.

Reasons For Jumps

Evolution Stage	Reasons for Jumps
Monolithic to Hollow	-reduced weight -reduced use of material -space to insert other material -hole to hang an object from -increase moment of inertia -pass something through the object -improve heat transfer
Hollow to Multiple Hollow	-improve heat transfer -improve strength properties -pass multiple things through object -increase surface area
Multiple Hollow to Capillary/Porous	-improve surface area -improve strength/weight ratio -improve heat transfer
Capillary/Porous to Active	-improve heat transfer -add new function -allow variation in properties

Notes:

Many systems have evolved some way along this trend. The emergence of foam-based materials (particularly foam-metals and foam-polymers) offers considerable evolution opportunities for many systems at earlier evolution stages.

'Active elements' represent a broad range of additional possibilities

SURFACE SEGMENTATION

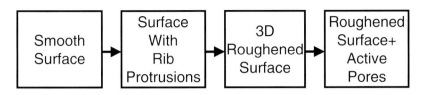

| Smooth Surface | → | Surface With Rib Protrusions | → | 3D Roughened Surface | → | Roughened Surface+ Active Pores |

Examples

Clothing materials, low-drag surfaces (e.g. evolution to shark-skin profile), road-markings, high friction surfaces (shoe-soles, tyres), bio-active surface coatings, self-cleaning surfaces, table-tennis paddles, golf-club grips.

Reasons For Jumps

Evolution Stage	Reasons for Jumps
Smooth to Ribbed	-easier to grip -reduce aerodynamic drag -improve traction -improve drainage -improve heat transfer properties -increase surface area -improve aesthetic appearance -increase noise (road-lines) -create deliberate weak-point -improve location when joining to another object (e.g. toothed-belt)
Ribbed to 3D Roughened	-reduce drag -improve traction -improve grip -improve aerodynamic controllability -self-cleaning (Lotus Effect) -improve heat transfer -increase surface area -incorporate identification marks
3D Roughened to Active	-improve control under different conditions -reduce drag -incorporate change indicators -add a new useful function

Notes:

Companion to Space Segmentation trend. Again, 'active' is a useful idea trigger.

OBJECT SEGMENTATION

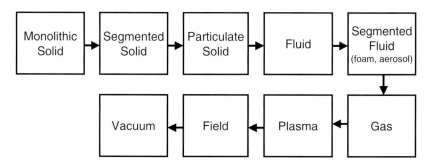

Examples

Bearing systems, Combustion fuels (coal to powdered coal to fluidised bed to gas), power transmission systems, conveyors, washing agents.

Reasons For Jumps

Evolution Stage	Reasons for Jumps
Monolithic to Segmented Solid	- easier to transport -easier to arrange/pack -increase surface area -increase perimeter -separate different functions -isolate stresses/loads
Segmented Solid to Particulate Solid	*as above*
Particulate Solid to Fluid	-improve transportability -reduce viscosity -increased system flexibility -improved compressive load handling -self-leveling capability -easier to control flow-rate -easier to mix with other substances (e.g. gels)
Fluid to Segmented Fluid	-increase surface area -separate different functions -isolate stresses/loads -increase mixing capability -increase dispersion rate -increase useful effect per mass of substance
Segmented Fluid to Gas	-increase surface area -reduced density -increase mixing capability -increase dispersion rate -increase effect per mass of substance -improve transportability

	-reduce viscosity -increase system flexibility -easier to control flow-rate
Gas to Plasma	-add new function -easier to mix -reduce density -increase energy flux-
Plasma to Field	-improve transmission of loads/energy/etc -reduce losses -increase flexibility -increase controllability -reduce use of substance
Field to Vacuum	(very few examples) -reduce use of substance

Notes:

Object segmentation is one of the over-riding 'do more with less' trends. It features major shifts from solid to liquid to gas to field states.

There is emerging evidence of an intermediate stage between 'field' and 'vacuum' which we might call 'sparse fields'. Certain computer applications are beginning to use this 'sparse' descriptor.

EVOLUTION MACRO TO NANO SCALE
(and beyond)

$10^2 \quad 10^1 \quad 10^0 \quad 10^{-1} \quad 10^{-2} \quad 10^{-3} \quad 10^{-4} \quad 10^{-5} \quad 10^{-6} \quad 10^{-7} \quad 10^{-8} \quad 10^{-9} \cdots$

Examples

Transistors, consideration of crystallography in construction of compounds, nano-tube material fibre inserts, micro-motors, nano-technologies – nano-robots, etc.

Reasons For Jumps

Evolution Stage	Reasons for Jumps
Any stage to the Next	- increased understanding of system structure - more effective use of resources - improve strength/weight ratio - reduced overall size of system - improve system performance efficiency - reduce losses

Notes:

This trend represents a general direction rather than containing a number of discrete stages. That being said, the world seems to be operating in jumps of 10^3 – such that we have micro- and now an emerging cluster of nano- technologies.

In a more general sense, it implies our increasing understanding of the world around us at molecular, atomic and sub-atomic levels.

Remember that the trend works in both a space (i.e. physical size) and a time context. In the case of evolution to the nano-scale in the time context we are interested in events taking place in ever smaller graduations of time.

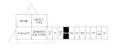

WEBS AND FIBRES

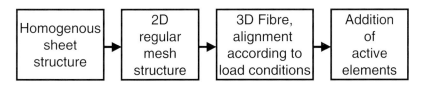

Examples

Aircraft wing construction (aluminium sheet to 3D lay-up carbon-fibre composite), Formula 1 car panels, chassis frame, chair design, golf-club shafts, solar arrays for space applications.

Reasons For Jumps

Evolution Stage	Reasons for Jumps
Homogenous to 2D regular mesh	-reduced use of materials -improved strength/weight ratio -increased flexibility -increased deformation capability
2D mesh to 3D fibre alignment	-alignment with dominant load paths leads to improved strength/weight - increased durability
3D to Active	-add new function -allow variation in properties

Notes:

Another trend that has emerged only relatively recently. Development has been paced by availability of design capability and (more importantly) manufacture technology.

'Active elements' phase has barely begun in any system.

DECREASING DENSITY

$$10^2 \quad 10^1 \quad 10^0 \quad 10^{-1} \quad 10^{-2} \quad 10^{-3} \quad 10^{-4} \quad 10^{-5} \quad 10^{-6} \quad 10^{-7} \quad 10^{-8} \quad 10^{-9} \ldots$$

Examples

Shift from Steel to titanium to TiAl alloys, steel to aluminium, metal to composites/plastics, evolution of plastics, polystyrene. Shifts taking place to some degree in just about every kind of product imaginable.

Reasons For Jumps

Evolution Stage	Reasons for Jumps
All the same	-increased strength/weight ratio -reduced consumption of material resource -increased component flexibility

Notes:

Another trend associated with the general theme 'doing more with less'. It has parallels with Inventive Principle 35B – changing the material used for a less dense one.

This trend is often used in combination with others related to achieving the same 'do more with less' goal – space segmentation, object segmentation, Mono-Bi-Poly (thinking about composites).

As illustrated in the trend graphic, this is a continuous evolution rather than one with discrete stages.

INCREASING ASYMMETRY
(To match External Asymmetries)

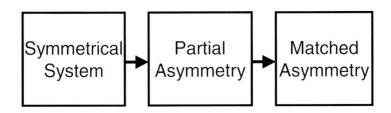

Examples

Most systems or components with ergonomic functional requirements – clothing, hand-grips, scissors, oven gloves, poke yoke assembly forms, cams, skewed normal distribution curves, spiral-forms

Reasons For Jumps

Evolution Stage	Reasons for Jumps
Symmetrical to Partial Asymmetry	-improved ergonomics -improved aesthetic appearance -poke yoke component assembly -ease of operation (spout on a jug) -more compact installation -varied motion control (cam) -orientation visibility
Partial Asymmetry to Matched Asymmetry	-improved ergonomics -improved aesthetic appearance -ease of operation

Notes:

The Asymmetry trend is relevant as many traditional manufacturing systems are tuned to mass-manufacture of symmetrical artefacts (e.g. turned on a lathe). Removal of these traditional constraints is resulting in significant shifts to matching form to suit the user.

The trend is heavily connected to human-interface issues in its engineering context.

The trend is very commonly observed in nature
(http://www.biology.ualberta.ca/palmer.hp/asym/asymmetry.htm#Small+Large).

BOUNDARY BREAKDOWN

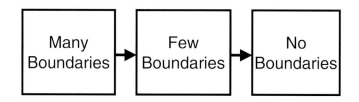

Examples

Turbine blades (evolution to 'single crystal' material structure – this is the trend operating at the micro-scale), manufacture flow-lines/cells, communication chains.

Reasons For Jumps

Evolution Stage	Reasons for Jumps
Many to Few	-improve reliability -improve strength properties -improve toughness -improve communications
Few to None	*as above*

Notes:

The main thought intended to be provoked through comparing this trend to a given innovation situation, is one of interfaces; interfaces generally mean weak-points and inefficiencies, and evolution suggests we gradually get better at eliminating them.

The trend can contain both continuous and discrete stages.

Note that this trend has connections to both space and interface aspects.

GEOMETRIC EVOLUTION
(Linear)

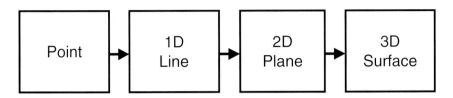

Examples

CAD systems, drinking straws, paper joining, clothes fasteners, spray nozzles, aerodynamic surfaces, pipes, door handles, car-lights, car windshields, cutlery.

Reasons For Jumps

Evolution Stage	Reasons for Jumps
Point to Line	-improve load distribution -improve flow distribution -improve integrity of a join -increase hydraulic diameter -increase surface area -change aspect ratio -create ability to identify/change component orientation -improve ability to see object
Line to Plane	-improve load distribution -improve flow distribution -improve strength properties -improve moment of inertia -improve location for two joining parts -increase surface area -add new function
Plane to 3D Surface	-improve compatibility with 'real world' effects -improve structural strength -improve aesthetics -improve ergonomics -improve surface area -add new function

Notes:

The geometric evolution is very closely linked to manufacturing technology. We live in a three-dimensional world, but many of the artefacts that we traditionally make to exist in it are dominated by one- and two- dimensional manufacturing systems. Many of these traditional limitations are disappearing with the emergence of new manufacture capabilities. In mechanical systems, there are currently considerable evolution opportunities in looking for the benefits to be had by shifting a 1D or 2D manufactured object to fully utilise the third dimension.

GEOMETRIC EVOLUTION
(Volumetric)

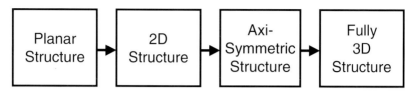

Examples

CAD systems, fuel tanks/containers, aerodynamic structures, watering can, furniture, car headlights, ergonomic keyboards, hi-fi speakers.

Reasons For Jumps

Evolution Stage	Reasons for Jumps
Planar to 2D	-improve load distribution -improve flow distribution -increase surface area -change aspect ratio -create ability to identify/change component orientation -add a new useful function-
2D to Axi-symmetric	-improve load distribution -improve flow distribution -improve strength properties -improve moment of inertia -improve location for two joining parts -increase surface area -add new function
Axi-symmetric to Fully 3D	-improve compatibility with 'real world' effects -improve structural strength -improve aesthetics -improve ergonomics -improve surface area -add new function

Note:

This trend like the previous geometric evolution (linear) one is very closely linked to manufacturing technology. We live in a three-dimensional world, but many of the artefacts that we traditionally make to exist in it are manufactured by machines limited to operate in one or two-dimensions. There are currently a significant number of opportunities for evolution along this trend as manufacturing systems evolve.

DYNAMIZATION

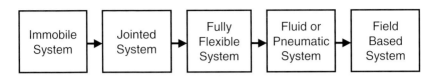

Examples

Steering systems, power transmission means, window blinds, doors/security systems, medical stent, ruler/measuring devices, chair, desk-lamps, sound recording (vinyl to tape to optical).

Reasons For Jumps

Evolution Stage	Reasons for Jumps
Immobile to Jointed	-fold to make more compact -maneuverability -increase positional flexibility -mechanical 2-way switching -solving physical contradiction (e.g. wide and narrow) -variable deflector (e.g. flap on aircraft wing) -compound properties (e.g. stiff and flexible parts) -damage protection
Jointed to Multiple Jointed	- more compact folding -positional flexibility -multi-way switching -compound properties
Multiple Jointed to Fully Flexible	-positional flexibility -smooth deflection -compact installation -continuous variability -impact load damage resistance
Fully Flexible to Fluid/Pneumatic	-positional flexibility -improve power/weight ratio -improve strength/wt -increase reliability -increase convenience
Fluid/Pneumatic to Field	-increase reliability -increase operation flexibility -increase efficiency -increase control precision -increase power density -increase ability to change system characteristics

Note:

Like object segmentation, this trend features major jumps from mechanical to fluid to gaseous to field based systems.

ACTION CO-ORDINATION

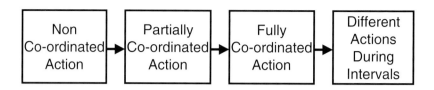

Examples

Manufacture processes, manufacture scheduling (run factory at full capacity irrespective of demand; manufacture to forecast; pull-based manufacture to order systems), refrigerator pump systems (controlling temperature), bearing lubrication systems, chemical reactions.

Reasons For Jumps

Evolution Stage	Reasons for Jumps
Non-Co-ordinated to Partially Co-ordinated	-reduce time wastage -increase system efficiency -improve response to external changes -improve safety -reduce likelihood of system damage -reduce system wear -increase user convenience
Partially Co-ordinated to Fully Co-ordinated	as above
Fully Co-ordinated to Action During Interval	-insert a new useful function -improve overall efficiency -increase user convenience -improve safety

Notes:

The key connecting word in this trend is 'action' – what actions are being performed in the system being investigated?

The 'Action during interval' evolution step could actually be seen as an example of the Mono-Bi-Poly trend. It is included here as a stage in this trend because the explicit evolution trigger 'can you find any intervals in your current system?' is not covered explicitly enough in the Mono-Bi-Poly trend.

This trend relates to both time and interface aspects of the trend clusters.

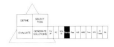

RHYTHM CO-ORDINATION

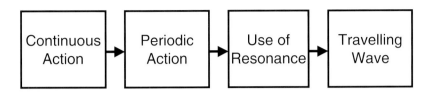

Examples

Bottle-cleaning operations, insect locomotion, vacuum cleaner suction actions (continuous to periodic), dough-mixers, paint-stripping, automobile braking systems, propulsion systems.

Reasons For Jumps

Evolution Stage	Reasons for Jumps
Continuous to Periodic	-reduction in energy usage -overcome a physical contradiction (separated in time) -increase efficiency of useful effect -introduce time measurement capability -reduce waste
Periodic to Use of Resonance	-take advantage of force lever offered by resonance: -increase magnitude of useful effect -increase efficiency of useful effect -reduce energy usage -reduce waste -reduce system complexity -reduce cost (resonance is a free resource)
Resonance to Travelling Wave	-increase efficiency -reduce system complexity -reduce energy usage -reduce cost

Notes:

Many systems will be found at the left hand end of this trend. This is at least partially because resonance is usually viewed as a 'bad' thing. The trend shows that (like the Inventive Principle 'Blessing in Disguise' – Chapter 10) somewhere resonance can be put to useful effect. There is considerable evolutionary potential in this trend for many systems.

Locomotion in nature offers many examples of this trend in action.

(Matching To External) NON-LINEARITIES

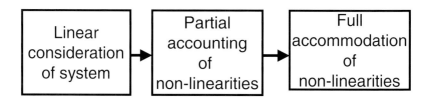

Examples

Safety razors that 'recognise' the presence of local bumps and hollows, aircraft with wake turbulence or wind-shear sensors, turbulators on wing suction surfaces.

Reasons For Jumps

Evolution Stage	Reasons for Jumps
All the same	-(all trimming options aimed at maintaining or improving functionality) -reduced complexity -reduced manufacture cost -improved reliability -improved maintainability -improved user safety -reduced likelihood of (cliff-edge) catastrophic failure

Notes:

Another emerging trends – the large majority of technical systems are designed to avoid exposure to non-linear areas of operation by being forced to stay within established envelopes of known safe operation. Unfortunately, we sometimes get these boundaries wrong, or accommodation of their existence unduly compromises the performance of the system. As described in 'Extending TRIZ to Help Solve Non-Linear Problems' (paper presented at TRIZCON2002, St Louis, April 2002, authors – Apte, P., Mann, D.L.), a growing number of designers are beginning to find ways of identifying non-linearities and producing contradiction-breaking designs to cope with them.

MONO-BI-POLY
(Similar)

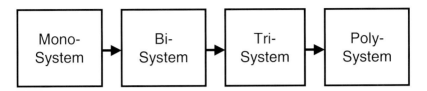

Examples

Turbine blades, compressor/fan blades, tines on a fork, teeth on a zip fastener, teeth on a comb, bristles on a brush, pages in a book, connections in a pipe, number of sections in a telescopic aerial, lenses in a camera, single to double to triple CDs.

Reasons For Jumps

Evolution Stage	Reasons for Jumps
Any stage to the Next	- improve amount of useful function deliverable -improved function distribution (e.g. load spreading) -improve user convenience -synergy effects -reduced cost per system component

Notes:

The principal issue with the M-B-P trend is that a point is reached, beyond which it is no longer possible to continue obtaining benefit by adding any more of the similar objects:

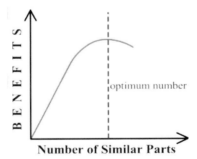

Number of Similar Parts

The equation determining what exactly this optimum number is may be relatively fixed (e.g. the number of tines on a fork is unlikely to shift from the optimum four), it may also be highly dynamic. This is especially so when considering that the top and bottom halves of the ideality equation both change as more things are added to a system. The conflict between increased benefits of adding more versus the almost inevitably increased cost with adding more can be a turbulent one – see the shifting 'optimum' number of blades to be found on wind-turbines for example.

Applies to both time and interface issues.

MONO-BI-POLY
(Various)

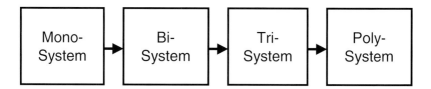

| Mono-System | → | Bi-System | → | Tri-System | → | Poly-System |

Examples

Swiss Army knife, computer software packages, computer peripherals, hi-fi systems, wrist-watches, mobile phones, keyboard synthesisers, cameras and lenses, home entertainment centres, power-tool attachments.

Reasons For Jumps

Evolution Stage	Reasons for Jumps
Any stage to the Next	-increased system functionality -increased operability -increased user convenience -reduced packaging -(synergy effects) -reduced number of systems -reduced net system size

Notes:
The principal issue with the M-B-P(Various) trend, like M-B-P(Similar) is that a point is reached, beyond which it is no longer possible to continue obtaining benefit by adding any more of the different objects:

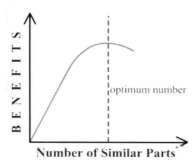

Applies to both time and interface aspects.

MONO-BI-POLY
(Increasing Differences)

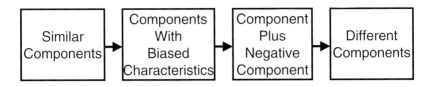

Examples

Coloured pencils (negative component = eraser on end of pencil), tool-set (negative components = (e.g. nail-puller on hammer), stapler with staple remover, one-way glass.

Reasons For Jumps

Evolution Stage	Reasons for Jumps
Similar to Biased	-increased system functionality -increased operability -increased ability to adapt to different use circumstances -increased user convenience -(synergy effects)
Biased to Negative	-add ability to achieve the opposite function -increased adaptability -increase operational flexibility -reduced packaging -(synergy effects) -increase user convenience
Negative to Different Components	-increased system functionality -increased operability -increased user convenience -reduced packaging -(synergy effects) -reduced number of systems -reduced net system size

Notes:

The jump to the 'negative' component (i.e. that component that delivers the opposite function to the exiting function) is a very important one – someone, somewhere can make positive use of a system that delivers the opposite function to that conventionally expected. For example, there is a whole emerging class of so-called 'negative materials' featuring negative thermal expansion coefficients, negative Poisson's Ratio, negative wear, etc.

The timing of these jumps to negative is difficult to predict as the size of market for the negative thing, if it doesn't already exist is unknown, and hence risk is high.

REDUCED DAMPING

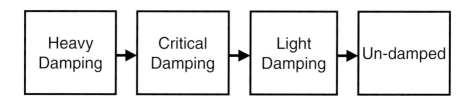

Examples

Aircraft flight control architecture, hydraulic systems, computer chip buffering.

Reasons For Jumps

Evolution Stage	Reasons for Jumps
All the same	-reduced energy loss in system -improved dynamic performance -improved response time

Notes:

The trend towards reduced damping demands a parallel increase in control capability in order to enable function to be delivered safely - in this sense it is fundamentally coupled to evolution along the controllability trend.

This trend is still at a relatively immature stage – being largely dependent on the emergence of sophisticated control algorithms and hardware.

INCREASING USE OF SENSES

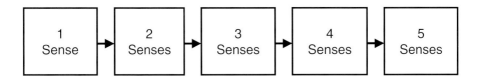

Examples

Silent movies – talking pictures – 'Sensurround' – addition of smell, taste, multi-media computers, virtual reality, theatre, communications in general (e.g. emergence of video-phones), food products.

Reasons For Jumps

Evolution Stage	Reasons for Jumps
Any stage to the Next	- improved interaction control - increased human involvement - 'sensual immersion' - improved realism of simulation-

Notes:

The trend is about increasing interaction of systems with human faculties. The trend relates only to the number of trends incorporated into a system not the sequence.

In all there are five key senses involved in the trend – visual, auditory, kinaesthetic (touch), olfactory and gustatory (taste). The acronym VAKOG is widely used to assist in the remembering of these senses.

INCREASING USE OF COLOUR

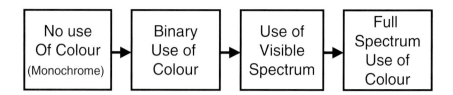

Examples

Photography, film, thermal management on space systems, manufacturing inspection systems, pressure/temperature sensitive paints, active camouflage systems.

Reasons For Jumps

Evolution Stage	Reasons for Jumps
Monochrome to Binary	-ability to make simple yes/no measurement -warning indicator -improved aesthetic appearance -improved radiation heat management
Binary to Visible Spectrum	-increased flexibility of measurement -improved aesthetic appearance-
Visible to Full Spectrum	-eliminate interference with human interfaces -add new function through employment of effects present (e.g. use IR to achieve heat-seeking capability) -increased range of measurement possibilities

Notes:

Full spectrum includes infra-red and ultra-violet – both of which are increasingly being used to achieve previously untapped benefits.

Colour is rarely viewed as a resource in many engineering systems; the trend shows that someone, somewhere has found an advantage in making use of colour.

INCREASING TRANSPARENCY

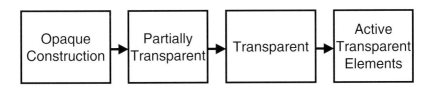

Examples

Building facades, automobile transparencies, see-through packaging, viewing windows in ovens, fire-glass, variable opacity (electro-chromic) glazing systems, cassette tapes, iMac, glass-bottomed boat.

Reasons For Jumps

Evolution Stage	Reasons for Jumps
Opaque to partially transparent	-increased natural illumination -save energy -increased visibility for safety -ease of inspection -aesthetic appeal
Partially transparent to transparent	-ease of inspection -save energy/energy management -aesthetic appeal -impression of reduced size
Transparent to active transparent	-add new function/integration of other functions -allow variation in properties

Notes:

Another recently codified trend. Originated by S. Dewulf and reported in TRIZ Journal, June 2002.

Architects talk about this trend towards increased use of transparency the 'perennial fight for light'. The search for a substance with the transparency of glass and the structural strength of aluminium is a long sought after goal.

CUSTOMER PURCHASE FOCUS

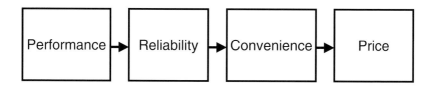

| Performance | Reliability | Convenience | Price |

Examples

Automobiles, hydraulic components, filters, light-bulbs, CDs, computer hard-drives, televisions, video/DVD players, mobile phones, just about anything that has become 'commoditised'.

Reasons For Jumps

Evolution Stage	Reasons for Jumps
All the same	-customers desire for more of the parameter has been fulfilled -competitive advantage -overcomes common problem of technology capability overtaking customer requirement

Notes:

This trend operates a little differently to most of the others. The jumps from stage to stage here are made when a given customer has received 'enough' of the current purchase focus. Most car-buyers for example care little about better car performance, and most have shifted to purchasing 'reliability'. Anyone still interested in high performance is unlikely to be unduly concerned by reliability, convenience or prices.

The trend is related to positions on the s-curve for a system:

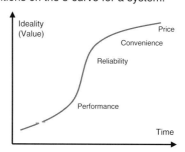

Different customers will be at different positions along the trend.
Trend is based on Windermere Associates model described in 'The Innovator's Dilemma by Clayton Christensen (Reference 13.2).

MARKET EVOLUTION

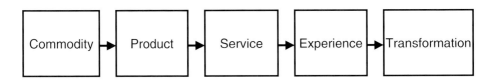

Examples

Commodities – steel, aluminium, timber, chemicals, generic drugs, filters, CDs, videos,etc.
Products – cars, phones, televisions, DVD players, washing machines, etc
Services - Clean clothes, power-by-the-hour, fast food, package holidays, home delivery, car rental, library, hotel shuttle, contract cleaning
Experiences – Disney, adventure sports, McDonalds,
Transformation – personal trainers

Reasons For Jumps

Evolution Stage	Reasons for Jumps
All the same	Customer expectations increase with time If you stand still, you are actually going backwards. In order to remain competitive, you should be looking to the right along the trend

Notes:

This trend is focused on the recipients of the products and processes we design. The trend emerges from the work of B.J.Pine in his book 'The Experience Economy' (Harvard Business School Press, 1999)

The idea that we are actually going backwards if we are standing still on this trend comes from the quality work of Kano – and the idea that things over time our expectations as customers increase such that the things that used to 'excite' us – air-conditioning in cars for example – rapidly become the norm and we become dis-satisfied if they are suddenly not there.

Appropriate use of the trend requires adequate customer data.

DESIGN POINT

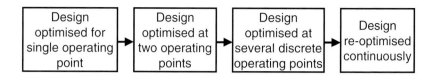

Examples

Aircraft optimised for 'cruise' operation, jet-engine design, variable valve timing in internal combustion engines, 'self-tuning' engines, electro-rheological suspension systems.

Reasons For Jumps

Evolution Stage	Reasons for Jumps
All the same	-improved performance at all operating conditions -reduced energy loss -increased user operational flexibility -broader operating range -increased operating safety margin -solving a physical contradiction

Notes:

This is another emergent trend. Many technical systems have their performance optimised at a single condition – most conventional internal combustion engines optimised to achieve optimum fuel burn at a certain level of rpm, various 'constant-speed', 'constant-flow', 'constant-x' systems (helicopter rotor, fans, electric motors, aerosol sprays, etc). This trend is emerging to help reduce inefficiencies as the system in question operates at points distant from the optimum design point.

The trend is related in several senses to the Mono-Bi-Poly trend. It is included as a specific reminder of the importance of thinking about design point, and because the idea of 'continuously re-optimised' designs does not emerge from M-B-P thinking adequately.

The trend also operates strongly in combination with the 'smart materials' trend.

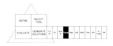

DEGREES OF FREEDOM

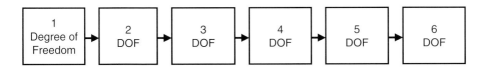

| 1 Degree of Freedom | 2 DOF | 3 DOF | 4 DOF | 5 DOF | 6 DOF |

Examples

Machine tools, flight simulators, gear-shifts in manual drive cars, robot limb joints, universal joint, cranes, computer mouse (still plenty of degrees left though!).

Reasons For Jumps

Evolution Stage	Reasons for Jumps
All the same	-increase operability -increase positional flexibility -improved co-ordination with human actions -improved dynamic response

Notes:

The degrees of freedom relate primarily to three linear dimensions (x, y, and z), and three rotations about these orthogonal axes:

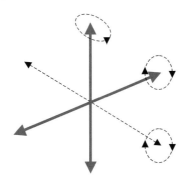

TRIMMING

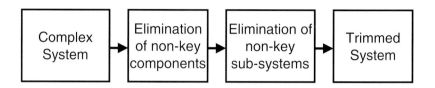

Examples

Machine-from-solid components replacing assemblies, castings, one-piece syringe, advanced computer keyboards, mini hi-fi systems, mobile phones.

Reasons For Jumps

Evolution Stage	Reasons for Jumps
Complex to Elimination of components	-reduced complexity -reduced manufacture cost -improved reliability -improved maintainability

Notes:

All trimming operations are aimed at reducing part-count/overall complexity of a system without negative impact on functionality.

The trend has strong links with Design for Manufacture and Assembly (Chapter 17).

The main thing to remember about the trend is that there are times in the evolution of a system when trimming is an appropriate action, and times when it is not:

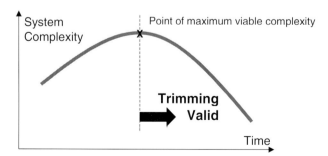

CONTROLLABILITY

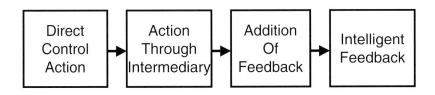

Examples

Switching devices, window open-close mechanisms in greenhouses, steering systems (intelligent feedback – systems that adapt and optimise to an individual user), bottle filling systems, petrol pumps, auto-focus cameras, street-lighting.

Reasons For Jumps

Evolution Stage	Reasons for Jumps
Direct Control to Use of Intermediary	-improved user safety -reduced user effort-
Intermediary to Feedback	-system self-correction -reduced likelihood of error/catastrophic failure -ability to control function delivery to specified requirements -improved user-proofing -reduced user involvement
Feedback to Intelligent Feedback	-adaptive systems -self-learning systems -self-repairing systems -reduced likelihood of failure due to system non-linearities

Notes:

The advent of cheap micro-processors means that many systems have now evolved to the 'feedback' stage. There is still considerable remaining evolutionary potential left in the remaining jump to intelligent feedback systems.

The Controllability trend is the most common example of the phenomenon 'the need for the system disappears' when the end of this trend has been reached. I.e. something else already in the system performs the function of the control system – the system becomes 'self-controlling'.

REDUCING HUMAN INVOLVEMENT

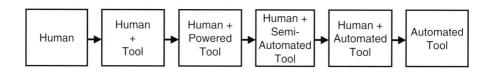

Examples

Use of computer aided systems, person to map to GPS to auto-navigation systems, DIY tools, machine tools, ready-prepared meals, domestic heating systems, cooking methods, genetic algorithms/self-learning software systems.

Reasons For Jumps

Evolution Stage	Reasons for Jumps
Any stage to the Next	-reduced human drudgery -reduced likelihood of 'human error' effects -increased accuracy -ability to deliver extremes of a function outside the human range – e.g. lifting, joining, throwing, etc -reduction of fatigue effects -reduced cost

Note:

'Tool' should be interpreted in the trend in its most general possible sense – i.e. as the thing that delivers an action onto an object.

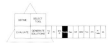

DESIGN METHODOLOGY

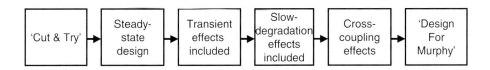

Examples

A general trend observable across many industries – automotive, fast-moving consumer goods, aerospace. Nuclear and space represent the state of the art in terms of 'if anything can go wrong, it will go wrong design philosophy.

Reasons For Jumps

Evolution Stage	Reasons for Jumps
'Cut & Try' to Steady-state	-improved use of design resources -reduced waste in development time/cost -reduced waste of materials -reduced product development time
Steady-state to transient to slow degradation to cross-coupling	-improve product reliability
Any of the above to 'Design for Murphy'	-improve reliability -enable easy shift to 'functional sales model'

Notes:

This trend is closely linked to drives for improved reliability in systems. See Chapter 20 for more details on this trend in operation.

Generally speaking, if the design methods you are using are not at the right hand end of the trend, someone out there has already identified ways to allow you to do a better job.

Examples of the different stages of the trend:-
Transient – taking account of temporary effects – acceleration, deceleration, start-up, stopping, etc
Slow-degradation – taking account of things like wear, fatigue, effect of contaminants, etc
Cross-coupling – recognising that things in a system that should in theory have no effect on one another can sometimes actually have a cross-linking effect. The design of the rear axle of a car, for example, at one time as thought to be completely independent of the front axle design. Today, most companies think the same thing about the rear-axle and the air-conditioning system (to take an extreme example) – prevailing logic says the performance of one ill not impact on the performance of the other. The cross-coupling effect says that one is actually quite likely to affect the long term behaviour of the other.
Design for Murphy – under normal circumstances, if a customer does something stupid with a product, they pay the consequences; under emerging 'service' markets, the supplier is increasingly liable for these consequences. It is thus becoming important to include consideration of 'if the customer can do something stupid with this, they will' into the design process.

REDUCING NUMBER OF ENERGY CONVERSIONS
(Tending to Zero)

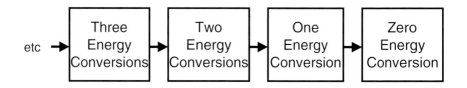

Examples

Car with internal combustion engine converts chemical to heat to mechanical,
Aircraft - chemical to heat to mechanical to pressure (prop) to chemical-heat-pressure
(turbojet), locomotives.

Reasons For Jumps

Evolution Stage	Reasons for Jumps
Any stage to the Next	-improved system efficiency -reduce waste/waste products -reduced overall system complexity -reduced weight -reduced harmful side effects -increase reliability -reduce cost

Notes:

Corollary - energy usage tends towards use of free and readily available sources - e.g.
increasing moves towards of wind, wave and solar energy sources.

Perhaps the most significant role of this trend is to encourage the problem solver to focus
on energy flows within a system and the management of those flows. This is particularly
important when managing system inefficiencies.

14.
Problem Solving Tools
Resources

"Do you mind if I use your back legs as a towel horse?
Rabbit to Winnie the Pooh after Pooh gets wedged in Rabbit's front door.

Resources play a big part throughout the systematic creativity process. We encounter them as an integral part of the problem definition process (Chapter 5) and conceptually, we are being encouraged to maximise the effective use of resources (defined as we have read earlier as 'anything in or around the system not being used to its maximum advantage – including the harmful things') in every part of the generate solutions part of the process.

The basic idea behind this 'problem solving' chapter is to achieve two basic goals:-
1) Provide a database of resource triggers to help us to recognise things that we might not normally view as 'resources'.
2) Recommend strategies successfully used by others to turn unexpected and harmful things into useful resources.

Resource Identification Triggers

There are two main ways of identifying resources within a system. The first way links in with the Trends of Evolution in the previous chapter. There we saw the concept of 'evolutionary potential' and the idea of a radar-plot as a means of describing how much further a given system is able to evolve. In terms of these plots (Figure 14.1), every bit of unused evolutionary potential represents a resource.

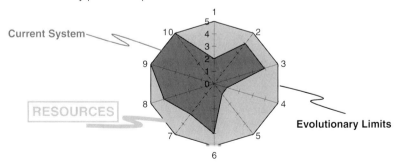

Figure 14.1: Evolutionary Potential Radar Plots as Resource Identifier

The second means of identifying things that can be utilised as resources is to provide a series of lists of things that other problem solvers in other fields have at some time successfully harnessed as resources. We present these lists here with the expectation that

you will peruse through them when in a position where you are looking to explore the complete resource space in and around the system you are evaluating.

For ease of use, the resource trigger lists have been segmented into the following major categories:-

- Resources in the Environment
- Low-Cost /Plentiful Resources
- Material Resources
- Transforming/Modifying Substances
- Manufacturing Resources
- Resources Associated With Humans

For all of the trigger lists, data has been arranged in terms of relevance to space, time and interface categories, in line with the importance of space-time-interface conceptual thinking in TRIZ. The basic recommended means of using the lists is simply as a series of memory joggers. The problem solver is effectively being prompted to ask the question 'is resource X present in my system, and if it is, could I harness it as a resource?'

Resources in the Environment

The atmosphere:-

Constitution of air (% by volume)

Nitrogen	N_2	78.084
Oxygen	O_2	20.946
Argon	Ar	0.934
Neon	Ne	0.0018
Helium	He	0.000524
Methane	CH_4	0.0002
Krypton	Kr	0.000114
Hydrogen	H_2	0.00005
Nitrous oxide	N_2O	0.00005
Xenon	Xe	0.0000087

Resource	Typical Value
Density (kg/m3)	1 ?
Temperature/Gradient (°C)	15
Pressure/Gradient (Pa)	101325
Altitude (m above sea level)	0
Velocity	0
Gravitational Force (m/s2)	9.807
Thermal Conductivity (W/mK)	0.0242

336

Index of refraction	1.00029
Peak Sunlight Intensity (W/m^2)	1600
Mean Sunlight Intensity (W/m^2)	250
Opacity (ppm particulates)	40
Speed of sound (m/s)	339
Viscosity (cP)	0.0171
Water vapour content (%)	4
Relative Humidity (%)	80

Other Environment Resources:-

Context	Resource
Space	Mass of earth, density Water – sea, river, rain
Time	Cycle of sun, moon, planets, stars, tides, Speed of sound (variation with density) Speed of light
Interface	Sound attenuation (frequency dependence) Nitrogen cycle Carbon Cycle

Low-Cost Resources

These resources can be useful if we determine that we are unable to solve a problem with a system using the resources it presently contains, and are fundamentally required to add something. The following are all readily available things:

Context	Resource
Space	Rock, stone, sand (silicates), earth, clay, chalk, dust Timber, biomass, natural fibres – hemp, hair, Water, steam, ice, salt, hydrates, cavitation bubbles Foams (Reference 14.1) Aerosols, Smoke Air, voids
Time	Sun-dial (shadow), resonance
Interface	Earth's magnetic field, sunlight, wind, rain, lightning UV, IR Barometric pressure/variation with altitude Ambient temperature/variation with altitude

Manufacture Process Type Resources:

Manufacture processes are often at the root of a contradiction between benefits and cost. As described in some of the Trends of evolution (and particularly geometric evolution) in Chapter 13, there are many evolution opportunities available through better design using all of the available dimensions, degrees of freedom, etc, but which are not exploited due to limitations of the processes used to manufacture the artefact. This list highlights manufacture processes that may enable such limitations to be overcome.

Context	Resource
Mechanical (Also Reference 14.1)	Conventional machine tools – lathe, mill, drill, grind, etc Forging – hot, cold Punches, dies and presses Electro-discharge machining Electro-chemical machining Explosive forming Sand-casting Centrifugal casting Lost-wax casting Single-crystal casting Soldering/brazing Friction welding Electron-beam welding MIG/TIG/arc welding Laser drill/cutter/heat-treatment Etching – Chemical, photo, laser Flame spray Ultrasound cutter Sintering/Firing Extrusion Film-blowing Moulding – injection, blow, compression, reaction-injection Shot-blasting/Shot-peening/Laser shot-peening Rapid prototyping – stereolithography, selective laser sintering, Fused deposition, inkjet systems/3D-printing, shape-metal deposition Nano-clustering
Chemical	Acylation Alkylation – oxygen, nitrogen Amination Bio-accumulation Blending Bromination Carboxylation, De-carboxylation Chiral Synthesis Chlorination Condensation Cyanation, Cyanoethylation Diazotation Distillation Enantiomeric Reduction, Resolution Fermentation Fluorination Fractionation Friedel-Craft Reactions Granulation Hydrogenation, Dehydrogenation Iodination Lithiation (BuLi, LDA) Methylation Nitration Organometallations

Oxidation	
Phosphorylation, Phosgenation	
Polymerisation	
Reductions (Metal Hydrides)	
Sulphonation	
Thiolation, Thiocarbonylation	

Materials

Inventive Principles 35 and 40 and trends like 'decreasing density' all indicate the more effective selection and use of materials when assembling systems. This list highlights basic material selection triggers.

Material Family	Principal Elements	Main Types
Metals & Alloys	Li, Be, Na, Mg, Al, K, Ca, Sc, Ti, V, Cr, Mn, Fe, Co, Ni, Cu, Zn, Ga, Rb, Sr, Y, Zr, Nb, Mo, Tc, Ru, Rh, Pd, Ag, Cd, In, Sn, Sb, Cs, Ba, La, Ce, Pr, Nd, Pm, Sm, Eu, Gd, Tb, Dy, Ho, Er, Tm, Yb, Lu, Hf, Ta, W, Re, Os, Ir, Pt, Au, Hg, Tl, Pb, Bi, Fr, Ra, Ac, Th, Pa, U, Np, Pl, Am, Cm, Bk, Cf, Es, Fm, Md, No, Lr	(Reference 14.3, 14.4, 14.5) (Emerging alloys – TiAl, NiAl, SMA)
Ceramics & Glasses	H, Li, Be, B, C, N, O, F, Na, Mg, Al, Si, P, S, Cl, K, Ca, Sc, Ti, V, Cr, Mn, Fe, Co, Ni, Cu, Zn, Ga, Ge, As, Se, Br, Rb, Sr, Y, Zr, Nb, Mo, Ru, Rh, Pd, Ag, Cd, In, Sn, Sb, Te, I, Cs, Ba, La, Ce, Pr, Nd, Sm, Eu, Gd, Tb, Dy, Ho, Er, Tm, Yb, Lu, Hf, Ta, W, Re, Os, Ir, Pt, Au, Hg, Tl, Pb, Bi	Oxides Silica (SiO_2)– fibre optics Aluminium, magnesium, mullite, zirconium Carbides Diamond, graphite, SiC, Tungsten carbide Nitrides Boron, silicon Glasses Silica, soda-lime, lead, borosilicate
Polymers	H, C, N, O, F, Si, P, S, Cl	Polyethylene, Polypropylene, Polystyrene, Polyvinyl-Chloride (these make up 85% of all polymers)
Semi-conductors	B, C, O, Al, Si, P, S, Zn, Ga, Ge, As, Se, Cd, In, Sn, Sb, Te, Hg, Tl, Pb	Silicon
Composites	Polymer/ceramic Metal/ceramic	GRP, Carbon-fibre Wood TiMMC, AlMMC

Special Properties/Modifications Resources

Resources for solving contradictions – particularly of the physical sort, where we want conflicting attributes – stiff and flexible, hot and cold, big and small, weak and strong, attract and repel, on and off, etc.

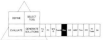

Context	Resource
Space	Asymmetry, local-modification to geometry
	Voids – bubbles, negative Poisson's Ratio
Time	Constant fields, variable fields
	Oscillating Fields – frequency, amplitude, phase, compound
	Pulsating Fields – period, amplitude, duration, compound
	Resonance – natural frequency, higher order harmonics,
	Travelling wave – single, multiple, compound
Interface	Strong Taste
	Strong Odour
	Colour change – thermo, electro, photo, pressure
	Variable transparency/opacity – thermo, electro, photo
	Luminescence/fluorescence
	Friction coefficient – low, high
	Restitution ratio – low, high,
	Deformable – tension, compression, torsional
	Breakable – fuse, fail-safe, designed weak-points
	Ferromagnetic – solid, powder, ferro-fluids
	Piezo-electric – forward and reverse
	Dielectric
	Variable viscosity – electro-rheological, rheopexic
	Anisotropy
	X-ray sensitive
	Radiation sensitive
	Electrical conductivity – super-conductivity, semi-conductive, variable
	Chemically reactive – exothermic, endothermic, reversible
	Liquid – absorbent, repellent
	Explosive
	Bio-compatible
	Adhesive –triggered by water, light, air, pressure, temperature

Resources Associated With Humans

Many systems used by humans make inadequate recognition of the resources that humans possess. Here are some of the things that can help to use existing human resources more effectively:

Context	Resource
Space	Mass, height, shape, physiology (Reference 14.5)
Time	Natural frequency of different body parts
	Pulse, pulse variation,
	Blink rate, breathing rate
Interface	Heat generation, variation in temperature
	Motive power – 0.75hp peak, 0.33hp mean
	Sweat
	Oxygen absorption
	CO_2 generation
	Urea production, water, solid waste
	Senses - VAKOG

'Unexpected' Resources and Turning Harm Into Good

Tales of the Unexpected – a simple but often effective problem solving strategy involves examining the components in a system, picking out an unlikely one and asking the question 'how can this component be turned into a useful resource?' This kind of provocation can often generate some surprising new thoughts.

By way of example, we were once asked to solve a problem at a charity-run walled garden situated on a hillside in the middle of nowhere. The garden had a number of outbuildings and running water but no electrical power. The local electricity supplier quoted the charity a completely unaffordable amount of money to lay a power-line to the garden. The anticipated power requirement was relatively low (boiling kettles, etc). The challenge was to get power to the garden with minimum expense.

An initial run through the problem explorer part of the systematic creativity process (Chapter 5) did not reveal any solutions of great merit, albeit there were several possibilities for generating electricity using wind-power. The only affordable one of these involved the creation of a crude vertical axis wind-turbine constructed from the two semi-circular halves of an oil-drum welded edge to edge driving a scrap alternator from a car. The calculations suggested that such a device was not going to generate sufficient power. The compromise solution was going to involve constructing two or three of the turbines. Then we decided to look again for resources. As a part of this re-visiting exercise, we made the very simple provocation 'how could we make the wall into a resource?' – the wall being, we thought, one of the least likely of the things present at the garden to help generate electrical power. But then simply forcing ourselves to keep trying to turn it into a resource, we eventually hit upon the idea of combining the oil-drum turbine with the wall. What we came up with is illustrated in Figure 14.2.

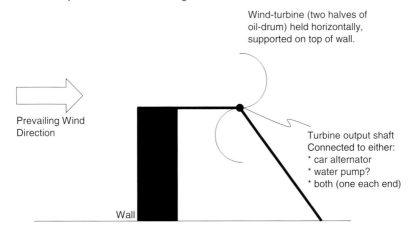

Figure 14.2: Novel Wind-Turbine Design Suggested by Using the Wall as a Resource

The basic idea produced three useful benefits; firstly it could act as a shield to the non-working side of the oil-drum wind turbine - thus increasing the efficiency very significantly as there was suddenly none of the wind force trying to resist the rotation of the drum as would normally be the case (in fact we later estimated an overall increase in aerodynamic efficiency from around 27% to over 60%); secondly it would minimise eye-sore impact; and

thirdly the wall would be able to support much of the weight of the turbine - thus the remaining support structure could be made very simple, light and, most important of all, cheap.

Moral of the story; even the most unexpected things in a system can turn out to be useful resources if we force ourselves to think about it hard enough. The same goes for things in the system we currently view as harmful:

Turning Harm Into Good – the same basic provocation 'how can this component be turned into a useful resource?' as described above can be taken a step further and applied to things in the system we are currently seeing as bad things. 'How can this bad thing be turned into a useful resource?' is thus a good start point for some serious thinking about turning harm into good.

Related to this basic start point are the follow up questions:-

- under what circumstances would the bad thing become a good thing? (and how could we make these circumstances happen?)
- who might view the bad thing as a good thing? Why?
- where might the bad thing be seen as a good thing?

Resonance is an attribute that most engineers are taught is a bad thing, which indeed it can be in the wrong situation. But, as can be seen from the rhythm co-ordination trend in Chapter 17, it can be become a useful resource if we think hard enough about it. In very simple terms, resonance is the natural property of all systems to be able to amplify a small input signal into a much bigger output signal. One of the tricks with turning resonance into a resource, therefore, is to identify those situations where such an amplification can be put to good use.

Cleaning bottles perhaps offers a good example of putting resonance to good use; traditionally, bottling plants cleaned out returned bottles by inverting them and injecting a jet of water up into them. This was found to be relatively inefficient, and required a large quantity of water. Then – in keeping with the rhythm co-ordination trend – it was discovered that by pulsing the water jet, not only was less water required, but that the cleaning action was also improved. Then resonance was identified as a resource and the idea of pulsing the water jet at the resonant frequency of the bottles came about. This design meant that the bottles resonated and thus helped to dislodge any dirt or contamination during the cleaning process. Thus the resonant frequency of the bottle was harnessed and put to good use. Cleaning operations in general, in fact, offer good examples of resonance being put to useful effect – vacuum cleaners, paint-strippers, chemical-strippers, etc could all be modified to make use of resonance.

Other examples of things traditionally viewed as 'bad' being turned into useful resources:-
- Pressure – especially in things like seals, there is a strong inclination to fight pressure. This results in bulky and complex designs; worse still, the higher the pressure, the bulkier and more complex the designs we produce. Smart seal designers recognize that if they harness the pressure rather than trying to fight it, much more elegant solutions can be achieved.
- Surface Tension – an attribute that all liquids possess that most designers tend to think of as a nuisance. In resource terms, surface tension effects represent unused energy sources that can be harnessed to achieve a useful function – for example, surface tension effects are used during the melted phase of the

manufacture of composites to create a pre-compression effect, which in turn enables a self-repairing capability to be provided in the finished material.

- Centrifugal Forces – in any rotating system, designers have a similar inclination to design components *in response to* the forces present. Again, this is fighting an ever-losing battle – the bigger and faster the speed of rotation, the bigger the system we have to design to cope with it. Smart designers recognize that the centrifugal energy is there to be harnessed; to work for the good of the system.
- Thermal Energy – almost all forms of energy conversion result in the generation of 'waste' heat, which is then the subject of considerable effort to successfully manage it out of harms way. Again, the tendency is to fight what is inevitably present, rather than view it as a potential resource.
- Failed components – might just be the biggest resource an engineer can ever be presented with. Unpleasant though a failure can be, it usually represents a unique opportunity to really understand what is happening in a system. A system that doesn't fail is one where the safety factors are never understood.

See also Inventive Principle 22 'Blessing in Disguise' in the reference section of Chapter 10 for other examples of things traditionally thought of as 'bad' being turned into something useful.

By way of practice at turning bad things into good things, try thinking about the absolute worst thing about a system you can, and then force yourself to see how it could be viewed as a resource.

What Do I Do?

Resources and the concept that everything in and around a system that is not being used to its maximum potential is one of the cornerstones of the TRIZ philosophy. In TRIZ terms, even the bad things in a system are good things, if only we can think about them hard enough.

The aim of this chapter is essentially to collate lists of things that we don't always think of as resources, but that someone, somewhere has somehow been able to successfully harness. The best way to use these lists is as simple solution triggers. In this regard it is recommended that you peruse the lists when you are unable to develop an elegant enough solution to the problem you are working on.

In the case of turning bad things into good things, the key provocation to be used is 'how can this bad thing be turned into a good thing?'

References

1) Perkowitz, S., 'Universal Foam', Vintage, London, 2000.
2) Pahl, G., Beitz, W., 'Engineering Design: A Systematic Approach', Springer-Verlag, 1996.
3) Alloy Digest 1952-1998, Asm International, CD-Rom, 1999.
4) Steiner, R., 'ASM Handbook: Properties and Selection : Irons, Steels, And High Performance Alloys', Asm International, 1990.
5) 'ASM Handbook : Properties and Selection : Nonferrous Alloys and Special Purpose Materials', Asm International, 1990.

6) Despopoulos, A., Silbernagl, S., '<u>Color Atlas of Physiology</u>', Thieme Medical Publishers, New York, 1991.

7) Brown, J., '<u>Advanced Machining Technology Handbook</u>', McGraw-Hill Professional Publishing, 1998.

15.
Problem Solving Tools
Knowledge/Effects

"You know how I'm smart? I've got people around me who know more than I do"
Louis B. Mayer

When the 'select' part of the systematic creativity process is directing us to the 'knowledge/effects' part of the TRIZ problem solving toolkit, we are basically being prompted to look beyond our current horizons to see if anyone has already solved the type of problem we are facing. We are in fact being offered three different options. The first is relevant to situations where we are looking to deliver a **function** more effectively than we are currently achieving. The second is that we are looking to improve the delivery of an **attribute** associated with a part of a system, and the third is that we are looking to see how closely someone, somewhere might already have solved our **direct** problem. The three different options require three related but different tools:

1) A database of functional effects – a collection of knowledge detailing known means of delivering certain key functions.
2) A database detailing known means of altering key attributes contained within a system or delivered by a component.
3) A means of effectively searching on-line knowledge resources.

This chapter contains all three elements. The next section provides the foundations of a functionally-classified Effects database. This is then followed by a similar database of attribute altering mechanisms, and then finally the chapter ends with a section describing effective means of searching on-line patent databases.

Database of Physical, Chemical and Biological Effects
(Classified by FUNCTION)

For those times when the systematic creativity process is suggesting we look for alternative ways of delivering a given function – for example if the way we are currently delivering it is deemed insufficient – then an encyclopedia of solutions arranged by function offers a useful start point to first identifying and then finding out more about what alternatives there may be. This kind of functional classification of knowledge is a very effective way of stripping away the boundaries that exist between different industries and scientific disciplines. Having used such a database to find possible new solutions, we might not understand those solutions, but at least we now know of their existence.

The following functionally classified knowledge database offers the first stage in this process. The table includes references wherever possible to knowledge sources where further information on a given function can be found. The list of effects should also act as search strings when using on-line methods of finding out more about a given function

deliverer. The table also includes space for you to add your own knowledge should you find effects not covered in the database in its current form.

Primary Function	Solid	Liquid	Gas	Field
Absorb/ Accumulate	Shape-memory effect	Exo/Endothermic Reactions Capillary Action Chemisorption Hydrogenation	Ultrasound Dissolution in Liquid	Aerosol Battery Capacitor Corona Discharge Fly-wheel Fuel-cell
Bends	Piezo-electric Effect Shape Memory Superplasticity	Bernoulli Coanda Effect	Bernoulli Coanda Effect	Magnetic Field Electrical Field Refraction
Breaks Down/ Cleans/ Corrodes/ Decomposes	Desorption Acoustic Cavitation Acoustic Vibration Cavitation Combustion Jet Erosion Spark Erosion Electrochemical Erosion Electron Impact Desorption Laser Evaporation Ionic Action Radioactivity Redox Reactions Hydrodynamic Cavitation Laser Gettering Ultrasonic Oscillation Friction Cryolysis Photo-Oxidation Optohydraulic Effect Explosion Thermo-destruction Dissolution Mechanical Action/Brushes Electrolysis	Acoustic Cavitation Acoustic Vibration Bio-destruction Cryolysis Mechanical Heating Hydrolytic Reactions Ozone Photo-oxidation Ultrasound Vacuum Refining	Adsorption Ultrasound Vibration	
Changes Phase of/ Melts/ Freezes/Boils / Evaporates/ Condenses	Heating Electric Arcing Electron Beam Thermo-nuclear	Heating Capillary Evaporation De-pressurisation Thermal Shock Ultrasound	Cooling Increase Pressure	Opto-elastic Effect Phase- Modulation Polarization Digitisation
Cools	Endothermic Reactions, Capillary-porous materials, Corona Discharge, Stirling Effect, Nernst-Ettinghausen Effect Piezoelectric Fan Peltier Effect Phase Transitions (Heat Pipe) Air-Flow -Impingement Jets, etc Fluid Spray Thermoacoustic Effect Transpiration Cooling (Evaporation)	Heat Exchanger Peltier Effect Phase Transitions Ranque Effect Thermomagnetic Effect Conduction Convection Air-flow	Heat Exchanger Dufour Effect Joule-Thomson Effect Ranque Effect Conduction Rarefaction Thermoacoustics	

	Conduction Convection Radiation		
Deposits	Adsorption Cathode Sputtering Chemical Vapour – Deposition Chemiepitaxy Corona Discharge Electrochemical Electrolysis Electrophoretics Electro-plating Electrostatics Oxidation Photochemical - deposition Plasma Deposition Spark Ablation Sublimation Transport Reactions Wetting	Gravity/ Differential Density Differential Viscosity Electrostatic Deposition		
Destroys/ Erodes/ Corrodes	Alexandrov Effect Bio-destruction Burning Cavitation Cryolysis Dissolving Explosion Hydrogenation Hyperthermia Optohydraulic Effect Oxidation Radioactivity Vibration Ultrasonics Acoustic Shock Photo-oxidation Resonance Coherent light Ozone	Bio-destruction Cryolysis Hydrogenation Optohydraulic Effect Oxidation Photo-oxidation Radioactivity Ultrasonics	Oxidation Hydrogenation Radioactivity	
Detects (see also Attributes list 'measuerment' column)	Acoustic Cavitation Acoustic Vibration Corona Discharge Doppler Effect Eddy Current Ferromagnetism Neutron Beam Scattering Photoluminescence Piezoelectric Effect Radioactivity Ultrasound X-Ray	Bernoulli Effect Corona Discharge Photoluminescence Piezoelectric Effect Radioactivity	Adsorption-resistive Effect Auger Effect Chromatography Corona discharge Ionization Light Absorption/ Reflection Penning Effect Photoluminescence Piezoelectric Effect Radioactivity	Acoustic emission Barkhausen Effect Light Diffraction Light Polarization Photochromism Photoelectric Roentgen- Luminescence Resonance Tenso-resistive Effect Faraday Effect Magnetostriction Wiegand Effect Electrets
Dries	Acoustic Vibration Capillary-condensation Centrifuge Convection Photopolymerization Hanque Effect Resonance Sublimation Ultrasonic Drying		Capillary- Condensation Chemisorption Desorption Ultrasonic Drying Ranque-I litch Effect	
Embeds	Diffusion Glow discharge Ion implantation Thermionic Emission Thermo-diffusion Ultrasonic Vibration			

Extracts	Fermentation Melting Precipitation Oxidation/Reduction	Absorption Centrifugal Separation Distillation Electro-osmosis Fermentation Funnel Effect Gravity/Settling Reverse Osmosis	Absorption Acoustics Capillary Condensation Chemisorption Ranque-Hilche Effect Turbulence Heating (Desorption)	
Heats	Combustion Eddy Current Exothermic Reactions Condensation Heating Conduction Convection Laser Microwave Radiation Peltier Effect Phase Changes Radiation Shunt Effect Solar Energy Strain Heating	Acoustic Cavitation Combustion Conduction Convection (Free & Forced) Electromagnetic-induction Joule-Lenz Effect Magnetostriction Microwave radiation Phase Changes Pressurisation Radiation Ranque Effect Shock Wave Solar Energy Thermosyphon	Combustion Conduction Convection Dufour Effect Explosion Optical radiation Pressurisation Radiation Ranque Effect Shock Wave Solar Energy Thermosyphon	
Holds/Joins/ Assembles	Mechanical Fastener (thread, twist, etc) Taper Mandrel Hooks Adhesive Foams Diffusion Bonding Ferro-magnetism Hot-pressing Melting (Transient Liquid Phase Bonding) Osmotic Pressure Shape-Memory Effect Solder/Braze/Weld Friction Welding Explosive Welding Laser welding Ultrasonic Vibration Thermal Expansion Adsorption	Chemical bonding Container Foams Magnetothermal Effect Osmosis	Chemical bonding Container Foams	Capacitor Parallel Junction
Locates	Thermal Expansion Brushes Electrostriction Eccentrics Friction Magnetics Magnetostriction Piezoelectric Effect			
Mixes	Acoustic Vibration Binding Agents Catalysis Coulomb's Law Electrets Stirring/Shaking Ultrasonic Vibration	Barbotage Binding Agents Catalysis Coulomb's Law Electrets Ferromagnetism Sono-chemistry Stirring/Shaking Ultrasound Vibration	Chemical Bonding Diffusion	
Moves/ Vibrates	Gravity, Inertia, Vibration, Birds Beak Effect, Brushes	Absorption Acoustic Cavitation Acoustic Vibrations Archimedes' Principle Bernoulli's Theorem	Acoustic Vibrations Archimedes' Principle Bernoulli's Theorem Cholosky Effect	Conductors Faraday Effect Gunn Effect Kerr Effect Light Conductors

	Corona Discharge, Coulomb's Law, Friction, Diffusion, Dopant Segregation, Electromagnetic induction Electrophoresis, Electrostatic fields Explosion Funnel Effect, Hyperboloid, Ion Conductivity, Magnetic Explosion, Photophoresis, Mobius Strip, Desorption, Resonance, Electrets, Thermophoresis, Coanda Effect, Triboelectricity, Pascal Law, Ferro-magnetism Diamagnetism, Fluidisation, Reuleaux Triangle, Boundary Layer Entrapment, Shape Memory Effect Spiral, Torque Oscillator	Boiling/Evaporation Capillary Condensation Capillary Evaporation Capillary Pressure Coanda Effect Condensation Coulomb's Law Deformation Dessication Electrocapillary Effect Electrolysis Electroosmosis Electrophoresis Electrostatic Induction Explosion Ferromagnetism Funnel Effect Gravity Hydraulic shock Inertia Ionic Exchange Jet Flow Lorentz Force Magnetostriction Mechanocaloric Effect Osmosis Pascal Law Pump Ranque Effect Resonance Shock Wave Spiral Super Thermal Conductivity Superfluidity Surface Tension Thermal Expansion Thermocapillary Effect Thermomechanical Effect Ultrasonic Capillary Effect Ultrasonic Vibrations Use of foam Weissenberg Effect Wetting	Coanda Effect Diffusion Ejector Electrocapillary Effect Electroosmosis Electrophoresis Electrostatic Induction Fan/Compressor Ferromagnetism Gravity Inertia Jet Flow Pascal Law Ranque-Hilch Effect Shock Wave Spiral Thermal Expansion Peristaltic Pump Vacuum Venturi Effect	Photoelasticity Refraction Reflection Electro-optics Magneto-optics Superconductivity
Orients	Anisotropy Graphoepitaxy Helix Lorentz Force Magnetism Mechanical Devices	Lorentz Force Magnetism Pressure Gradient Thermal gradient Venturi	Pressure Gradient Thermal gradient Venturi	Lens Polarization Refraction
Preserves/ Protects	Adsorption Chemisorption Coatings Cryogenics Deposition (Electro-chemical) Diffusion Barrier Filter Foams Gels Hard/soft Multi-Layer Coatings Hydration Hydrogen Peroxide Hydrophobia Isolation Kragelsky Effect	Accumulator Adsorption Chemisorption Ferro-fluids Filter Foams Isolation Ozone Preservatives	Accumulator Filter Foams Isolation	Capacitor Filter Isolation

	Magnetism Surfactants Vacuum Packing			
Prevents	Deformation Strain Limiters Thermal Expansion	Foam Gels Thermal Expansion Valve	Foam Valve	Adsorption Birefringence Diffusion-junction Metal-Hydrides Pool-Frenkel Efffect Punchthrough -Effect Thermal-Decomposition
Produces	Agglomeration Chemiepitaxy Crystallization Diffusion Electrolysis Osmotic Pressure Precipitation Redox Reactions Spark Discharge Thermo-diffusion Transport Reactions	Capillary Wave Effect Condensation Dissolution Distillation Reverse Osmosis Transport Reactions	Acoustic cavitation Arc Evaporation Boiling Corona Discharge Dehydration Electrolysis Evaporation Ionization	Chemiluminescence Ohms Law Eddy Currents Electrokinetics Electro-dynamic Effect Electroluminescence Electromagnetic-Induction Electrostatic Induction Fluorescence Frictional Electricity Capacitance Effect Induction Magneto-hydrodynamic Effect Thermionic Emission Photoconductivity Photoluminescence Piezoelectric Effect Pockels Effect Pyroelectricity Radioluminescence Seebeck Effect Sonoluminescence Tribo-electricity Triboluminescence Noise Effect Radioactivity
Rotates	Torque Force Bernoulli Effect Screw converter	Centrifuge Ranque-Hilch Effect	Centrifuge Ranque-Hilch Effect	Magnetism
Separates/ Removes/ Polishes	Acoustic Waves Adsorption Boundary-Layer-Momentum Centrifuge Coanda Effect Corona Discharge Electrets Filter (mesh) Friction Inertia Magnetic Field Magnus Effect Melting Reuleaux Triangle Ultrasound Vibration	Capillary-Porous Materials Cavitation-Fragmentation Centrifuge Coagulation Density-Gradient/Gravity Temperature Gradient Electroosmosis Electrophoresis Electrostatics Hydrophilics Hydrophobics Liquid membranes Osmosis Distillation Resonance Transport Reactions	Absorption Corona Discharge Crystallization Desorption Diffusion Electrets Hydrates Ranque-Hilch Effect Streamer Effect Ultrasound	Birefringence Prism
Stabilises	Corrugation Ellipse Friction Hysteresis Inertia Damping Pendulum Screw Converter Gyroscope	Capillary Pressure Coanda Effect Crystallisation Electro-rheology Ferro-fluidics Magneto-rheology Suspensions	Coanda Effect Electron Beam	Earthing Thermoresistive Effect Absorption Magnetic- Hysteresis

Database of Attribute Altering Effects
(Classified by ATTRIBUTE type)

For those times when the systematic creativity process is suggesting we need to improve the way we achieve a change of some description to an attribute of either the system or one of its component parts, a database of attributes and the things we are most likely to want to do to them is required. We present such a database here. The database is ordered by basic attribute type. For each attribute, we present known ways of 'changing', 'increasing', 'decreasing', 'stabilising' or 'measuring' it. As 'increase' and 'decrease' are specialised versions of 'change', the convention used in the table is that if a given effect is capable of achieving both increases and decreases of the attribute it is listed only under the 'change' category. Thus the 'increase' and 'decrease' data columns list effects that are capable of delivering primarily those types of change.

Attribute	Means of Changing	Means of Increasing	Means of Decreasing	Means of Stabilising	Means of Measuring
Weight		See 'Deposits' function	Holes, Composites Wear See 'Removes'		Balance, vibration, Acoustic waves Resonance Buoyancy
Volume	Phase transition, Diffusion, Dissolution, Hyperboloid Shape-memory, Magneto-optics Ionization Auxetics	Ellipse, Torus Thermal expansion	Thermal contraction, Cavitation Nesting Capillary Con-traction	Poisson Effect	Cavitation, Vibration, Dielectric permeability Reverberation Archimedes
Surface Area		Mobius strip, Segmentation Ellipse, Spirals, Corrugation Protrusions 'Fractalisation'	Spheroid Capillary – Contraction		Geometry Geometer Shadow-graph
Length	Ellipse, Shape-memory effect Magnetostriction, Electrostriction, Piezo-effect Magnus Effect Cam Profiles Deformation	Thermal expansion	Thermal contraction	Zero Thermal Expansion Coefficient Materials	Archimedes force, Vibration, Diffraction Gratings Electrets, Interference, Light emission, Doppler Effect, Luminescence, Electrical fields, Magnetic fields, Heat radiation, X-ray Shadowgraph Electrical resistance, Calorimetry Moire Effect, Ultrasound, Rheoelectric Effect Neutron Diffraction Fresnel Diffraction Domain Effect Capacitance
Surface Finish	Friction, Adsorption, Shot-peening, laser shot-peening, Diffusion, Bauschinger Effect Ultrasonic – Abrasive-Treatment Ferromagnetism			Coatings, Lotus Effect	Laminarity, Transition to turbulence, Bernoulli Effect, Shadow graph Interference Fringes Friction Light Polarization

Density	Porosity Auxetic Voids	Compression forming,	Evaporation		Mass/displacement, Ultrasound, Vibration Densimeter Sound Velocity Resonance
Speed	Gravity Inertia Mechanical- Effects Forces		Viscosity Friction	Force Balance	Piezo-electrics Acoustic Vibration, Accelerometer Barnett Effect Magneto-Resistance Effect Coriolis Force Doppler Effect Dorn Effect Hall Effect Karman Effect Bernoulli Effect Ultrasound Eddy Currents Lorentz Force Torquemeter Fabry-Perot- Interferometer Electromagnetic- Induction Corona Disharge Triboelectric Effect Laser-Doppler Anemometry Magneohydrodynamic Effect Stroboscope
Force	Kragelsky Effect, Johnson-Rahbeck Effect Electrokinetics Capacitance Effect Lever Wedge Crank Hydraulic Effect		Reverse Piezoeffect Torus	Feedback	Barkhausen Effect Inertia Piezo-electrics Elastic Strain Resonance Forced Oscillations Fibre-optic Bending Villari Effect Magneto-optic (Kerr Effect) Photoelasticity
Pressure	Inertia, Bernoulli Effect Phasetransitions, Alexandrov Effect Osmosis, Centrifugal forces, Toricelli Boyle-Mariotte	Thermal expansion, Shock wave, Absorption	Decomposition		Mechanical vibration, Gels, Piezo-electrics Electrets, Electrokinetics Corona Discharge Light Rings Moire Fringes Bourdon Spring Weissenberg Effect Magneto-elastic Effect Pascal Law Bernoulli Tenso-resistive Effect Radiation Phase -Shift
Pressure Gradient	Electro-rheology, Magneto rheology	Shock wave,			Pressure sensitive Paint Bernoulli
Temperature	Dissolution, Decomposition of hydrates, Phase transitions, Radiation, Convection, Conduction Peltier Effect	See 'Heats' Function	See 'Cools' Function	Phase Transitions, Curie Point, Ferromagnetic Powder, Foam/insulation, Electromagnetic induction	Thermal expansion, Thermochromism, Phase-transition, Curie Point Pyroelectric Effect Radiation Frequency Phosphor Afterglow Seebeck Effect

	Eddy current Joule Heating				Curie Point Light Wavelength Thermoresistance Electrolyte
Temperature Gradient	Heat-pipe Composites			Conduction	Thermal imagery Thermochromism Temperature Sensitive Paints Tomography
Strength	Annealing Cold-forming Griffiths Effect	Ultrasound Pressurisation Corrugation Magnetic-Casting	Weak-point	Stress-relief Holes	Tensile testing
Brightness	Surface Finish Film Coatings	Electro/Photo-Luminesence			Photochromism, Acoustooptic Effect Luminescence Photoplastic Effect Kerr Effect
Energy	Inertia Deformation Gyroscopic effect Bernoulli Effect Hooke's Law Poissons Effect Coulombs Laws Boyle-Mariotte Newtons Laws Coriolis Force Magnus Effect Centrifugal Force Hysteresis Steam Pressure Biot-Savart Effect Peltier Effect			Fly-wheel Battery Fuel Cell	Tensoresistive Effect
Power	Ionization	Solar, wind, wave, nuclear, Etc Hartmann Nernst-Etinghausen	Storage Media		Seebeck Effect Bolometer Electrochromic radiation
Homogeneity	Corona discharge, Adsorption, Electrolysis	Gettering Filtration			Speed of Sound Conductivity
Lubricity	Plasma	Nitrogen, Sulphur, Chlorine Ion Implantation PTFE Parylene			Friction Coefficient Munson Roller
Conductivity – Electrical	Temperature Diode	Purification Thin Films	Composites		Electrolysis (resistance) Electrets Faraday Effect Hall Effect Pockels Effect Ohm's Law Parasitic Capacitance Resistance Tomography
Conductivity – Heat	Porosity	Plasma Etching	Insulation		Thermal Expansion Scanning Microscopy
Magnetic Properties	Hydration Electromagnetic-Induction		Curie Point		Tensoresistive Effect Magnetometer Hall Effect Magnetostriction Ampere's Law
Porosity	Nano-construction Gels	Holes Foams	See 'Separate' Function		Porosimeter Water-Capacity
Viscosity	Acoustic Cavitation	Cooling Electroviscous-	Ultrasound Heating		'Falling Ball' (Timing) Viscometer

	Electro-rheology, Magneto-rheology, Temperature, Thixotropy Toms Effect 2-Phase Flows Vibration Ultrasound	Effect	Toms Effect Vapour Injection		Paramagnetic-Resonance-Spectrometer
Hardness		Shot-peening Alternating-Magnetic Field Laser shot-peen Hard/Soft Multi-Layer Coatings Nitriding Cr, Tu, Mn, Ni, Sc Additives		Multi-layering	Vickers, Brinell (Mohs Scale) Continuous Stiffness Nano-indentation Durometer
Sound/ Ultrasound	Resonance Aerophonics Vibraphonics Piezoelectric Resonant- Macro-sonic-Synthesis		Anti-phase	Feedback	Sound-level Meter Gels
Colour	Photochromism Electrochromism Christiansen Effect Interference Fringes			Heat Treatment Chelating Agents Blanching	Spectrophotometer Chromaticity Sensor Light Absorption Photoionization

Patent Search Strategies

The recent availability of on-line patent databases opens up the prospect of easy access to potentially vast amounts of data. To some, the amount of data available can be overwhelming. TRIZ-based search techniques can help to considerably ease the task of searching for knowledge on patent databases. We present here a useful strategy for helping to maximise the effectiveness of time spent looking through such data:

0)   Before you start, gather together a clear definition of the specific solution required, the useful function(s) you are looking to deliver, and the constraints which will limit the breadth of your search. Think also about which countries you want to search against – European is a good default as it now includes patents from other sectors.

1)   It is a good idea to start by scoping the amount of intellectual property that might be relevant to your problem or opportunity. Do this by thinking about your specific requirement (e.g. aerosol nozzle), and progressively abstracting this out to one of the generic functions listed on the following sheet (e.g. aerosol nozzle ® produce spray/mist ® mist/droplets/particles)

2)   Use the defined constraints for your problem to limit the search scope. For example, if you are not able to look at a markedly different solution to the one you have now, there is little point in abstracting out to the generic function. For example, if you are unable to change anything about an aerosol container other than the nozzle, there lu littlu puint in looking nt nolution options other than those related to aerosol nozzles.

3)   If your problem allows you scope to think about 'ideal' solutions, however, start your search with patents where other inventors have had similar aims. 'Self' is a very good search word in this regard. There are still a small enough number of patents of the self-x type (where x can be any verb related to delivery of a function – e.g. 'self-clean'), to make this a viable and effective search strategy.

4)   If your constraints permit you to look outside your current scope of solution types,

start a search based on search words describing the function being delivered (e.g. 'move liquid' or '(produce) small droplets')

5) You might also like to include certain qualifier search words. For example, if you are looking for solutions that deliver very fine droplets, you might include 'micron' as a search word. Similarly, 'low cost', (high) 'temperature', or 'stainless steel' offer useful words that will limit the search to include only those solutions that fit your constraints.

6) Order your patent search to present the most recent patents first. Finding a 'good' recent patent will be helpful because it is likely to contain references to 'good' earlier patents. (Note you might also like to start a search on patent applications rather than patents granted if you are looking for really up to date solutions options.)

7) Remember that very few search engines include anything more than a crude array of synonyms. For example, most will pick up 'seals' if you search on 'seal', but none (so far) will also find patents that use 'prevent leak' instead of seal. Ditto 'self' and 'automatic'.

8) It is usually preferable to search for your chosen words in the whole patent text. If this is producing too many hits, you might like to consider restricting the search of one or two of the key words to just the title. (Health warning on this one – an increasing number of patent agents are filing patents with titles (and indeed abstracts) which bear as little relation to the invention as possible).

Example

Situation: I want to find examples of a device to pump a liquid soap at the lowest possible manufacture cost. It is also required to deliver a reliable and fixed measure of soap for every pump action made by the user. Minimum user effort is highly desirable. As is the ability to use existing manufacture capabilities – which include little more than plastic moulding or simple turning type manufacture operations.

* Specific requirement – fixed measure, liquid soap pump
Abstracted requirements – pump liquid soap & move viscous liquid

* US patent database
'liquid' and 'soap' and 'pump' = 1211 hits
('move' or 'pump') and 'viscous' and 'liquid' = 6975 hits
'pump' (in title) and 'liquid' = 1604 hits
'pump' (in title) and 'liquid' and 'cost' = 570
'pump' in title and 'soap' = 32 (too confined now)
'self' and 'pump' in title = 43
('self' and 'pump' and 'soap' = 0 (!))

A preliminary look through 'pump' in title and 'liquid' and 'hand' highlights the following ideas shown in Figure 15.1.

The search also highlighted things like 6,257,458 '**Self**-priming **hand pump** for dispensing fluid to a bovine')

('Hand' is an important constraint in thinking about actuation power for the pump, and as such makes a more useful contribution than 'low-cost' to this particular search – because it implicitly means that the power source has been removed from the device to the user.)

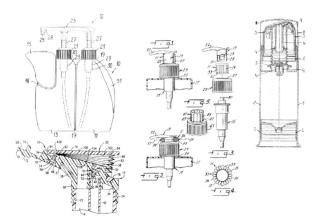

Figure 15.1: Typical Hand-Pump Patents

16.
Problem Solving Tools
Algorithm for Inventive Problem Solving (ARIZ)

Every part is disposed to unite with the whole, that it may thereby
escape from its own incompleteness.
Leonardo Da Vinci

Nothing appears to cause argument in the world of TRIZ like the Algorithm of Inventive Problem Solving, ARIZ. Conceptually, there is little disagreement – ARIZ exists to help tackle 'complex' problems, and it does it through a series of systematic steps that take problem owners from potentially vague beginnings through to a successful conclusion. Thereafter, however, the details of what these steps are and in what sequence they should be carried out, is a matter of some considerable disagreement – with just about every TRIZ expert endorsing their own variation on the theme. In several senses, one could argue that the 'systematic creativity' process described in Chapter 4 of this book and linked to almost every other chapter is also ARIZ-like in its scope and motive. We hope, however, that that process operates at a somewhat higher, more holistic level than any variant of ARIZ. In that context, we view ARIZ as a tool that can form a useful complement to the systematic creativity process, rather than as a replacement.

This chapter describes a simplified version of ARIZ. The description fits with the manner in which we expect to see the tool used; that is as a fall-back option if, after a user has been through the necessary problem definition steps, arrived at the 'select solve tool' part of the process (Chapter 9), and discovered that they do not know how to proceed. In other words, we will use ARIZ as the emergency back-up to help us when we are stuck.

The chapter is split into three basic parts. The first and shortest part provides a very brief background on the history of ARIZ. We will use this solely for the purposes of setting the context for the second part – a step-by-step description of the ARIZ we think best fits into its emergency back-up role within systematic creativity. The third part will then feature a case study example of the process in action.

ARIZ – Background
ARIZ started out as Altshuller's attempt to detail a generic series of steps that would enable any user to first properly define, and then solve a complex problem. The resulting method was something that evolved year-on-year until around 1985, with new and upgraded versions being given a code description 71A, 73C, 85C, 85V and so on. Actually with the 85V version (Reference 16.1), Altshuller is said to have believed the method was 'good enough' and any work subsequent to that version may be seen to have shifted focus to better encapsulate psychological effects. In any event, the method builds on the belief that a clearly defined problem equals the formulation of its main physical contradiction, which the experience of this author believes not to be wholly generically applicable.

It is important however, because the evidence from many problems is that the elimination of a 'good' physical contradiction can do rather more than just eliminate the problem being focused on. In other words, solving a 'good' physical contradiction often leads to several, unexpected additional benefits. One particular experience of this author involving the resolution of a physical contradiction aimed at improving the efficiency of a filtration device, saw not only a doubling of separation efficiency, but also a halving of volume, 40% reduction in weight, 40% reduction in pressure loss through the system and 60% reduction in ice-protection power requirement – none of which were focused on during the process of eliminating the contradiction in question. In short, solving physical contradictions often leads to synergistic benefits.

More complete descriptions of ARIZ may be found in References 16.2 and 16.3. We will not seek to duplicate the efforts of either author here. Neither will we try to reproduce the history of ARIZ – a fine version of which can be found in Reference 16.4.

Some of the initial steps of ARIZ (the attention here will focus on the 85V version) share much with the problem definition steps described in Chapters 5, 6 and 8 – for example, ARIZ 85V, Step 1 says:

'Evaluate the initial situation, construct the hierarchy of the system, and locate the sore point'

Which effectively says, conduct a function analysis and use it to find the 'sore point'. We will skip that stage of ARIZ as the equivalent steps in chapters 5 and 6 in this case, we believe offer a somewhat higher degree of assistance in what is widely recognized to be the most critical part of the process. Our description of ARIZ in the context of its use as a back-stop, therefore begins with its second step:

ARIZ Process – Within a 'Systematic Creativity' Setting

(NB rather than trying to mimic the original ARIZ step numbers – which could potentially confuse – we list only the steps relevant to our systematic creativity application.)

a) Define the mini-problem.
From the functional and attribute analysis model of the system, identify the key harmful, insufficient or excessive functional relationship – what is the one that is causing you to have drawn the FAA in the first place, what is the one that, if it wasn't there any more, you would consider the problem to have been solved? This can be a difficult process, and to be honest, requires more than a little faith that solving a physical contradiction concerning this relationship will also solve some of the other adverse relationships present in the system. A good principle to keep in mind is that it should be something that is close to the Main Useful Function (MUF) of the overall system under evaluation – the section on functional hierarchies in Chapter 6 should suggest to you that the MUF delivering parts of the system will still be around when everything else has eventually evolved away.

b) Define the Problem Space and Interval
For the selected key problem functional relationship selected in the previous step, identify the operational space and operational interval. These are, respectively, the relevant physical space around the problem, and the relevant time space around the problem. In the case of the operational space, it is often useful to make drawings (preferably from several different angles) of the problem, and then to draw an enclosing

dotted line to denote what is in and what is outside of the conflict zone. It is helpful to focus this space as closely to the problem relationship as possible, so trying to make it as small as possible is a good objective – it could, for example, be a few nanometers big. For the operational interval, the task is similar in that the aim is to draw a time envelope defining the boundaries of when we do and don't have a conflict. Of particular interest are the time when the conflict is occurring (to define one boundary of our time-window) and the time immediately before the problem occurs, or (less likely, but by no means impossible) immediately after it has disappeared. As with the operational space, the objective is to define these boundaries as close together as possible. Taken together, the operational space and time define the boundaries within which the problem is observed to exist.

c) Define a Technical Contradiction

Keeping your thinking within the operational space and time from the previous step, think about the negative functional relationship under evaluation and, looking at the system component *from* which the relationship arrow leaves, identify the useful thing(s) that this component delivers. If there are more than one other things (positive or negative) that the component in question delivers, pick the one closest to the MUF of the system. The selected useful function plus the previously selected negative functional relationship together define a technical contradiction – in that you want the useful thing, but in the process of obtaining that, you also get the negative thing. Record what this technical contradiction is. If there are insufficient functional arrows leaving the component in question to formulate a contradiction, check the component attributes in order to establish which of them is involved in producing a conflict. In order to check that whatever contradiction derived is a true contradiction, think about what happens to the useful function at the time (from step b) above) immediately before or after the time the conflict occurs – i.e. immediately outside the defined operational interval; if the useful function has either become insufficient, excessive or has disappeared altogether, then it is safe to assume that your chosen positive and negative pair (or an attribute) are in contradiction with one another.

d) Define the Physical Contradiction

Select one of the pair of positive and negative functional relationships from the previous step and use this as the basis for defining a physical contradiction. Although there is no general rule dictating which of the two relationships to use during this process, it is more usual to configure the physical contradiction around the negative relationship – if only because the idea of 'wanting the MUF and not wanting the MUF' or rather the 'not wanting' part of the contradiction, is often meaningless. Use the already defined operational space and interval to explore the boundaries of when or where you do and don't want the different requirements of the chosen contradiction parameter. Record the formulated physical contradiction in the form *'I want condition A at* (define space, time or circumstance where you want condition A), *and I want condition –A at* (define space, time or circumstance where you want condition –A)'. –A is taken to represent the opposite function to A – for example if A='hot', then –A='cold'. (See Chapter 11 for more details on formulating physical contradictions.)

e) Define the Ideal Final Result Outcome

Thinking about the physical contradiction defined in the previous step, define the Ideal Final Result (IFR) outcome to this contradiction. This should take the form of a statement like '*I achieve condition A and condition –A without complicating the system*'.

f) Define The X-Component

The x-component is an interesting concept that exists in classical TRIZ only in the context of ARIZ. Its basic function is to help break out of psychological inertia. The x-component should be viewed as 'something' that is magically able to come along and solve your problem. At this point in the process, the user is asked to put all preconceptions about what is and isn't physically possible on one side when thinking about the x-component. In effect, what the user is doing is using the concept as a way of defining the specification for what it is we would like this magic component to achieve. The definition of the x-component should be closely tied to the negative functional relationship defined in a) and physical contradiction defined in step d). Record the resulting specification for the x-component in a form something like; *'the x-component is able to eliminate the harmful function B and/or to solve the physical contradiction, C'.*

g) Analysis of Resources

Having defined conceptually what the x-component is required to do, the next step in the process involves a search to establish whether there is something already in or around the system capable of fulfilling the specification defined in the previous step. The system resources should previously have been recorded during the problem explore part of the overall systematic creativity process detailed in Chapter 5. The slight difference in the way we now use those resources we have identified, is that we are now looking to compare them to the specification outlined in step f). There are various ways in which to conduct this comparative x-component/resource search. The way recommended here is to begin the search within the operational space and interval boundaries, and to move gradually beyond these boundaries to look at things, next, things already in the system, and then things we might easily add to the system – see here the list of 'easily available' substances from Chapter 14. The generally recommended search strategy is illustrated in Figure 16.1. If we can find a resource matching the x-component specification, chances are we have solved the problem.

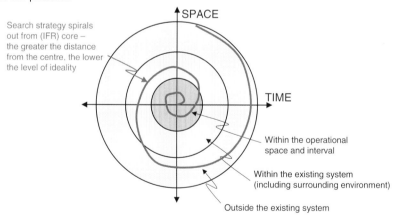

Figuro 16.1 X Componont/Rooouroo Matoh Soaroh Stratogy
(Note: the IFR defined in step e) defines the minimum disruption point at the centre of the circle)

h) Modification of Resources

This step is similar to the preceding one, but takes things a step further by prompting the problem solver to think harder about the resources issue. This step assumes that a suitable resource has not been identified in the previous step. The new questions provoked in this 'modification' step are:-

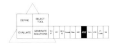

i)   would it be possible to reproduce the specification of the x-component by modifying one of the things already in the system?

ii)   would it be possible to reproduce the specification of the x-component by combining two or more of the things already in the system?

As with the preceding step, the most logical sequence of events here involves starting within the operational space and interval and gradually working outwards to other system components and then things we could add to the system. Typical 'modifications' to resources are detailed in the trigger sheet in Chapter 9, they will include things like phase transitions, local changes in geometry, or any of the evolutionary steps illustrated in the trends of evolution – which, in conjunction with the concept of evolutionary potential (Chapter 13) also suggest the presence of resources (e.g. ' a smooth surface is a resource'). As in the previous step, if we can find a modified resource matching the x-component specification, chances are we have solved the problem

i) Use Principles for Eliminating Physical Contradictions

Apply the strategies described in Chapter 11 for the elimination of physical contradictions on the physical contradiction defined during step d).

j) Use Principles for Eliminating Technical Contradictions

Apply the strategies described in Chapter 10 for the elimination of technical contradictions on the technical contradiction defined during step c).

k) Use Knowledge/Effects

Examine the useful function in contradiction with the negative functional relationship defined in step a) and examine the content of Chapter 15 in order to establish whether there are other ways of delivering that useful function that may avoid the generation of the negative effect.

l) No Solution?

If no solution has been obtained by this stage, the most pragmatic strategy to adopt is to return to either one of the options emerging from the preceding steps (e.g. say we determined there were two possible contradictions) or to go back to the original FAA model and identify an alternative negative functional relationship on which to base the ARIZ analysis. Repeat the ARIZ steps a) to k) for the new mini-problem arising from the newly selected alternative negative function.

Summary

In several senses, the version of ARIZ presented here represents 'just' another way of linking together some of the steps already contained within the bigger 'systematic creativity' process. It differs in several minor (introduction of x-component, combination of resources) and one key respect, however. The key difference builds from the underlying assumption within ARIZ that we wish to solve the problem with the *minimum level of disruption* to the system (as opposed to the systematic creativity process where we use the constraints defined in the initial problem explorer to drive the direction and strategy). A useful image to keep in mind as you progress through the various ARIZ steps is the convergent-divergent picture illustrated in Figure 16.2.

The basic idea is that we use the process to gradually define a progressively more exacting problem – the extreme limits of which being our definition of the Ideal Final Result

– and then, as we shift into the solution part of the process we migrate away from this ideal only when we are unable to obtain solutions at or close to that ideal definition.

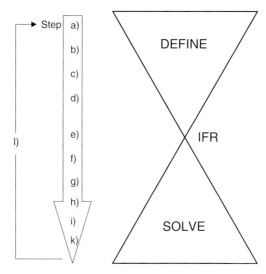

Figure 16.2 Overall Convergent-Divergent Structure of ARIZ Process

One final point regarding the mechanics of ARIZ; our brains tend to want us to stop going through the process once we hit upon a solution that looks promising. It is always useful to avoid this tendency and carry on with subsequent steps, in the same way that it is useful to cycle more than one time around the systematic creativity process.

ARIZ – Case Study Example

If TRIZ is in large part about eliminating contradictions, one the whole community of exerts has thus far failed to solve involves 'good' case study examples of ARIZ in action. The roots of the contradiction lie in the role of ARIZ as a tool to help tackle complex problems; complex problems tend to make readers focus on the problem rather than the process, while simple problems focusing on the process tend to be frustrating because it very quickly becomes apparent that you don't need ARIZ to tackle it. In other words, we would like a case study which is both complex and not complex. We will examine a human-powered flight problem which is actually neither.

Figure 16.3 Typical Human Powered Aircraft

The state of the art in human powered flight is defined by aircraft like the Gossamer Albatross (Reference 16.5) or the Raven. One has flown across the English Channel, and

the other is able to achieve around about the 100-mile mark. Strictly speaking, any analysis of the problem of improving the capability (range) of either aircraft ought to involve the full systematic creativity process as detailed in Chapter 2. Lack of space and our desire to focus on the mechanics of ARIZ, however, dictate that we work through the problem using just the ARIZ steps. Let's say, by way of making the problem more realistic, that we have conducted the three essential problem definition steps described in Chapters 5 through 7 and when we have reached Chapter 9 'Select' we don't know which way to go. In those circumstances, we should come here, to Chapter 16.

Referring to the steps detailed in the previous section, we should then proceed through this problem as follows:-

a) Define the mini-problem – the main useful function contained in the system 'human powered aircraft' is the one that gets the human (and aircraft) off the ground. The only parts of the system currently capable of delivering this function are the wings – as they are the things that have been designed to generate lift. The problem we are looking at – increasing capability – relates to the wings in that, at present, the wings are delivering *insufficient* of the useful function 'lift'; and that we would like more of this function. This 'increase lift' thus forms the basis of our mini-problem.

b) Define the Problem Space – here the requirement is to define the operational space and interval. We will define the operational space as that space contained within the dotted line illustrated in Figure 16.4. This space describes a half-section of the aircraft (the aircraft is nominally symmetrical, and so in a bid to legitimately minimize the size of the operational space, we will consider half of the system) and includes the air immediately around the wing , the air pushed over the wing by the propeller (we will assume this is a front-propeller aircraft), and, because the aircraft is likely to fly at low altitude, we should include the ground beneath the wing surface.

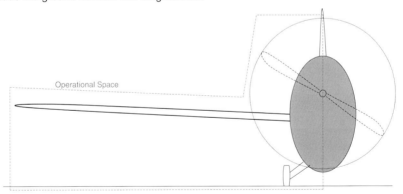

Figure 16.4 Operational Space Around Human Powered Aircraft Wing

With regard to the operational interval we should be looking for a time when the conflict occurs and the time immediately before it occurs. It would appear that we have two choices here; the first is that the problem of insufficient lift begins when the pilot becomes fatigued – before he is fatigued, the aircraft is staying airborne and hence the wing must be producing sufficient lift. The second choice is when the aircraft is just on the verge of take-off; immediately before the aircraft leaves the ground, when the undercarriage is still on the ground, we could say we have 'sufficient' lift, which then becomes 'insufficient', the

moment the aircraft leaves the ground and the lift provided by the wings has to balance the weight of the craft. Either of these would form a legitimate focus for the subsequent analysis. As the second one implies a problem where we have insufficient lift all the time the aircraft is airborne rather than when the pilot becomes tired, we will pick this one – as it should also help solve the first problem. We should, of course, record the first operational interval as if we fail to have success solving the second one, this one will provide an alternative entry into the ARIZ process.

c) Define a Technical Contradiction – in order to identify a technical contradiction we need to examine some of the functional space around our problem wing. In particular we need to examine the functional relationship arrows leaving the wing. In this regard, we might extract a portion from a previously conducted FAA model as shown in Figure 16.5.

Figure 16.5 Functional Relationships Around the Aircraft Wing

Although there are likely to be several functional relationships acting *on* the wing (not shown), 'lifts' in fact seems to be the only function delivered *by* the wing. This is a problem in terms of defining a technical contradiction. According to the rules in the process description above, the next option involves examining the attributes of the wing. Figure 16.6 illustrates a partial list for consideration.

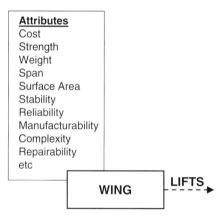

Figure 16.6 Attributes of the Aircraft Wing

(Note: the attributes list should inherently bear considerable resemblance to the list of 39 parameters contained in the Contradiction Matrix from Chapter 10.)

In order to identify our technical contradiction, we need to establish at least one of the listed attributes in conflict with our desire to increase lift. The most obvious conflict (with apologies to any aerodynamicist readers who probably reached this conclusion five minutes ago), the one most likely to hazard our ability to achieve lift appears to be weight. Thus, the chosen technical contradiction exists between **lift** and **weight**; in that we want high lift *and* low weight and conventional logic says we can have one or the other. So, the

thing we would like to improve is lift (in terms of the Contradiction Matrix, 'Force'), and the thing stopping us is 'Weight'.

d) Define the Physical Contradiction – definition of a physical contradiction is somewhat easier seeing as we were only able to find one functional relationship delivered by the aircraft wing, and we found a technical contradiction by looking solely at the wing: A good physical contradiction, therefore, must center around the wing. In such circumstances, the physical contradiction '*I want a wing* and *I don't want a wing*' is a sound choice. In more detail, we have 'I want a wing (to provide lift) and I don't want a wing (because it is heavy)'.

e) Define the Ideal Final Result Outcome - '*I achieve condition 'wing' and condition 'no-wing' without complicating the system'.*

f) Define The X-Component – '*the x-component is able to eliminate the harmful function 'insufficient lift' and/or to solve the physical contradiction, 'wing and 'no-wing''.*

g) Analysis of Resources – here we should refer to the 9-Windows based list of resources that we should have compiled during the problem explorer part of the systematic creativity process that preceded our entry into ARIZ. We will not seek to duplicate such a list, merely reproduce some of the resources identified that might be relevant to the problem at hand (a complete analysis would examine all of them – here we are simply picking out a few that appear to have some similarities to the specification of the x-component from the previous step). More important than completeness, for the purposes of this case, is the process adopted; in keeping with the search direction progressing outward from the operational space and interval as illustrated in Figure 16.1, we have compiled a table comprising the three different search spaces. The table has also been divided into two data columns – the first for listing resources as identified in the problem explorer, and the second emerging from a trends of evolution based 'evolutionary potential' analysis.

Search Space/Time	Substance & Field Resources (from Problem Explorer)	Evolutionary Potential Resources (from Trends of Evolution)
Inside the operational space and interval	• Ground Effect • Air inside wing cavities • Air from propeller (swirl) • Control surface actuators • Length of wing • Undercarriage support location? • Over-tip leakage from wing-tips	• Smooth surface over wing • Solid section wing spars (evolve to foam metal structure?) • No use of colour in wing surface • Matching asymmetry • Unjointed/inflexible system • Largely 2D structure (add 'vertical' dimension – e.g. winglets) • Flapping wing? • Local quality of surface at wing-tip (as in bird). Also curvature
Within the overall aircraft system	• Pilot body heat • Pilot breath • Energy transferred from pedals to propeller (re-direct some?) • Lift from fuselage • Tail plane and fin	• Smooth surface of fuselage • Unjointed/inflexible fuselage • Solid section spars and struts • Mechanical control actuators (fly by light?) • Asymmetrical flow pattern from propeller

		• Variable speed propeller
Outside the system	• Sun • Thermals from ground heating • 'Tensegrity structures' – incorporate tension cables to help support wing • 'Lighter than air' gases	

Again, the point is process, but nevertheless, hopefully it should be possible to see that the table describes many things that are not currently being utilized in the design of human-powered aircraft. They may be seen to possess significant amounts of untapped evolutionary potential, for example.

h) Modification of Resources – the next step involves the re-examination of the resources identified in the previous step in the context of their possible beneficial effect on the insufficient lift problem when either modified or used in combination. Again we are more interested in process than actual solutions, but below are some examples of how combining resources may result in synergistic benefits for the problem at hand:-

- Use the energy of the sun to heat the air inside the cavity of the wing – make the top half of the wing transparent, and the bottom half opaque in order to trap the greatest possible amount of heat
- Divert some of the energy currently transmitted from the cyclists pedals to the propeller to drive a small fan that is then used to blow a very small amount of air out over the surface of the wing (or part of) in order to enhance lift coefficient. (The fan could also be reversed and boundary-layer suction could be used instead.) The mathematics of introducing boundary-layer blowing or suction turn out to be very interesting; providing elegant means of moving the necessary air around are employed (i.e. no additional pipe-work introduced), the lift coefficient can be increased by a factor of several times – thus offering the opportunity to make the wing span considerably shorter (hence also reducing weight both directly and, because the moment is smaller, meaning less structure is required at the wing root) for the same lift performance.
- Combined use of tensegrity structure and the idea (from the 'dynamization' trend) of a wing that unfurls as speed of the aircraft increases along the runway – such that the wing roots have a much lower moment to support.

i) Use Principles for Eliminating Physical Contradictions – taking the 'wing and no-wing' contradiction as a start point, use the physical contradiction solution strategies described in Chapter 11 to identify solution possibilities. Using the separation in space, time and condition questions, it should be possible to find conceptual solutions in all three directions:

Separation in space – I want a wing close to the fuselage (low moment) and I don't want a wing a long way away from the fuselage (high moment).

Separation in time – I want a wing when the speed is high enough to generate sufficient lift, and I don't want a wing during acceleration along the runway, or when the aircraft is stationary.

Separation on condition – I want the wing if I want lift, and I don't want a wing if there is no requirement for lift.

All three definitions should, in combination with the appropriate Inventive Principles (see Table 11.1) enable us to generate several useful solution directions. The fourth physical

contradiction elimination strategy – transitioning to an alternative system – should likewise generate several solution opportunities.

j) Use Principles for Eliminating Technical Contradictions – the technical contradiction defined in step c) was between lift ('force' in terms of the Contradiction Matrix) and weight. The 'force' parameter is the one we are trying to improve as we have decided we have insufficient lift; the weight is the thing stopping us and so is the worsening feature. In terms of whether we should be looking at the 'stationary' or 'moving' weight options in the Matrix, because there is definite relative motion in the system (air over wing, and wing over ground), we should select the 'weight of moving object' parameter. (Note here that although step j) is very much in the 'solve' part of the process, TRIZ continues to encourage us to refine our problem definition.) The Matrix then gives us Principles 8, 1, 37 and 18 as most likely contradiction elimination strategies.

k) Use Knowledge/Effects – here our search should focus on ways known from other fields of enhancing the function 'lift', and then other ways besides 'wings' of delivering lift.

l) No Solution? – even though we have been focusing on process rather than generating actual solutions to the human-powered aircraft problem, it appears evident that we have nevertheless identified a number of conceptual solution opportunities using ARIZ that the existing experts in the field have not yet identified or exploited. If, on the other hand, we had failed to generate any such solutions, step l) of the ARIZ process would return us to previous steps in order to force exploration of other problem definition opportunities (for example is step b) we identified two possible operational intervals and chose to pick one; step l) would send us back to try the discarded opportunity).

What Do I Do?

As stated at the beginning of the chapter, the 'systematic creativity' process described in this book is intended as a more complete replacement for the classical form of ARIZ, and as such the use of ARIZ within the overall system is somewhat different from the original intent.

If you are interested in using one of the classical ARIZ approaches, you would be advised to look to one of the supplied references to find a version you like.

If you are primarily interested in obtaining a benefit (i.e. solving a problem), we suggest you think of the version of ARIZ presented here as something you will use only when the 'select' part of the systematic creativity process directs you to this chapter (i.e. when you have been through the three preceding problem definition steps and still don't know how to tackle the problem at hand).

If you are looking to use the ARIZ described here, follow the steps a) to l) and repeat as necessary until you have achieved a clearer view of what your problem actually is and have (hopefully) generated some good solutions.

It often happens that going through some of the definition steps within ARIZ clarifies the problem situation to an extent that it becomes possible to re-visit the systematic creativity 'select' step and be guided by that in terms of which solve tools to be used. The key to recognising that this has happened is the (usually sudden) dawning of the 'its obvious, why didn't I think of that before?' moment.

References

1) Altshuller, G., 'To Find An Idea', Nauka, Moscow, 1985 (in Russian)
2) Salamatov, Y., 'TRIZ: The Right Solution at the Right Time', Insytec, The Netherlands, 1999.
3) Ikovenko, S., 'Algorithm for Inventive Problem Solving', tutorial session at TRIZCON2000, Nashua, NH, April 2000.
4) Zlotin, B., Zusman, A., 'ARIZ on the Move', TRIZ Journal, March 1999.
5) Burke, J.D., 'The Gossamer Condor and Albatross: A Case Study in Aircraft Design', AIAA Professional Study Series, 1980.

17.
Problem Solving Tools
Trimming

Going, going...

Trimming (or 'pruning' or 'part-count reduction') is one of the conceptually more simple of the TRIZ tools. In several senses it may be seen as something that is not unique to TRIZ - being one of the triggers in Osborn's SCAMMPERR model (the 'E' there to represent 'Eliminate something'), and a large element of the Design for Manufacture and Assembly work of Boothroyd and Dewhurst (Reference 17.1). The tool also has links to the 'Trimming' trend described in Chapter 13. The trend describes how systems eventually evolve to contain fewer and fewer components, while managing to maintain or in some instances actually increase functionality. The trend also contains a note of caution that sometimes in the evolution of a system it is correct to 'trim' components, while at other times it is not possible. This examination of the 'trimming' tool, then, considers itself only in that scenario where the reduction of part count in a system is a viable option.

In a bid to maximise the useful effect of the tool, we will describe what is an amalgam of best practice from other similar innovation strategies. Following this description, a second section of the chapter will examine some of the rules we need to be aware of when evaluating the what, where and how of trimming. A third section provides two simple case study examples of 'trimming' in action.

1) Trimming Tool

The trimming tool has a function and attribute analysis model as its essential start point. Some might argue that the simple trimming provocation 'how could the system work if component X was trimmed?' is a far simpler start point – and undoubtedly it is, but unfortunately it is a simplification than filters-out rather than distills useful data, and consequently usually leads to a variety of downstream problems. As far as this book is concerned, the only way you will be directed by the systematic creativity process into this trimming chapter is after a function model has been constructed. It is that fundamental to the process.

Once the model exists, the underlying principles of the trimming tool are then very simple. The main objective is to eliminate unwanted components from a system. We need to decide which components are potential candidates from trimming, and in what order we should examine them, but first it is useful to examine the provocations contained in the tool to start the process. The crucial first trimming provocation is

Why don't we eliminate this component?

Essentially, then, we have a series of seven trimming questions to ask about any of the components we decide to try and eliminate within the system under analysis. Those seven questions are illustrated in Figure 17.1 below.

- Do I need the function offered by the part?
- Can something else in or around the system perform the function?
- Can an existing resource perform the function?
- Can a low cost alternative perform the function?
- Must the part move relative to other parts
- Must the part be of a different material or isolated from
  its mating parts?
- Must the part be separate from mating parts to facilitate
  assembly or dis-assembly

Figure 17.1: Combined TRIZ/DFMA Trimming Questions

Let us have a look at each of them in turn:

Do I need The Function? An important first question. If we are looking to eliminate a particular component, **all** of the functional connections between that component or its attributes and other components or their attributes (i.e. all of the 'useful' arrows pointing out of the component – see illustration below) will disappear. The question is about establishing whether those functions are actually required.

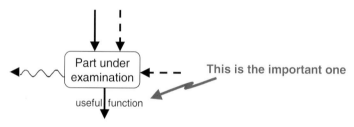

Note how it is only outgoing arrows on useful functions that we are required to question. We don't mind if outgoing arrows representing harmful functions disappear (these are probably among the things that are prompting us to consider trimming the component in the first place!), and likewise, we don't mind if the incoming arrows disappear as these are functions that exist only because the component does –in many instances, they are only present because the component functions inadequately without them.

Can Something Else In or Around the System Perform The Function? Here we are explicitly looking at the other components already drawn on the FAA model to see if they are able to perform the useful function(s) that we would lose if the part under consideration was to be trimmed. The implicit assumption here is that we have determined from the first question that we do want the function. If the FAA model has been drawn in a hierarchical manner (see Chapter 6, section 3), the search for something else in the system to deliver the function should start from the components closest to the trimmed part, gradually working away to the extremes of the model. Experience suggests, that if an answer exists, it will tend to be found at a position higher up the hierarchy, but this should not be considered to be an absolute rule.

Can an Existing Resource Perform the Function? In several senses, this is similar to the previous question, but it extends that question to look beyond just the other

components drawn on the FAA model. In the terms of our definitions of what resources are (see Chapter 14 and the resources section in the Problem/Opportunity Explorer in Chapter 5), this question provides three new opportunities to identify something already in the system that may be able to help deliver the function(s) we require to have performed:

   a) is there something in the attributes of one of the other components that might make it able to perform the function?
   b) is there something in the environment around the system that can be used as a resource?
   c) Could some of the unused evolutionary potential (see chapter 13) in other existing components be used as the resource that can help deliver the function. In other words, if we evolve one of the other components along one or more of the trends of evolution, could it then perform the function we require?

Can a Low Cost Alternative Perform the Function? This question relates fairly specifically to the 'low cost' and 'easily available' resource idea tables detailed in the reference section of Chapter 14. The question is more one of substitution than trimming, but if the component we are looking to eliminate can be replaced by a cheaper alternative, then we will certainly have the opportunity to trim cost.

Must the Part Move in Relation to Other Parts? This is an adaptation of one of the questions emerging from DFMA. The key to successful application of this question in the trimming context is the identification of functional relationships in the FAA model that indicate movement between components. This is of course not the same as a functional relationship 'component moves another component' – which would have been picked up by the first question (with which this one does overlap somewhat). Rather, the prompt here is to think about components which are not directly related in terms of functional relationships, but which nevertheless feature some form of relative motion.

Must the Part be of a Different Material or be Isolated from Mating Parts? This question works in a similar manner to the previous one, and again overlaps somewhat with the first question 'do I need the function?', but here there is a specific suggestion to think about material attributes.

Must the Part Be Separate to Facilitate Assembly/Dis-assembly? This question demands that the user thinks about the 'past' and 'future' elements in the 9-Windows, and any requirements that may be present during assembly and dis-assembly of components. Some useful provocations can emerge from this kind of thinking – for example a provocation to trim the hood of an automobile sounds impossible because the function 'allow access to engine during maintenance' would be lost if the hood is eliminated, but turns out to be very useful if either the need for opening and closing the hood disappears, because either the need for maintenance disappears, or some other form of engine access is devised.

Trimming Sequence

Chapter 9 provides guidelines on when trimming will be used, but not on determining which specific components should be trimmed or in which specific order. Such specific details are unfortunately not able to be pinned down definitively in any generic sense. What can be determined is that there are useful guidelines that do appear to be generically applicable. We examine three in particular here:

1) Number of harmful, excessive and inadequate functions connected to the component to be trimmed – those components with the highest number of such functions (especially with incoming arrows – i.e. where the component is the *object* of a functional relationship) are a prime candidate for trimming.
2) Relative value (usually financial) of the different components. The highest value components represent the biggest trimming benefit opportunities.
3) Component position in functional hierarchy – the higher the position, the higher the potential prize of successful trimming.

The relative priority of these three guidelines is highly dependent on the specific circumstances surrounding a given problem. The case study example at the end of the chapter uses one method of prioritisation; your problem may require a different one.

2) Trimming Rules

A) Function Capturing

The biggest single factor affecting the success or otherwise of a trimming action is functionality, and specifically knowing that **all** of the functions present in a system are known and recorded. Unfortunately there are no hard and fast guidelines to help in this task; there are simply too many possibilities. The only real 'secret', therefore, is that the function and attribute analysis that should have been carried out before commencing any trimming operation has been comprehensive and, preferably, also been validated by more than one person.

By way of introduction to a useful test we can apply to help in this 'functional completeness' analysis, we return to the bicycle saddle from Chapter 10. An initial function analysis of the saddle design (stripping away the surrounding detail (e.g. height and orientation adjustment functions) to concentrate purely on the saddle for a moment) might well look something like the FAA model reproduced in Figure 17.2. The diagram suggests that the only useful function of the saddle is 'supports rider'. The harmful function 'impedes legs' is the indication that there is a contradiction present – and thus the reason that the design featured in the chapter on eliminating contradictions. The point here, however, is that if we are to attempt any kind of trimming on this system, we need to ensure all of the functions are captured.

Perhaps surprisingly, many designers in the bicycle business would agree with the functional description of the saddle as 'supports rider' as being the only reason for the saddle being there. On company recently took this belief as a justification for trimming the nose of the saddle. Unfortunately, the nose of the saddle does have a useful function, albeit one that requires a definite use of 9-Windows thinking to recognise: anyone who cycles may be aware of the exertion of a force by the side of their legs onto the side of the saddle as they attempt a high-speed cornering operation. Essentially, the leg is helping to react a 'keep travelling in a straight line' force from the bike. The nose of the saddle has, in this situation, got a very definite useful function called 'react side-force'.

The saddle manufacturer that trimmed the nose of the saddle, therefore, took this function away from the cyclist. Okay for an exercise bike; not so good for a road-bike.

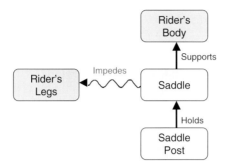

Figure 17.2: Simplified FAA Model of Bicycle Saddle

The general point from this first trimming rule, then, is make absolutely sure you have recorded all of the useful function arrows pointing away from the component you are aiming to trim. We recommend you use the 9-Windows concept to help you to make sure 'all' really does mean 'all'.

B) Law of System Completeness

The TRIZ Law of System Completeness (Reference 17.2) describes four essential elements of a system as shown in Figure 17.3. The Law requires that all components are present and that 'if any component is missing, the technical system does not exist, if any component fails, the system does not 'survive'' (Reference 17.3).

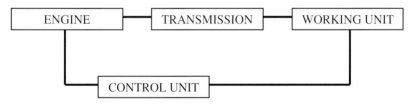

Figure 17.3: The 4 Essential Elements of a Technical System
(as defined in classical TRIZ)

By way of example, a technical system to achieve the function 'clean teeth' requires a working unit (or 'tool' in several texts) – the tooth-brush; an engine – our muscles; a transmission – our arm/hand/etc; and a control unit – in this case a combination of our brain, our nervous system and our view in the mirror. Take any one of the four away, and we are no longer able to deliver the required function.

More recent work reported by Savransky (Reference 17.4) has implied that actually the system is not complete with just the four elements, and that a fifth essential element is required. Savransky calls this fifth element 'casing'. Incidentally, both Stafford Beer's 'Viable System Model' (Reference 17.5) and Game Theory (Reference 17.6) both also describe the need for five elements to define a complete and viable system. Reference 17.7 discusses the three different perspectives in more detail for those interested in

gaining a broader perspective. We might interpret this description more evocatively as a connection between the defined system and its surroundings. In keeping with other conventions developed throughout this book, we will use 'interface' as a suitably descriptive name. By way of example of what we mean by this fifth essential system element, in the case of the above 'clean teeth' example, we see that we are only able to successfully achieve the function because of the presence of teeth and thus there has to be an interface between the tool and those teeth. There is considerable commonality with the substance-field model concept here of course, and the definitive law of system completeness rule we will recommend here combines all of these elements.

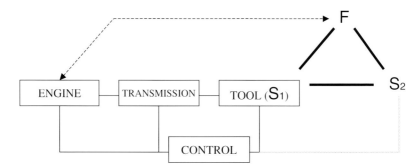

Figure 17.4: The Complete Viable System Model

This picture highlights the tool and 'S1' as the common link between the Law of system Completeness and the Substance-Field Model; the two things are in fact the same. There is a similar link between the engine and the field required to make the function happening.

The net effect of this combination is that the Law of System Completeness is only strictly speaking correct if S2 – 'the object' or 'interface' is present. This is consistent with the above description of the need for a fifth essential element.

The essential 'field' element of the model may come from the 'engine', but not always. In the teeth-cleaning example, with the toothbrush as S1 and the tooth as S2, the field connecting them is a mechanical field producing relative motion. While at source the energy providing this relative motion is coming from human muscle, it is still useful to think of the two as 'possibly' rather than 'definitively' connected.

The 'control' element is interesting also with regard to the way it gets us to think about its relationship with S2: Returning to the cleaning teeth example, it should be evident that while it is perfectly possible to deliver the function without any connection between the teeth (S2) and the control system – most teeth cleaning systems exhibit precisely this disconnection such that we don't know other than by visual or tactile examination after the event whether we have clean teeth or not – a far more effective solution emerges when the object (S2) is included in the control loop – as shown by the dotted red line. This line is in fact the 'feedback' line suggested by the controllability trend. Either way, this final picture should give us a useful image of what actually defines a viable and effective system.

From the perspective of the 'trimming' tool, the main point of this system viability test is that if we are seeking to trim any of these essential elements from our system, we

fundamentally have to find replacements for them, as without them, the system cannot be viable.

C) Coupled Functional Requirements

The development of Axiomatic Design by Nam Suh (Reference 17.8) was an attempt to produce a series of rules that would enable designer's to discriminate between 'good' and 'bad' design practice. The method essentially provided two useful rules (actually, Suh called them 'axioms' – TRIZ can be used to show there are very definite examples of good design practice that do not follow these axioms, although they do remain as 'useful guidelines') to define good design practice. To simplify these rules somewhat, they basically state good design:-
1) achieves independence between different functional requirements, and,
2) achieves the functional requirements with minimum complexity.

The first of these rules provides the most useful element to help in the process of system trimming.

The classic example of 'good' design practice emerging from this first rule is the mixer tap. A conventional hot and cold tap system represents 'bad' design practice because the two functional requirements from the system – 'dispense water at the correct temperature', and 'dispense a controlled amount of water' – are not independent. In Axiomatic Design terms, the functional requirements are said to be 'coupled'. This is 'bad' because it means the user has to make two adjustments in order to deliver both functions, but adjustment of either (tap) has an influence on the other. In other words, if the mixed water coming out of the two taps is too hot, the user reduces the flow of hot water, which then has affected overall flow rate. The mixer tap represents an example of 'good' design practice because the user is now able to control temperature and flow-rate independently of one another.

Suh unfortunately resorts to matrix algebra as the principle mechanism for determining the independence of functions (unfortunate because 'matrix algebra' and 'designer' seem to mix like oil and water in around 95% of cases). FAA modelling offers a rather more visual perspective on whether designs are coupled or not, and it is that we will focus on now in order to elicit the useful rules that Axiomatic Design offers during use of the trimming tool (those wishing to delve further into the details of the arguments – for example, does the user really want a controlled flow rate or simply a maximum flow rate, may care to check out Reference 17.9).

Figure 17.5, meanwhile, provides a simplified FAA model of the coupled hot and cold tap system.

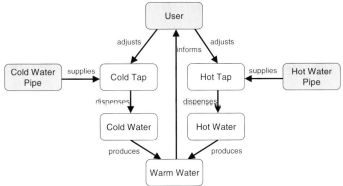

Figure 17.5: Simplified FAA Model of Hot and Cold Tap System

The first thing we look to from this figure is what are the factors that show us that the design is coupled and therefore doesn't meet the independence rule? The answers to this question are twofold:

1) the main product (a known amount of warm water) is produced through a combination of other things, and,
2) there are multiple (in this case two) control actions

In abstracted form, these two answers present a good test of a coupled design, and can be used in this way. From the trimming perspective, the existence of such coupling effects should then present us with the following good rule:

If there are coupled elements in a system, one or more of those elements is a prime candidate for trimming.

Note how the FAA model alone does not indicate the coupled function issue, and also that if we try and re-draw the picture to represent time issues, we will draw the same thing – i.e. the picture does not change as a function of time.

The second useful rule to take from this example and therefore from Axiomatic Design, is that after we have successively trimmed the system – see Figure 17.6 showing the equivalent FAA model for the mixer tap – we should continue to endeavour to maintain independence between the functional requirements. In other words, at least one of the two answers above, should no longer be true – so that either the product comes from one thing, or there is one control action, or both.

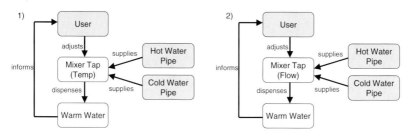

Figure 17.6: Simplified FAA Model of Mixer Tap System

Note also how to truly reflect what happens in the mixer tap, the FAA model is drawn at two different times – the usual mode of operation being that the user first adjusts the tap to the right temperature, and then adjusts for desired flow rate.

3) Trimming Case Study Examples

We will now examine two case study examples of the Trimming tool in action. The first case – looking at a simple paper stapler – focuses on trimming of a relatively simple mechanical system. The second case – looking at a hypothetical manufacture process – examines a system where the time dimension plays a much more important role. Both cases have been chosen to also bring out a number of additional, hopefully useful, thoughts regarding trimming and our effective deployment of the technique. For the sake of brevity, in both cases, we do not present the whole of the preceding problem definition

activity that lead to a decision to use trimming – our purpose being to focus on process rather than specific outcome.

Paper Stapler

Figure 17.7 illustrates a typical paper stapler. The device is a relatively cheap commodity item at the mature end of its current s-curve. Its primary function is 'join paper' (in a semi-permanent manner).

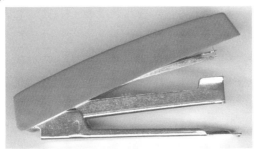

Figure 17.7: Typical Stapler – Prior to Trimming Analysis

The first thing we have to do before it is possible to begin a trimming analysis is to construct a functional model of the device. We do this using the procedure defined in Chapter 6. The resulting model drawn for the stapler under consideration is reproduced in Figure 17.8.

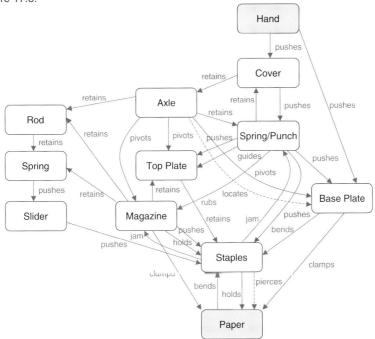

Figure 17.8: Function Analysis for Exemplar Stapler Prior to Trimming Analysis
(Blue boxes represent components we have decided cannot be changed)

For function analysis models like this, where there is little influence of time on the problem, we are basically presented with two main directions when we begin to contemplate trimming. The first is to focus on the elimination of the negative things happening in the system, while the second is to focus on reducing part count in a way that has greatest impact on the cost of producing (or whatever other attributes we choose to focus on) the system. In the case of this stapler, those two approaches lead to quite different foci:

If we choose to focus on the 'eliminate negative effects' part of the current system, the function analysis shows us immediately that just about all of the harmful, excessive and insufficient functions contained in the system center around the staple. Thus, we might say, to eliminate the bad things in the systems, the most useful trimming provocation is 'why don't we eliminate the staple?' Immediately this suggests a shift that will lead to a solution which is not a stapler anymore. This is not necessarily a bad thing. The first thing it encourages us to do is to ask the question 'are there any other ways of delivering the function 'join paper?' The other things the provocation should encourage us to investigate are the Trends of Evolution – and specifically 'in what direction will a staple evolve in, and a t what point does it stop being a staple? The answer to both of these questions leads to some very interesting concepts – none of which the industry appears to have yet seen or exploited.

Fortunately we are less interested in new intellectual property than examining the mechanics of Trimming here, and so we can leave you with that thought from the 'trim the bad things' route. We will turn our attention to the other route – the one about reducing part count to reduce cost. In order to achieve success in this direction, we need to supply some more data into the function analysis model. Specifically, we need to supply some cost attributes for each of the components. Figure 17.9 illustrates how this has been done. In simple terms, each component identified in the function analysis model has a whole series of attributes – manufacture cost, running cost, weight, size, level of reliability, etc – some of which will be relevant to the problem and some not. The cost attributes, and particularly manufacture cost, are particularly useful metrics from a trimming perspective. In Figure 17.9, the cost attributes have been highlighted for each component (other attribute data remains hidden for the purposes of clarity only).

The task once the relevant attributes have been identified involves selecting the most appropriate of the current components for trimming. The simplest rules here are to opt either for the most expensive components or the components generating the fewest useful functions first. In this case, the cost route would lead to the trimming provocation 'why don't we eliminate the staple magazine?', while the 'fewest useful functions' option would lead to us selecting either the top-plate, rod, spring or slider – each of which exists in the system to deliver just one useful function (as evidenced by the fact that each has only one useful arrow departing from it).

In most cases like these we are faced with a trade-off between ease of achieving the trimming result and the resulting benefit we achieve – difficult trimming equals big benefit, and vice-versa. The only exceptions to this general rule appear to be systems which have not been the subject of any kind of function analysis before. In these situations, it would seem that almost any kind of analysis can result in big benefits.

For the stapler example, however, we will pick a component at random in order to illustrate the mechanics of the trimming process. We will make the provocation 'why don't we eliminate the top-plate?'.

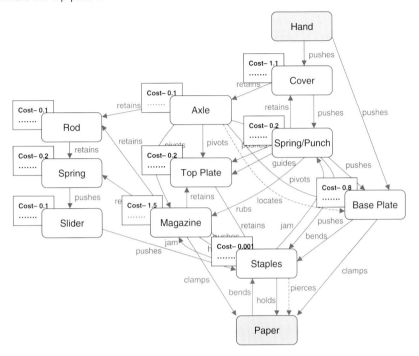

Figure 17.9: Function Analysis for Exemplar Stapler with Cost Attributes Added

The immediate answer to this question is that if we trim the top-plate, we will lose the useful function 'retains staple'. Looking at the questions in Figure 17.1, the next thing we need to then ask is 'do we want this function? If we decided the answer is yes (answering no might take us across to the 'eliminate staple' route outlined earlier), the next question is then can we find something else already in the system to deliver the function in place of the top-plate.

A good way to focus the search of other components that may be able to take on the function is to start with the ones that are physically closest and to work away to the most distant ones. The closest components are in the majority of cases the ones already functionally related to the trimming candidate and are the ones most likely to be capable of taking on the function. In this case, the closest components to the top-plate are the cover, the magazine and the staples.

The next thing to do is examine the attributes of the top-cover, establish which of them are relevant to the delivery of the useful function, and then to see if any of the other components in the vicinity possess similar attributes. In this case, for example, the 'retains staples' function requires that the top-plate is made of metal with a smooth surface. The (plastic) cover is thus probably not a suitable component to take on the new function

(although the question of whether it is possible to make the cover from a stronger plastic might arise). The magazine, on the other hand is both physically close and has similar attributes. Positive answers to the other trimming questions – like do the magazine and top-plate have to move relative to other, or be different to facilitate assembly – would appear to suggest that the useful function currently delivered by the top-plate, could in fact be delivered by the magazine without adverse effect. (Incidentally, a useful parallel provocation to the 'why don't we eliminate the component' trimming question is 'what's stopping us from trimming this component.)

Hopefully this random example should demonstrate the mechanics of trimming in action. We will examine one more example in order to make another useful point about trimming and function analysis in action.

If we adopt the provocation 'why don't we eliminate the cover?' we can go through a similar process of identifying the useful functions performed by the component, establishing whether we actually need them, and if we do, identifying whether something else could deliver the function. In the case of the cover, it should be possible to transfer the function 'retains axle' to something else. The function 'pushes spring/punch' is more interesting because we can soon see that we are only delivering this function in order to transfer the 'push' action to something else. I.e. something else is already performing this function (and because the load carrying attributes must be the same, the strength must be equivalent). Does this then mean we can trim the cover? Strictly speaking, yes. Certainly from a function perspective. But then we are likely to have immediate doubts about the validity of trimming the cover. The point here involves those doubts. They are the things that we should interpret as suggesting that there are other functions we have not registered in our model. If we then force ourselves to answer the question 'what else does the cover do?' it probably won't be long (especially if we look at its list of attributes) before we register the fact that the cover has an aesthetic function. The model as it stands does not register the relationships between cover and user – 'cover attribute 'apearance' pleases user' and 'cover surface finish pleases user' to name just two – because the 'user' does not feature in the model. If we add a new box, then, labeled 'user' and draw a 'pleases' relationship between the appearance attribute of cover to the user, the trimming operation becomes a little more difficult. Especially since, if we examine the attributes of the other components in the system, none of them (as yet) possesses the aesthetic capabilities of the cover.

The point of this final thought being that it is absolutely essential to double-check the completeness of any FAA model before concluding that a part can be trimmed. 'What's stopping me?' is a very good double-check question. A relationship between the part and something from the super-system that we haven't thus far included is a very usual reason why something is stopping us.

Case Study 2 – Time-Based Problems

Figure 17.10 illustrates a hypothetical coated paper manufacturing process which we have selected as a possible candidate for trimming. Paradoxically, many process-based situations are potentially full of trimming opportunities, but trimming is often experienced as a 'difficult to achieve' activity. They are 'full of opportunities' because it is often the case when analyzing processes that the function of many of the steps is only there because some other step is performed inadequately. This is particularly true in chemical reaction problems, where it is very common to see a simple main function (e.g. 'react A with B to

get C') becomes entangled with a host of ancillary functions to compensate for the imperfections in the initial reaction. On the other hand, trimming can be difficult because, unlike trimming a component from a system, in processes a single trimming operation might be removing a whole series of components at a time.

It is often useful in fact before constructing a complete FAA model (or series of models) for a process operation to identify the main useful function, ask whether you would like to perform it better, and, if the answer is yes, establish from the knowledge part of the TRIZ tool-box whether anyone else has performed a similar function better elsewhere. The most extreme example of the potential benefits of doing this came from an extremely complex piece of chemical plant containing several million dollars worth of equipment in which 90% of the processes present were there solely to mop up the problems caused by performing the main useful function in a sub-optimal way.

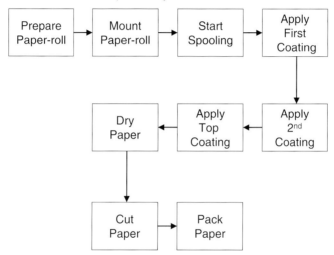

Figure 17.10: Operation Sequence for Hypothetical Paper Coating Process

The system outlined in the figure, meanwhile, is one that has been optimized stage by stage over a period of several years. All of the steps in the process have been optimized towards the upper limits of their (s-curve defined) fundamental limits in terms of rate of output delivered. Each stage also contains a highly sophisticated piece of plant to perform the desired useful function. Several of them (particularly the coating application processes) have ancillary processes (not illustrated for clarity) to achieve such functions as 'remove excess coating', 're-process excess coating', etc.

We could apply Trimming at two main levels in this kind of situation. The first would be the level where we look to eliminate these ancillary functions – applying provocations like 'eliminate the excess coating removal operation'. This would force us to then examine the FAA model for the particular operation. This kind of activity represents an optimization of the process step. Very often this kind of trimming operation will have more to do with reduction of waste than it will in delivering the main useful function any better (i.e. it will not increase process throughput rate). See Reference 17.10 for a very good example of this kind of trimming operation in action.

The second kind of trimming is the one operating at a higher hierarchical level. This is the level where our interest is usually focused on improving throughput – which, after all, is the reason the whole system exists.

Our start-point for trimming at this level is similar in several senses to the procedure detailed for systems like the stapler above, in that we have a choice whether to focus on trimming parts of the system with the most problems or whether to focus on those parts that are affecting the overall throughput. As described in Chapter 5, when identifying the 'sore points' within process-based systems, we are generally speaking looking for the bottlenecks.

In the case of this hypothetical system, if we assume that the attributes for each part of the process tell us the drying process is the bottleneck (as it seems to be in many other similar systems – especially painting processes), we might use the provocation 'eliminate the drying process' as a start point for a trimming analysis.
Here we immediately see that operating trimming at this high level in the system hierarchy forces us to ask some very difficult questions. On the other hand, if it were possible to trim the bottleneck, we would have a profound impact on the throughput of the process.

These kinds of trimming leaps are indeed difficult to make. It is the kind of thinking, on the other hand, that results in the sorts of improvements generated when float-glass production replaced 'conventional' processes involving mechanical systems to form and transport the glass (Reference 17.11).

Provocations like 'eliminate the drying process' or, to look at other operations in the Figure, 'eliminate paper-cutting operation' or 'eliminate paper roll mounting' force us to re-think things at a quite fundamental level. The most interesting thing when we force ourselves to do this, is that it is still common to find instances where someone, somewhere else has already thought (and achieved solutions to) the same big thoughts. (By way of a brief diversion from the mechanics of trimming, the sorts of solutions identified by others to the sorts of process problem posed for this paper coating example all involve a further shift in hierarchical thinking – in this case, zooming in to look at the molecular level delivery of the required functions.)

In summary, when thinking about trimming in the context of processes, the idea of hierarchy is fundamental to our thinking. Trimming at the higher levels, perhaps unsurprisingly, are the most difficult to realize, but on the other hand, they are usually the only ones to make a significant effect on overall process throughput.

What Do I Do?

Conceptually, Trimming is one of the simplest of the TRIZ tools to operate. The whole thing basically operates from the provocation 'why don't we eliminate X?' where X could be a component or a process step.

All of the necessary ground-work for Trimming should have been done in the construction of Function and Attribute Analysis models during the problem definition part of the systematic creativity process.

The strategies open to us once we have decided to attempt trimming of an element from a system involve working through the questions detailed in Figure 17.1.

These questions may then lead us on to other parts of the TRIZ toolkit (for example the question 'can something else in the system perform the function?' often leads to the idea of 'self-x' functions and Chapter 18 or to the knowledge/effects part of TRIZ in order to find out if anyone else has already achieved a solution to your trimming problem.

References

1) Boothroyd, G., Dewhurst, P., Knight, W., 'Product Design for Manufacture and Assembly', Marcel Dekker, September 2001.
2) Altshuller, G. ,'Creativity As An Exact Science', Gordon and Breach, 1984.
3) Salamatov, Y., 'TRIZ: The Right Solution At The Right Time', Insytec, The Netherlands, 1999.
4) Savransky, S., 'Engineering of Creativity', CRC Press, 2000, p41.
5) Espejo, R., Harnden, R., 'The Viable System Model', John Wiley & Sons, New York, 1989.
6) Nalebuff, B.J., Brandenburger, A.M., 'Co-opetition', Harper Collins Business, 1996.
7) Mann, D.L., 'Laws of System Completeness', TRIZ Journal, May 2001.
8) Suh, N., 'The Principles of Design', Oxford University Press, 1990.
9) Mann, D.L., 'TRIZ and Axiomatic Design: Commonalities and Contradictions', paper presented at Axiomatic Design conference, Cambridge MA, June 2002.
10) Mitchell, I., 'Edge Suck-Off', paper presented at TRIZCON2000, Nashua, May 2000.
11) Utterback; J., 'Mastering The Dynamics of Innovation', Harvard Business School Press, 1993.

18.
Problem Solving Tools
Ideality/Ideal Final Result

"Its like, how much more black could this be? And the answer is none. None more black."
Nigel Tufnel in Spinal Tap.

Chapter 8 examined the use of the Ideality and Ideal Final Result (IFR) concepts in the context of their application in a problem or opportunity definition context. In this chapter we examine aspects of both that are relevant to their use in a problem solving context – that is their application in the role of helping to generate solutions.

In all, there are three main aspects of Ideality and IFR that offer problem solving tools. These are:-
1) structured thinking questionnaire
2) 'self' solution trigger tool
3) connection to resources and system hierarchy tool

Each of the three will be described individually in the following sections:

Structured Thinking Questionnaire

Chapter 8 detailed a questionnaire for helping to define problems from an ideality perspective, followed by a series of examples of the tool in action for a variety of different problem situations. The questionnaire is repeated here in Figure 18.1.

1) **What is the final aim of the system?**

2) **What is the Ideal Final Result outcome?**

3) **What is stopping you from achieving this IFR?**

4) **Why is it stopping you?**

5) **How could you make the thing(s) stopping you disappear?**

6) **What resources are available to help create these circumstances?**

7) **Has anyone else been able to solve this problem?**

Figure 18.1: Ideal Final Result Problem Definition Questionnaire

Although the questionnaire exists primarily as a problem definition tool, it can also be a useful provider of solution triggers. The main one of these comes with the 'what's stopping you?' question and it's 'why?' follow-up. Simply forcing ourselves to think about these stoppers and their removal can often be a powerful means of generating solution ideas.
The second solution trigger provided by the questionnaire is one with a much more explicit set of problem solving directions to offer:

'Self' Solution Trigger Tool

This section discusses the importance of systems that incorporate solutions incorporating the word 'self' – self-cleaning, self-balancing, self-aligning, etc – in the context of their relationship – in the true TRIZ sense – to the concept of ideality. We discuss the state of the art regarding technical system design solutions achieving self-x delivery of useful functions, following an extensive analysis of the US and other patent databases.

Anyone that has used the Ideal Final Result part of the TRIZ suite of tools will have come across the word 'self'. If we accept that the Ideal Final Result occurs when we achieve the desired function without cost or harm, then we often derive statements like 'the system achieves the function itself', or 'the problem resolves itself' when conceptualising ideal solution directions. Although in practice we may have to back away from such an ideal end point, there is a growing database of solutions where others have not. Systems that have solved problems 'by themselves' represent an important part of the global knowledge database.

It is these solutions that we discuss here in the context of the way they can help to generate good solution directions and ideas. The basis for establishing the validity of the tool has been an analysis of the US patent database. That analysis has taken as its start point, the range of solutions featuring 'self-X' properties, where X may be just about any useful **function** other inventors have required a system to perform.

Before examining the patent database in detail, it is first necessary to clarify the relationship between 'things that do things for themselves' and the TRIZ concept of ideality. We must do this, because examination of the patent database quickly reveals a large number of 'self-X' solutions that have little in common with the concept of an Ideal Final Result solution.

By way of example, we will look first at the case of barrier filters. The main useful function of a barrier filter is to separate contaminants of varying descriptions from a flow of air or oil or other substance – Figure 18.1. Barrier filters are used in a massive variety of industries in a wide variety of different roles. While in many senses sophisticated at the sub-system level, barrier filters are a nevertheless relatively crude means of achieving the desired separation function when examined as a system - they are bulky, fragile, block-up easily, and their performance worsens considerably after they have been collecting debris for a period of time. Because of these last two effects in particular, significant efforts have been expended in achieving 'self-cleaning' barrier filters.

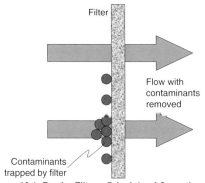

Flow with
contaminants
removed

Filter

Contaminants
trapped by filter

Figure 18.1: Barrier Filter – Principle of Operation

In its standard form, a barrier filter is relatively easy to design and install. The main challenges faced by the designer involve achieving an acceptable flow through the surfaces of the filter, and ensuring that there are no leaks or air escape routes which would allow contaminants to inadvertently by-pass the filter.

The majority of 'self-cleaning' barrier filters operate by essentially reversing the direction of flow through the filter such that instead of being pushed against the barrier by flow in the normal direction (green arrows in the figure), the contaminants are pushed away from the filter by a flow in the other direction. This flow reversal is usually known as 'back-washing' or 'back-flushing'. Although successful (to varying degrees) in 'cleaning' the filter, introduction of a 'self-cleaning' capability usually means a considerable increase in the complexity of the overall filtration system. It means, for example, that we need to introduce a means of reversing the flow; it means introducing means of capturing the contaminants that get blown away from the filter; it means ensuring that the seals we use to ensure they work in one direction now have to work in two; and it means addition of a considerable amount of hard (and often soft) ware to work out or tell the user when to conduct a back-flush operation.

So, although we may have introduced a 'self-cleaning' capability – i.e. the filter assembly cleans itself, we have not necessarily derived an 'Ideal Final Result' solution because the system has become markedly more complex.

How, then, do we discriminate between such a 'self-cleaning' design and what TRIZ might define as an Ideal Final Result 'self-cleaning' design?

One useful way derives from the trend of evolution in which systems are seen to evolve in such a way that they must become more complex before they can become simple again. Figure 18.2 illustrates the basic characteristic (see also the Trimming trend in Chapter 13) of 'complexity' versus time for a typical system.

Thus we see that the current 'state of the art' 'self-cleaning' filter designs have followed the traditional evolution path which implies that if we add new functionality – in this case 'cleaning' – then the system must become more complex. Conversely, a 'self-cleaning filter' conceived from an ideality-driven route would get us to think much harder about whether or not it is possible to achieve 'self-cleaning' without complicating the system.

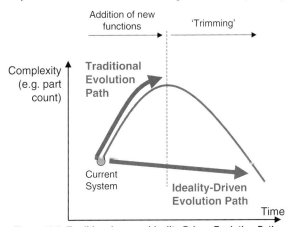

Figure 18.2: Traditional versus Ideality-Driven Evolution Paths

TRIZ, in other words, gets us to think rather harder about bypassing the traditional ways of doing things. The traditional way of doing things gives us a state of the art illustrated in Figure 18.3a. It bears little relation to the IFR-driven 'self-cleaning' filter shown in Figure 18.3b. The 'real' (ideality-driven) 'self-cleaning filter' – where the filter material really 'cleans itself' may not be possible today (actually it may be – it just may not be a barrier anymore), but the big point is that at least we should ask the question.

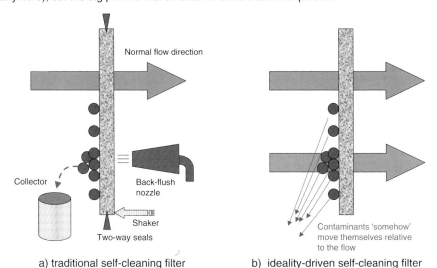

Figure 18.3: Traditional versus Ideality-Driven 'Self-Cleaning' Filter Concepts

Another Example

It is not possible to buy a self-cleaning filter of the type illustrated in Figure 18.3b at this point in time. In order to demonstrate that other industries have successfully achieved such Ideal Final Result driven solutions, we will shift slightly to look at another 'self-cleaning' solution; this time a self-cleaning oven. Self-cleaning ovens have been around for a long time. Like the filter above, several ovens seek to achieve the self-clean function through addition of more complexity – usually the incorporation of fans and vents to ensure a flow of air adjacent to the walls to be kept clean – but more recently, there have been drives to achieve the function without adding complexity. In this sense, the invention reproduced in Figure 18.4 emerges from asking whether there are ways of achieving the 'self-clean' function using existing resources. In this case, the answer is yes – the oven has a thermostat and the ability to cycle temperature, so why not use this existing capability in a way which encourages the walls to bake and then break-off the various contaminants that cause us to think the oven is not clean.

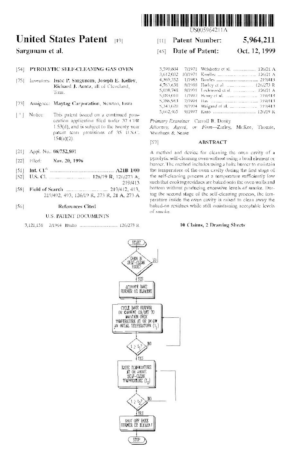

Figure 18.4: US Patent 5964211 'Pyrolytic self-cleaning gas oven'

Patent 5964211 represents a solution much closer to the ideality-driven rather than traditional innovation approach.

Self-X Patents'

A study of 'self'-based patents (including the synonyms of 'self' – 'automatic', 'auto-', etc) on the US patent database has been conducted in order to establish the state of the art in terms of what functions the world knows how to get systems to deliver 'by themselves'. The searches covered the period from 1985 to the present day.

The first part of the study examined the proportion of 'self-X' patents to be found in the database. The findings are recorded in Figure 18.5.

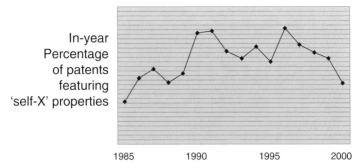

In-year Percentage of patents featuring 'self-X' properties

1985   1990   1995   2000

Figure 18.5: Relative Proportion of 'Self-X' Patents as a Function of Total Patents

The figure shows that the proportion of 'self-X' patents is on a gently rising line. This is consistent with increasing ideality being an overall driver for innovation, albeit perhaps not as dramatic as one might hope or expect. The figure, and the fact that the overall patent rate has increased dramatically, however, hides the fact that the overall number of 'self-X' patents has more than trebled in the last 15 years. The message in this sense is that a growing number of inventors are recognising the importance of designing systems capable of doing things by themselves.

The study then moved on to examine what sort of things it is that inventors are getting their inventions to do by themselves. Figure 18.6 illustrates the resulting breakdown. Over 2000 patents have been studied on a case-by-case basis in compiling the figures. It has not been possible to discriminate absolutely between 'traditional' and 'ideality-driven' solutions, but, rather, the point has been to examine the **functions** that inventors have been trying to get their inventions to deliver. The data is presented in descending order of frequency, such that 'self-aligning' is the most frequently occurring 'self-X' patent type.

The figure highlights a number of interesting points. Firstly, while there may be some debate over the inclusion of the 'self-contained' category – which doesn't necessarily contain a function – it is interesting to note that 'self-contained' occurs significantly less frequently than the most common 'self' function, 'aligning'. There are in fact close to 200 patents focused on delivering a 'self-aligning' capability.

'Self-aligning' may be seen as a whole family of similar patents (adjusting, positioning, centring, levelling, opening/closing, etc) associated with a physical movement. In just about all cases, the degrees of movement being achieved are relatively small. This is perhaps significant in terms of defining the state of the art – several inventors know how to make physical things move themselves, just not very far.

Another big class of 'self-X' functions is then concerned with the delivery of (relatively easy to obtain) non-physical changes. Such functions primarily consist of measurement-based functions such as 'self-test' and 'self-time' (many computer applications), or, on the mechanical side, 'self-regulate', 'self-limit', or 'self-calibrate'.

Moving down to the less frequent applications then are inventions which make use of new and emerging scientific knowledge. This category includes, for example, things that expand or contract by making use of shape-memory alloys or polymers, things that clean themselves using the Lotus Effect, things that heat themselves using a sodium acetate (or similar) phase transition energy storage means, things that self-learn as a result of increasing use of genetic algorithms and expert systems in computing, and so on.

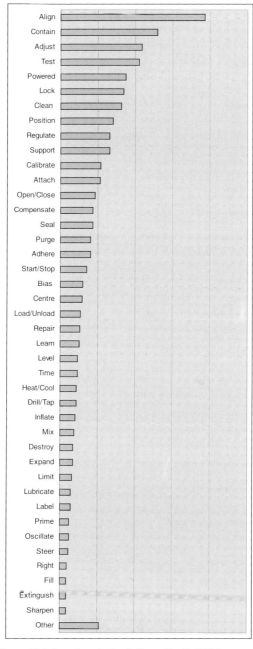

Figure 18.6: Functions Being Delivered by 'Self-X' Patents

A final group of 'self-X' types – self-balance, self-seal, self-repair, for example – represent relatively recent innovations, which have not as yet reached the eyes of the majority of problem solvers. Self-balancing things are particularly interesting in this context. Just about any industry that designs things that rotate faces a balance issue at some stage – either during manufacture (where we set tight tolerances in order to reduce out of balance forces) or assembly, or test (most sectors invest significantly in machinery to facilitate balance operations), or in service. Few, if any, on the other hand appear to have recognised the existence of several, highly amenable to transfer to other industry sectors, good patents in this area.

The 'others' category includes a wide range of 'self-X' functions with only one or two references. These include functions like mold, sinter, polish, illuminate, deodorise (!), which again represent capabilities (or potential capabilities) that have thus far not been widely exploited by other problem solvers.

'Self' and Your Problem

Solutions that achieve functions 'by themselves' are very important in the sense of a world in which the overall technology evolution driver is increasing ideality.

In this sense, the concept of Ideal Final Result, and the idea of looking for solutions which incorporate the word 'self' – i.e. the problem solves itself – is a very powerful tool in the TRIZ armoury.

Some problems contain constraints which make it difficult if not impractical for the problem owner to consider using the IFR method, but that being said, the 'define the IFR and then work back' schema illustrated in Chapter 8 is a useful start point for a good number of problems. Ideal Final Result thinking encourages problem owners to first register the function that they are wishing to deliver, and then gets them to think about how the system could deliver that function by itself – i.e. without the addition of the increased complexity inherent to traditional problem solving methods.

The 'self-X' solutions of others to be found on the patent database are testament enough to the fact then that someone may already have successfully achieved the 'self' delivery of a function we wish to achieve ourselves.

'Self' is a very important word in the context of looking for good solutions to problems; if a system can solve a problem 'by itself', it will be a more ideal solution than one that requires the inclusion of external factors which serve to complicate the system.

There is a difference between traditional and ideality-driven definitions of 'self'. Traditionally, if we add new functions, the system has to become more complex. The ideality-driven definition gets us to think harder about whether we can achieve the additional functionality using resources that already exist in or around the system, and without increased complexity.

The patent database provides a good start point (knowledge resource) for highlighting the sorts of 'self-X' functions being achieved by other problem solvers.

Someone, somewhere is increasingly likely to have thought about and solved your 'self-x' problem. As such, adding the word 'self' to the front of any function you are looking to deliver within a system is a simple yet extremely powerful solution trigger.

Resources and System Hierarchy Tool

As described in Chapter 8, the ideality part of TRIZ is closely linked to the identification and maximal utilisation of resources within a system. The underlying concept of increasing ideality involves the desire to achieve functionality with ever fewer resources. The identification of resources is thus a very important aspect of TRIZ philosophy. There are three main routes to the identification of resources. Two of these three ways are discussed in other chapters; Chapter 14 specifically discusses the identification of resources through use of a series of resource trigger databases – things that other successful problem solvers have successively found to be resources; Chapter 13 discusses the TRIZ technology trends and the concept of evolutionary potential – the unused evolutionary steps in a given system (by way of reminder, this evolutionary potential concept encourages us to see a smooth surface or a monolithic structure as resources – because both possess the ability to evolve towards roughening and hollowing respectively.

The third route to the identification of resources is more closely linked to ideality and is thus described here.

The basis of this ideality/resources link is the hierarchical nature of systems. Figure 18.7 illustrates a typical system hierarchy diagram for a system called 'transport' or (at a more abstract level 'freedom'). The hierarchy plots a simplified structure from transport down to car to the sub-systems of cars and, finally, to an example component – in this case 'windscreen wipers'.

The construction of this type of hierarchy is a very useful first step to the identification of resources that will hopefully enable us to evolve systems and system components towards ideality.

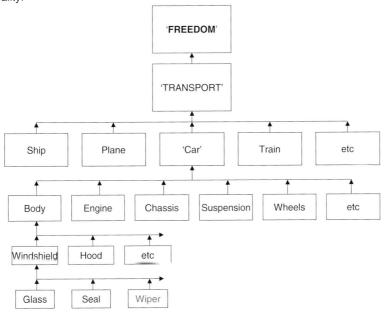

Figure 18.7: Simplified 'Transport' System Hierarchy

In certain circumstances (e.g. if we do not work in the automotive industry) we might chose to explore the IFR concept at the hierarchical level of car; in which case the IFR car is that we achieve the function ' transport' (or more specifically personal transport) without the presence of a system called car. For most practical purposes, defining the IFR at this level is not particularly useful. Defining it at lower levels of the hierarchy, on the other hand, can prove to be extremely useful.

As an example, we will examine an ideal final result windshield wiper. Our definition here would involve achieving the function(s) of the windshield wiper ('clean windshield' primarily) without the need for the wiper assembly. This definition can turn out to be much more practically realizable.

The main point, and the principal connection between this kind of IFR definition and a solving tool is that the hierarchy offers us the opportunity to identify other things that already exist in the system that may be able to fulfill the function of the component or assembly we wish to evolve to its IFR.

Thus, in the case of the components drawn in the figure, we might hypothesise that something else in the system – for example the windshield *itself* – might be able to achieve the function of the windshield wiper – Figure 18.8.

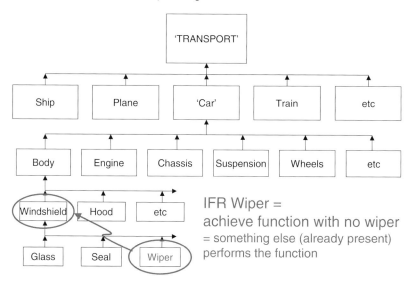

Figure 18.8: The Hierarchy Mechanics of Evolution Towards Ideality

There are obvious links to the idea of Trimming (Chapter 17) here of course. The difference – and thus the additional problem solving idea offered by this combined ideality/resources thinking – comes with the crucial image of first the construction of this kind of system hierarchy, followed by an evolution process in which the things at the bottom of the hierarchy are progressively evolved to their IFR and disappear. Thus we have an image of a hierarchical structure progressively being eaten away from the bottom up.

In terms of the search for resources to help evolve a given component to its IFR then, the key part of this hierarchy tool is that we should be looking at other parts of the hierarchy (particularly those things at a higher hierarchical level) to see if they can take on the useful functions of the component we wish to eliminate.

What Do I Do?

Using the ideality and ideal final result concepts in a problem solving context involves one or more of three possibilities:

1) Use the questionnaire in Figure 18.1 as a means of obtaining a more complete understanding of your problem situation and how to then achieve the defined goal.
2) Add the word 'self' onto the front of a function you require to have performed and use this 'self-x' function description as a trigger to first see if anyone else has already solved a similar problem (e.g. by searching patent databases), and second, as a prompt to generate ideas (akin to the 'self-service' Inventive Principle in Chapter 10.
3) Construct a system hierarchy as a means of seeing if there is a resource somewhere else in the system that may help you to achieve an IFR outcome for the component or assembly you are investigating – in other words, can something else already in the system perform its useful function(s).

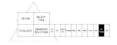

19.
Problem Solving:
Psychological Inertia Tools

There are six people in the world. Five of them are hamburgers.
Captain Beefheart

Introduction

The psychological inertia breaking tools contained in TRIZ are used in two main scenarios. The first involve situations where we are having difficulty solving a problem; perhaps a situation in which we have passed through the 'generate solutions' part of the process and have not generated anything that looks like an answer. The second involves use of one or more of the PI tools specifically as a problem solving tool because they fit into our particular way of doing things. Generally speaking, the first scenario is the only one in which the overall systematic creativity process will direct you to this chapter.

In either scenario, the basic underlying idea behind the tools is that our brains are somehow 'blocked', and that we need a something to give us a jolt. In the problem solving as 'digging for treasure in a field' analogy, the psychological inertia tools are there to help us make a systematic shift to another part of the field. More than this, the tools are hopefully going to send us to a part of the field in which the probability of finding new or better treasure is high.

There are many forms and types of psychological inertia breaking tools in creativity methods outside TRIZ. The work of Edward DeBono, Tony Buzan and, to a lesser extent Robert Dilts (see the bibliography at the end of the chapter for more information) are worthy of specific mention. In the majority of circumstances the strategies recommended by these other authors can be included in this part of the TRIZ process, either as a replacement or, preferably, a supplement to the TRIZ-generated tools.

We will confine our discussion to just the TRIZ tools. We will examine four different tools. One – the 9-Windows or system operator tool – has been the subject of a whole chapter earlier in the book and, in keeping with its importance, a 9-windows image features on every page. We will confine our discussion of the tool in this chapter to just its specific application as a psychological inertia breaking strategy. The other three tools within the armoury are:-

- Smart Little People
- Size-Time-Interface-Cost Tool
- Why-What's Stopping Analysis

We will start by looking at the 9-Windows tool in its purely psychological inertia breaking context.

9-Windows/System Operator

As initially discussed in Chapter 3, our brains sometimes play some cruel tricks on us. Take a look at Figure 19.1, for example, and write down what you can see.

Figure 19.1: What Can You See?

Because everyone has seen something like this picture before, the usual response is something along the lines 'aha, yes, I can see both things – two faces and a vase'. There are two types of psychological inertia happening here; the first comes from exactly that familiarity – we are simply too used to seeing this kind of annoying puzzle. The second, however, is somewhat more serious. It comes from a rule that in all probability your brain has just imposed on itself, even though it is a rule that was never stated, nor was it actually there. That unstated, self-imposed rule was 'I must form images from the *whole* picture'. Admit it, its one you applied.

But the rule was never there. Just as similar 'rules' are never there in many of the 'problems' we look at. The simple truth about the Figure 19.1 image is that there are lots of images there that can be formed from just a part of the picture. Maybe now we have dispensed with the false rule, you can see things like

- a man in a pork-pie hat or a light fitting? (bottom half of picture)
- a whale's tail? (top half of picture)
- profile of an overweight person? (bottom right quarter of picture)

Or maybe you can zoom out and see the picture as that of a small key-hole? Or how about a close up of the back of two cars parked back-to-back?

The point? We often need a little help to break us out of the ways we 'normally' look at things. In terms of the 9-Windows/System Operator tool, that 'normal' way involves someone giving us a problem and us heading straight for the system-present window at the center of the 9 boxes – Figure 19.2.

In other words, we immediately begin to think about the 'system' – where system is very often the first image your mind conjures up when the problem in described to you; 'the car won't start' leads to an immediate mental image of a system called 'car'. Similarly with respect to time; 'the car won't start' leads to an immediate mental image of someone sat in the drivers seat, turning the key, and nothing happening (except, maybe you can hear the engine turning over and not firing).

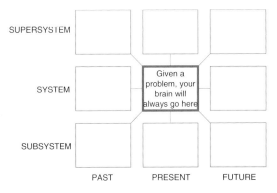

Figure 19.2: Where Our Brains Go When We Give Them A Problem To Solve

The Figure should give you a clue on how the 9-Windows tool can help us to overcome the system-present trick our brain plays on us. Very simply, what the 9-Windows asks us to do is think about the problem from the perspective of the other 8 boxes, asking the question in each 'is the *real* problem here?'

In other words, while the *manifestation* of the problem we are experiencing ('my car won't start') may well appear in the middle box, the root cause of the problem requiring to be solved may well be in another box.

Chapter 3 talks about the practiced ability of TRIZ experts to be able to continuously changing their frame of reference and viewing perspective on a problem, and Chapter 2 talks about how some of the solution triggers provided by TRIZ help push us to different Windows. The 9-Windows tool is mentioned again specifically in this Chapter, because chances are, if the overall systematic creativity process has directed you to this Chapter that a little reminder about using the 9-Windows wouldn't go amiss.

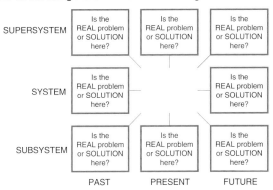

Figure 19.3: 9-Windows From A Problem Solving Context

Smart Little People

As previously discussed in Chapter 4 on the 9-Windows concept, the Smart Little People (SLP) tool can be viewed as simply a special case of encouraging the problem to zoom

into the fine details of the sub-system of a problem to view what the problem looks like from there. As a psychological inertia breaking tool, Smart Little People is actually a little bit more sophisticated.

The tool has its origins in several places. Certainly Altshuller had a version of the idea, but then so did Synectics and the 'Schmoos' cartoonist. Some people, in fact, seem to naturally be able to place themselves into this miniscule role in a problem setting. For the rest of us, the tool works something like this:

- isolate part of the problem which fails to perform the required action
- imagine the chosen part as a crowd of 'smart little people'
- divide the little people into groups acting according to the problem conditions
- see how little people may resolve the contradiction
- translate from little people to technical answer

With this tool, the user is first asked to think about the zone of conflict. This is a challenging start point. The real challenge is to zoom in to the smallest possible size of conflict zone – sometimes this might involve zooming in to molecular or atomic level for example.

The problem solver should be able to sketch this zone of conflict, and then able to select from a menu of different SLP types (see Figure 19.4 below) and to place as many SLPs onto the sketch as possible. The SLPs may be separate from one another, or the problem solver may chose to connect them depending on which model best mimics the real situation.

Once the problem solver has finished populating the picture with SLPs, imagine the SLPs are able to change their shape – e.g. from jumping to stretching to standing to squatting, etc – as per the different SLP types. If the SLPs are connected to one another, they should change their shape together – e.g. all stretch or all squat, etc. Another useful addition is to imagine 'good' SLP and 'bad' SLP, and examine how the two different 'character' types would behave in the problem situation. Some users also like to equip their SLPs with additional tools - shields, parachutes, swords, jet-packs, etc. The basic idea is that these smart little people images should offer ideas to the problem solver.

Tip-toe
Stand
Crouch
Sit
Lay

Arms/Legs:
Together/Apart
Up/Side/Down
Doing Different Things
Gripping/Free
etc

Figure 19.4: Example Smart Little People Forms

The best way to illustrate the Smart Little People concept and psychological inertia tool is probably through a good study example. Figure 19.5 illustrates a typical diffuser – a device used commonly in aerodynamic systems when a designer wishes to decelerate a moving fluid or gas. The problem with most diffusers is that as, say, gas enters the diffuser and begins to decelerate along the increasing area passage, the flow tends to separate from the walls – which then results in significant pressure loss and generally poor performance. For the majority of diffuser designs, the maximum allowable angle of divergence (shown

as angle α in the Figure) is around 3 to 4° before problems start to occur. This very low divergence angle means that diffusers tend to be quite long and bulky.

We could chose to examine this problem as a contradiction (think we're trying to improve is pressure; thing stopping us is length, for example), or we could try to get some ideas using the Smart Little People tool:

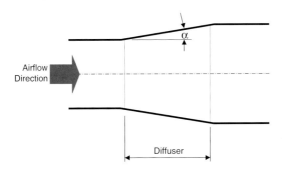

Figure 19.5: Typical Air Diffuser

The first thing the tool asks us to try and do is identify the zone of conflict. In the case of the diffuser, the problem really begins at the point where the flow along the diffuser walls is just on the verge of separating – before this position the flow is attached to the walls as we desire, and after the separation point, it is too late to do anything. The conflict zone is illustrated in Figure 19.6. Having identified this separation position (at least conceptually – we may well not know its precise physical location at this stage), the SLP then tells us to model the problem as a group of smart little people.

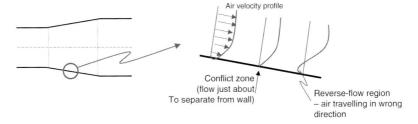

Figure 19.6: Zooming-in to the Diffuser Zone of Conflict

The first connection made is that the part of the system capable of moving should be turned into smart little people. In this case, that means the air passing along the diffuser walls. Thus we imagine the airflow as a group of these people all holding on to each other. The smart little people closest to the diffuser wall are imagined walking along the wall – Figure 19.7.

As we then focused in on the smart little person approaching the separation problem, the image that came to mind was of that person being increasingly stretched, trying to hold on to the person above (who is also moving ever more quickly) and trying to keep a grip on the wall. As shown in the Figure, the person is eventually on tip-toes trying to stay

attached to the wall and to the friend above. And then the person is forced to make a choice – keep feet on the wall or stay attached to the more rapidly moving friend above.

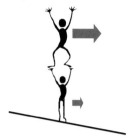

Figure 19.7: Smart Little People Helping To Define The Diffuser Problem

The person always chooses the friend, and is then swept up and off the wall.

So with this description, we now have a mental image of the smart little people behaving as the system behaves. The next part of the process requires us to imagine how the people might now solve the problem.

A first thought here might be 'why not make the walls out of a group of smart little people too, and have them keep a hold of the problem person so as not to be dragged away?' This might help to some extent (and indeed it is possible to modify the surface finish of the wall to help the problem person keep a grip a little bit better; but not much). But a useful thing to keep in mind at this point is that if a part of the system (in this case the wall) is not able to move, it should not be modeled as little people. So then what? The only way of keeping the problem person attached to the wall would be if there was some other way of keeping him held there. Unfortunately, the friend above cannot help – he (or she!) justs wants to keep moving and, in any event, the person above him is moving even faster and is also pulling him away from the wall. So what to do?

In this scenario, what we would ideally like are some other smart little people to help hold the problem person next to the wall. If we can't make the wall into people, and we don't want to add any different people to the situation, is there some way we could position other friendly people in a position where they may be able to help? One possible idea might be to dig some SLP-sized trenches and fill them with people who will grip onto the ankles of the passing problem person – Figure 19.8a. Or, to take this a stage further, is there some way of lining the whole wall out of little people – Figure 19.8b?

Figure 19.8: Smart Little People Helping To Solve The Diffuser Problem

So although these are probably not the only ideas we could think of if we were looking at the problem for real, at least we now have some conceptual solutions. The last part of the SLP process then requires us to translate these ideas into practical ones. The first one is perhaps easiest to imagine – cut some trenches in the walls of the diffuser and hope that some smart little people are inclined to jump in them, stay there and then hope they help keep a hold of the problem person (as it happens, if we size the trenches correctly, this is exactly what the air passing along a diffuser will do – it will enter the trenches and form little vortices that help to attract the air close to the wall).

The second option also turns out to offer a practically realisable solution to the problem – the 'fence diffuser' achieves unprecedented diffusion angles simply by trapping a rotating vortex of air in the gap shown in area A in Figure 19.9 below.

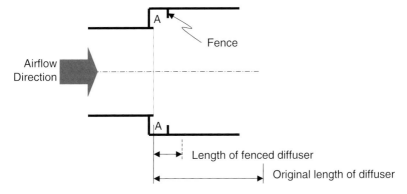

Figure 19.9: Fence Diffuser Concept – Translating the SLP Solution To Reality

You might like to see if you can use the contradictions part of TRIZ (or s-fields for that matter) to get to the same solutions. In the meantime, the number of other published examples of the Smart Little People tool in action is relatively small, but you may care to check out the two examples in Reference 19.1, or see Chapter 4 for the example of Smart Little People being used to solve a helicopter blade erosion problem.

Size-Time-Interface-Cost (STIC) Tool

The Size-Time-Interface-Cost (STIC) tool is an extension of the size-time-cost tool described in other TRIZ texts (see Salamatov for example – Reference 19.1). We make the extension to include 'interface' as a new category based on its philosophical importance in the overall context of the systematic creativity whole we are describing in this book.

The basic idea contained within the tool is that we tend to think of whatever problem it is that we are looking at in the context of its current size, the timeframe in which it currently operates, the number and form of interfaces that it currently has, and its current cost. We might see all these as the center point in a field with four dimensions (a little bit difficult to visualize perhaps – which might explain why the original tool had three dimensions to it). The tool is trying to get us to shift to the extreme edges of the field in order to see if we can find a better solution in one or more of those new viewing positions.

The tool gets us to take each of the four STIC parameters and systematically place ourselves at the extreme edges of each in turn. In each of the new positions, we then ask ourselves the question; 'how would I solve the problem if….?' Each extreme point provides us with a new if question. Taken all together, the questions the tool is prompting us to ask are; How would I solve the problem if…..

Physical Size (S) was	Zero	infinite
Time (T) to deliver function was	Zero	infinite
Number of interfaces (I) was	Zero	infinite
Allowable cost (C) was	Zero	infinite

Each of the eight questions is then used as the basis for a systematic brainstorming session. An example will probably help to illustrate how to use the tool in the most effective manner:

The economics of long-haul flight currently mean that there is a demand for bigger aircraft carrying more passengers. Unfortunately, as aircraft get bigger the problems of taking-off and landing on exiting runways become ever greater. Landing a big aircraft on a fixed length of runway in particular becomes very demanding. How might we use the STIC tool to help us to think of possible alternative solutions to the problem?

These are the sorts of questions the tool is prompting us to think about:-

(S→∞) - How would we stop the aircraft if the runway length was 10km? Would it stop itself if it were this size? How could we make the aircraft think it was this size?

(S→0) - How would we stop the aircraft if the runway was 1m long? Or if the aircraft was 1m long?

(T→∞) - What happens if we let the stopping time be 10hours?

(T→0) - How could we stop the aircraft if the stopping time was less than 1 second?

(I→∞) - How would we stop the aircraft if it had infinite interfaces with the runway? How could we make the aircraft think it had this many?

(I→0) - How would we stop the aircraft if it had no interfaces with the runway?

(C→∞) - How could we stop the aircraft if the cost of the 'stopping object' was unlimited?

(C→0) - How could we stop the aircraft if the 'stopping object' cost is reduced to zero?

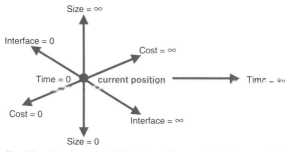

Figure 19.10: Size-Time-Interface-Cost PI Tool as a Means of Shifting to a Different Problem Perspective

Undoubtedly some of the solution directions will generate ideas that make no sense no matter how long you spend looking at them. Undoubtedly also, it is very rare that none of the eight direction shifts prompted by the questions produce an idea that turns out to be a very useful one.

By way of example of some of the things the tool may prompt us to think about in relationship to the above aircraft landing distance problem are:-

$(S\to\infty)$ - 'uphill runway'/'bowed' runway, 'moving runway'

$(S\to0)$ - land the aircraft vertically, use wind,

$(T\to\infty)$ - no useful ideas generated

$(T\to0)$ - anchor, lots of parachutes, retro-rocket,

$(I\to\infty)$ - many wheels (How could we make the aircraft think it had this many? - lower air-pressure in tyres to increase ground contact), ground-effect in reverse, foam runway,

$(I\to0)$ - aerostatic aeroplane, airship, magnetic levitation

$(C\to\infty)$ - no useful ideas generated

$(C\to0)$ - water/sea-plane

Depending on the individual or group using the tool, the likelihood of maintaining the energy to keep generating new ideas for all eight questions is relatively low. If you are trying to use the tool and find yourself saying things like 'oh, well, it obviously can't be possible to solve the problem if there's no money to do it', chances are you have reached the low-energy point. The temptation is to call it a day at this point. You can of course do this. A better strategy in such situations would be to go and do something different for a while and come back to the session later. Or it might mean splitting a group into smaller group and dividing the trigger questions between the different parts.

Why-What's Stopping Analysis Tool

The Why-What's Stopping? Tool is one that has its initial roots outside of TRIZ. A version of the basic idea behind the tool may be found in several places. We include it here because it is the best thing we've found to help establish a hierarchy of problem statements in order that we might identify from that hierarchy 'the' problem we should be tackling. As we will see, this is important because very often we will discover that the problem we start with turns out not to be the one we should be solving. You will also find the Why-What's Stopping tool inside the Problem Explorer part of the Problem Definition sector of the book. In that context, the tool is trying to provide some guidance at the beginning of a project. Here it is being used in the context of the situation where we have been through all the problem definition, tool selection and solution generation stages and still not generated a workable solution.

The 'Why-What's Stopping' tool represents a modified version of the analysis tool first developed by Basadur (Reference 19.2). The tool provides users with a structure through which to visualise an initial problem statement in the context of its broader and narrower context. The tool is aimed at overcoming the highly common situation which starts with

statements like 'the problem is…' and continues a few seconds later with a headlong plunge into problem solving mode. This phenomenon is one of the most important manifestations of psychological inertia. Countless situations point to the fact that the initial problem definition turns out to be anything but the 'right' one. So, the tool takes the initial 'the problem is…' statement and forces the user to think about the broader and narrower problem. A typical schema is reproduced in Figure 19.11 below.

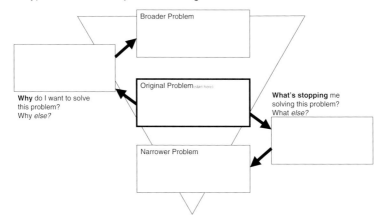

Figure 19.11: Why-What's Stopping? PI Tool Framework

Basically, the user uses the 'Why?' question to broaden the problem and uses the question 'What's Stopping?' to narrow the question. In keeping with the Deming (Reference 19.3) 'ask why 5 times' philosophy, the schema can be broadened or narrowed multiple times. (In line with Deming's statement, it would be very unlikely that we would have to repeat the why cycle more than five times to get to the root cause – in practice it will usually take less.) At the end of the process, the user has obtained a vertical stack of hierarchical problem definitions, from which a much clearer picture of what the 'right' problem is should emerge.

It is often useful to combine this mode of questioning with not just the '5-why's', but also the '5W's plus an H' approach: Who, What, When, Where, Why, and How. For more details on the combination of these approaches into TRIZ and systematic creativity in general, the reader may care to check out Reference 19.4.

For the purposes of breaking psychological inertia, we will retain our focus on the 'Why-What's Stopping?' approach. An example problem should hopefully help illustrate how the tool can encourage us to view a problem from different perspectives. In keeping with what seems to be something of a TRIZ theme, we will look at the problem of home delivery pizzas. The problem with home delivery pizzas is that they usually arrive on the doorstep cold. This is the problem the customer sees, and so we will define that as our original problem.

The tool then encourages me to head upwards in the direction of broadening the problem by asking 'why' questions, and also downwards in the direction of narrowing the problem by asking the 'what's stopping' questions. It is important to notice the 'why else' and 'what else' questions – the intended implication being that we should be looking for as many possible answers as possible.

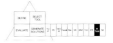

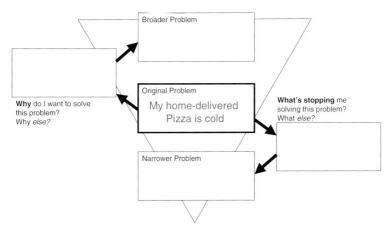

Figure 19.12: Why-What's Stopping? Tool at the Beginning of the Cold Pizza Problem

Figure 19.13 illustrates a possible combination of questions and answers for the initial cold pizza problem. Some of the solution directions suggested by the tool are consistent with some of the things the industry is already doing (ribbed boxes, heated containers, etc), but interestingly, some of them are not. The (seemingly daft) idea of delivering cold pizza for example is actually quite interesting if customers can be sold the benefits of having a freshly assembled but uncooked pizza delivered to their door for them to put in their oven as soon as it arrives. Similarly, the definition of a need for robust, low-energy heating systems might well suggest the idea of a portable microwave, or, simpler still, use of a microwavable container made of a cheap resource like wheat – which is used quite commonly in things like microwavable, stay warm clothing.

The basic point of the tool then is that it encourages exploration of the space around the initially perceived problem. As in this case, a better problem than the one initially identified often emerges.

Note that it is also possible to take one of the broader problem definitions and ask the 'what's stopping?' question on this in order to expand the scope of the problem exploration exercise. Similarly, it is possible to expand the scope of the narrower problem definitions by asking the 'why do I want to solve?' question.

See Chapter 5 for another example of the Why-What's-Stopping tool in action – this time in its purely problem definition assistance role.

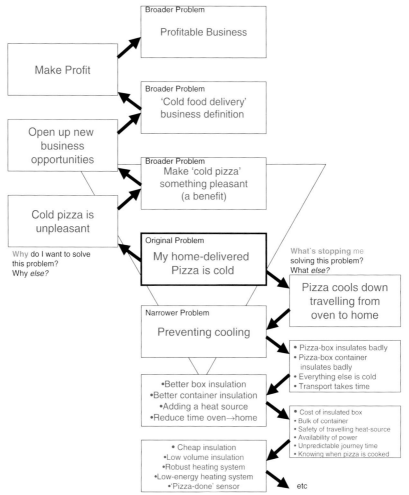

Figure 19.13: Why-What's Stopping? Analysis for the Cold Pizza Problem

What Do I Do?

As discussed In Chapter 3, psychological inertia appears to be a fundamental phenomenon of the human brain. Awareness of the problem is a start, but many people find they need active strategies to help them to overcome psychological inertia.

Four main tools are recommended in the overall process we have labelled 'systematic creativity'. The 9-Windows 'system operator' concept is required throughout, and thus received its own chapter earlier in the book. In this chapter we have examined three other

tools – Smart Little People, Size-Time-Interface-Cost and 'Why-What's Stopping' Analysis. These are collectively the four we have found to be most useful in countering psychological inertia, for the greatest number of users. Everybody's psychological inertia appears to have its own uniquely individual quirks, however, and so the most effective way of using the techniques in this chapter is to try each of them out and see which fits best into your way of doing things.

The PI tools are most useful in helping us to re-frame a problem if we have not been able to generate solutions using any of the other tools in the systematic creativity armoury, but some people will find they have a particular affinity to a certain tool and will naturally incorporate it into their everyday use. This is to be commended – the greater the number of working tools in the toolkit, the greater our chances of deriving better solutions.

For readers who find that none of the tools recommended here fit into their scheme of things, check out the bibliography at the end of the chapter for a more comprehensive list of what the wider world knows about overcoming psychological inertia.

Whatever PI tools you are attracted to, the real requirement is to use them as often as possible.

References

1) Salamatov, Y., 'TRIZ: The Right Solution at the Right Time', Insytec nv, The Netherlands, 1999.
2) Basadur, M., 'The Power Of Innovation', Financial Times Prentice Hall, 1995.
3) Deming, W.E., 'Out of the Crisis', Cambridge University Press, 1986.
4) Apte, P., Shah, M., Mann, D.L., '5W's and an H of TRIZ', TRIZ Journal, June 2001.

Bibliography (in descending order of importance)

1) DeBono, E., 'Serious Creativity', Penguin Books, 1992.
2) DeBono, E., 'Po: Beyond Yes or No', Penguin Books, 1972.
3) DeBono, E., 'The Mechanism of Mind', Penguin Books, 1969.
4) Dilts, R., 'Tools For Dreamers', Meta Publications, 1982.
5) Dilts, R., 'Strategies of Genius', Volumes 1-3, Meta Publications, 1996.
6) Koestler, A., 'The Act of Creation', Penguin Arkana, 1964.
7) Hall, L.M., Bodenhamer, B.G., 'Figuring Out People: Design Engineering with Meta-Programs', Crown House Publishing, 1997.
8) Lawley, J., Tompkins, 'Metaphors in Mind: Transformation Through Symbolic Modelling', The Developing Company Press, 2000.
9) MacKenzie, G., 'Orbiting the Giant Hairball', Viking, 1998.
10) Root-Bernstein, R. and M., 'Sparks of Genius – the 13 Thinking Tools of the World's Most Creative People', Houghton Mifflin, Boston, 1999.
11) Gelb, Michael, 'How to Think Like Leonardo da Vinci – Seven Steps to Genius Everyday', Thorsons, 1998.
12) Allan, D., Kingdon, M., Murrin, K., Rudkin, D., 'What If? How to Start a Creative Revolution at Work', Capstone Publishing, 1999.
13) Charlotte, S., 'Creativity – Conversations with 28 Who Excel', Momentum Books Ltd, 1993.

14) Foster, R., Kaplan, S., 'Creative Destruction: Turning Built-to-Last into Built-to-Perform', Financial Times Prentice Hall, 2001.
15) Horn, R.E., 'Visual Language – Global Communication for the 21st Century', MacroVU Inc, Washington, 1998.
16) Oech, R., von, 'A Kick in the Seat of the Pants', Harper Perennial, 1986.
17) Buzan, T., 'Use Your Head', BBC Books, 1997 updated edition.
18) Claxton, G., 'Hare Brain, Tortoise Mind', 4th Estate, London, 1997.
19) Wallace, D.B., Gruber, H.E., 'Creative People at Work', Oxford University Press, Oxford, 1989.
20) Grand, S., 'Creation: Life and How to Make It', Weidenfeld, 2000.

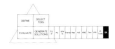

20.
Problem Solving Tools
Subversion Analysis

"The most important numbers are unknown and unknowable"
W.E.Deming.

The instinct of most people discovering TRIZ is that there is probably very little that it can offer to help during the solving of reliability-based problems. After all, what does the former Soviet Union know about 'design for reliability'? The answer, because it appears to most occidental eyes that reliability was never a big issue in the former Soviet Union, is probably not a lot. Certainly the instinct of this author when faced with a reliability problem is to head for a method other than TRIZ as a first instinct.

This instinct is in fact only partially correct, and TRIZ – being based on a distillation of best practice wherever it might exist – does have several things to offer from a reliability perspective. This chapter discusses those things in the context of the bigger 'what is it that I should actually do when facing a reliability problem?' issue. The text is divided into four main sections. The first section discusses the concept of design for reliability in its most general sense; the second section examines how the Contradictions part of TRIZ can be used to help solve reliability problems; the third section examines a method combining the best of Western reliability methods with the philosophical and methodological concepts contained in TRIZ; and a short fourth section discusses some of the implications on design for reliability prompted by evolution trends away from selling products to selling services.

Reliability

Reliability appears to be one of the dominant aspects of system design in many industry sectors. This is in part due to the fact that customers are increasingly expecting the things they buy to not break down, but also because in maturing industries, improvement of reliability is one of the few options for improvement available to the manufacturer. Historical analysis of the patent database quickly reveals the general pattern – first illustrated in Chapter 7 – that reliability only seems to become the dominant design driver when a system is approaching maturity – Figure 20.1.

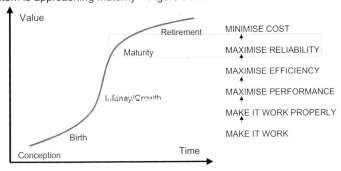

Figure 20.1: Reliability Consideration On System Evolution Curve.

A very big consequent problem in terms of designing to improve reliability is that it is something that is comparatively to design into an already mature system. The world is rapidly discovering that effective 'design reliability' almost demands consideration of reliability issues from day one.

The second big problem with regard to design for reliability issues is that there is comparatively little design database upon which to build an effective design methodology. In no doubt grossly over-simplified terms, 'reliability' is often viewed as 80% of the design challenge, and around 20% of the design knowledge database. In other words, in most fields it is now possible for a designer to turn a performance design specification (e.g. carry a certain load over a certain distance in a certain time, at a certain level of energy efficiency) into a working product relatively predictably. These days, because of increased cost reduction pressures, the designer of that system is reasonably well able to also design that system to achieve a required cost level. There is considerable design database to help the designer to achieve both goals. Asking the designer to now achieve a certain level of reliability – a three-year maintenance free life for example – and suddenly the design database to help is no longer present. In many instances, it may never be present. Does this mean that we should forget about reliability, or that we should perhaps think about it in a different way. The message presented here veers very much towards the latter.

Before justifying this decision, it is perhaps useful to define a few important reliability metrics: Reliability is defined as the probability that a component, device or system will perform as prescribed duty without failure, for a given time when operated correctly in a specified environment. Since reliability is a probability, it is defined as a number between 0 and 1.

A reliability of 0 indicates that a component will definitely fail, whereas a reliability of 1 means that the component will definitely not fail. Different products are typically designed to achieve different levels of reliability – as shown in Figure 20.2

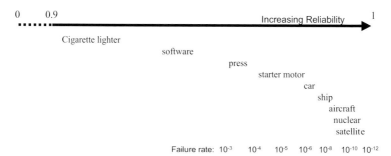

Figure 20.2: Typical Reliability Performance for Different Systems

In terms of the standard TRIZ adage 'someone, somewhere has already solved something like my problem, it appears clear from the figure that it is the space, aerospace, and nuclear industries that set the standards in terms of design for reliability. We will return to the implications and findings of this assessment later in the Chapter.

Meanwhile, sticking with reliability metrics, we can also say that:

Reliability $(R) = 1 - Probability\ of\ failure\ (F)$

Many reliability metrics are described in terms of failure rates per number of operating hours. Different industries tend to use different methods of presenting data. We will use the conventions of the space and aerospace industries – describing failure rates in terms of a probability of failure per hour operation. Thus 10^{-6} is used to record a failure rate of 1 failure per million operating hours. In other sectors it might be 'failures per operation carried out'.

In the very simplest conceptual terms, it may appear strange that we need to be talking about reliability at all; component reliability depends upon the relationship between the duty or load and the corresponding strength of the component. Figure 20.3 shows possible load and strength distributions of a sample of components, plotted on a common axis. There is no interference between the curves; all of the components have strengths greater than all possible loads. This then may be seen as the ideal situation; if a system is designed with these curves and this separation in mind, there can be no possibility of failure. This being the case, we must ask why it is that reliability, or rather the failure of so many systems continues to be such a big issue.

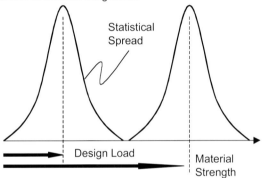

Figure 20.3: Strength-load diagram with no interference.

What actually happens is shown in Figure 20.4. In this scenario there is an interference region indicating that some components may have strengths less than the loads applied. Consequently there is a risk that some component failures will occur. This intersection between the to curves occurs due to two primary drivers – firstly, thinking about the ideality

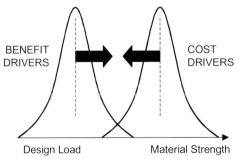

Figure 20.4: Strength-load diagram with interference.

equation, a requirement for increased 'benefits' (e.g. load carrying capability) tends to push the design curve to the right, and secondly, the demands of competition and cost reduction tend to cause organizations to pull the strength curve to the left.

In practice, of course, it is common to try and cut off the tail of the strengths curve by inspection and testing, and to limit loads with relief valves, over-speed governors, temperature cut-outs etc. The paradox in both cases, is that these actions tend to create their own reliability problems. In other words, we look to solve one set of problems and in so doing introduce another set.

An issue related to this paradox is also worth discussing briefly in setting the scene for understanding reliability and doing a better job of designing for reliability. Historically, the way we design systems is that we perform some often quite complex and sophisticated calculations to determine how strong we need to make the components in the system. Then we multiply in a 'fudge factor' that basically says 'we don't really understand what's going on, so let's add in some margin'. If we then build the system and it doesn't fail, what tends to happen next tie around is we say 'hey, the fudge factor was too big last time, so this time let's make it a bit smaller (and hence use less materials/money)'. This process then tends to repeat (in the case of bridge design over a period of a hundred years or more) until, surprise, surprise, a failure occurs. Usually this failure occurs at a load somewhere between the one we calculated and the one with the fudge factor added – as shown in Figure 20.5. Once the failure has occurred, we then work out what was wrong with our calculation process and try to rectify it. Then the process begins again.

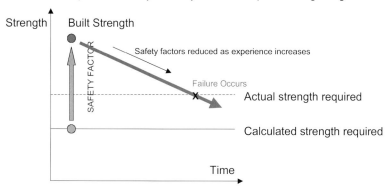

Figure 20.5 : **Typical Fudge Factor Design Philosophy.**

The famous Tacoma Narrows bridge is an example of this process in action; prior to Tacoma Narrows, bridge design calculations did not take sufficient account of aerodynamic loading. Post-Tacoma Narrows, they do, and there have been no more failures due to this effect. According to Reference 20.1 – a good source of information on both bridges and this 'reducing fudge factor' phenomenon – there has historically been a gap of around 60 years between bridge failures due to a previously unplanned failure mode. The prediction almost came true recently with the Millennium Bridge in London, which had to be closed when it was observed that the bridge moved violently when lots of people standing on the bridge saw that it moved and all acted together to make it move more. This 'bridge-users act together' phenomenon simply was not factored into the design calculations.

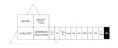

2) Reliability Contradictions

There is an emerging school of thought that says you can analyse and analyse a system from now until eternity and still not understand what is causing a reliability problem. This is the theme expressed by the WE Deming quote at the beginning of the chapter – the most important reliability numbers – cost of customer dissatisfaction, failure rate of a component when used in 'real' operating conditions, etc – are indeed both unknown and to all practical (affordable) intents and purposes unknowable. This despite the emergence of a whole host of (usually software based) tools to help designers to better quantify reliability issues. Too often these tools are used as after the event analysis tools rather than before the event, influence the design synthesis tools.

By way of an example of this 'unknowability' of important reliability numbers, this author always thinks about a telling example from days spent working in the aerospace industry.

The idea suggested here, however, is that if it turns out to be impossible to really get to the root cause of a given reliability problem, so long as I can identify a contradiction associated with the problem, I might still be able to improve the situation. The idea is based on the belief that if the strongest reliability improvement solutions are those that move away from the traditional compromise based optimization solution approaches (optimization can fundamentally never work if we don't have the data to drive it) and think instead about changing the paradigm. It also turns out that finding a root contradiction is considerably easier than finding a root cause. The next section will detail some of the signs that will help to identify these contradictions. The reader should also, however, keep in mind the strategies for utilizing the standard TRIZ contradiction tools described in chapters 10 and 11.

The simple consequence of this kind of contradiction-eliminating thinking is that the Contradiction Matrix already contains a specific line of data concerned with inventive problem solving situations in which reliability is the desired improving factor. Table 1 extracts the most likely of the Inventive Principles contained within TRIZ that have been used to successfully solve reliability problems. The table is intended as a simpler alternative to the preferable route of explicitly defining the root contradiction in a reliability problem and then using the full Matrix to generate a more specific list of solution triggers.

35 - **Change of Physical and Chemical Parameters**
  (change of aggregate state, change of concentration or consistency, change of flexibility, or change of temperature)
10 - **Prior Action**
  ('if your object is subjected to harmful factors of environment, create conditions that will protect the object from those harmful factors beforehand')
11 - **Beforehand Cushioning**
  ('if your object is unreliable, create conditions in advance that will protect the object')
 3 - **Local Quality**
  (make the object non-uniform, make the environment non-uniform, if multiple functions are to be performed, divide the object into parts according to those functions)
28 - **Mechanics Substitution**
  (replace mechanical solutions with other physical solutions – acoustic, optical, magnetic, thermal, etc)
40 - **Composite Materials**
  (use composite materials instead of uniform ones.)

Table 20.1: **TRIZ Inventive Principles Most Likely To Help Eliminate A Reliability Contradiction.**

See the Reference section at the end of Chapter 10 for a list of examples of these Inventive Principles in action.

3) Design For Reliability

There are many models of reliability which, when fitted to data relating to past experience of component failure rates, can be used to predict future reliability trends. One of the simplest such models assumes that component failures occur randomly at a constant rate throughout the system's lifetime. This constant failure rate is usually referred to as λ.

Component reliability, R is then modelled as:
$$R = e^{-\lambda t}$$
Probability of failure, $Z(t)$, is given by:
$$F = 1 - e^{-\lambda t}$$

The failure rate, $Z(t)$, is given by:
$$Z(t) = \frac{-dR(t)}{dt} \leftrightarrow \frac{1}{R(t)} = \lambda$$
Time to failure, θ, is given by:
$$\theta = \int_0^{\times} R(t)\,dt = \frac{1}{\lambda}$$

As with all models, this is an approximation and only describes part of the component life cycle. Figure 20.6 shows the *Bath Tub Curve*, used to illustrate the variation in failure rates of components during the lifetime of a system.

Figure 20.6: The Bath Tub Curve.

The model outlined above only attempts to describe the component failure rate behaviour during the flat portion of the curve, i.e. during the normal useful life of the system. In addition to the normal running time there are periods of higher component failure rates, both during the initial running-in period and also later when the system starts to wear out. The assumptions built into this curve and the problems associated in trying to model the running-in and wear-out phases further serve to re-enforce the 'most important numbers are unknown and unknowable' quote at the beginning of the chapter. It is very tempting indeed in fact to suggest that there is little true value in any of the mathematics associated with this kind of reliability modeling.

The associated methods and strategies for modeling reliability are nevertheless valid. We will briefly examine the best of the below, before moving on to show how other TRIZ thinking can be used to strengthen these methods.

System Analysis

Engineering systems of any description are often complex. By way of example, we will examine here a typical analysis for a hydraulic system. The usual start point will be a hydraulic circuit diagram. This will typically show the components contained in a circuit and their interconnections, but will not show the component sizes and ratings, the lengths of line or the location of components and connections. If the system contains multi-state components (e.g. a three position directional control valve), these are only drawn in one state or position. There is usually no explanation of how the system is supposed to operate in its various states. The hydraulic circuit diagram is thus only a very limited start ppoint for a reliability analysis.

Different approaches may be used, in order to break the system down into more manageable sub-units for the purposes of reliability analysis. These include:

i) An *Operational* or *Functional diagram* or an *Event Tree* which may be used to show the normal operating mode. The functional diagram or event tree may be supplemented by simplified circuit diagrams and drawings or photographs to identify components. There should be a status statement before and after each diagram to identify the condition of multi-state components.

ii) A *Fault Tree* which can be drawn to show the possible causes of a system malfunction. Ideally, all possible causes are shown; in practice an attempt is made to show the more likely causes of failure, events of very low probability being eliminated.

iii) *Failure mode, effects and criticality analysis* (FMECA, or more usually these days FMEA) which can be carried out for individual components. For each identified failure mode, the local effects and the effects on the system should be established. The severity of the failure may be classified in order to determine priorities for corrective action.

iv) Time domain computer simulation can be used at the design stage to allow the system's dynamic performance to be examined quantitatively. This technique can be used to size components and check that the system meets the specification. Computer simulation can also be used to examine the effect of component failures, including the interaction of multiple failures - a task beyond the scope of conventional FMEA.

We will examine fault trees and FMEA:

Fault Trees

Fault tree analysis (FTA) is particularly useful at the design stage, since it should identify likely causes of system failure. It corresponds to a question of the type "How could this failure event occur?" The general pattern of analysis usually follows a number of steps:

i) System definition - A circuit diagram is required, giving the components and their interconnections. In order that the normal operating sequence may be understood, it may be necessary to draw an event tree for each operating state, noting the position of any multi-state components. The system may then be checked in a qualitative manner, to determine whether it will function in the required way. This is usually followed by a quantitative analysis to determine whether the system will meet the specification. Details will be required of component sizes, rating and performance to set against the load specification and duty cycle.

ii) Selection of top event - The top event is an operational failure (or partial failure) of the system. It may represent either a complete breakdown or a failure to meet the

performance specification: e.g. a loaded actuator fails to move, moves in a sluggish manner, or moves in an erratic and uncontrolled manner. A new fault tree is associated with each new top event. Hence it is important to select those top events which have the most serious consequences, particularly those which are more likely to happen.

iii) Fault tree construction - By following the circuit from the component associated with the top event along the lines which lead either to the supply (pressure) or the return (tank), the top event may be linked to more basic fault events. The event statements are linked through logic gates. OR gates require only one input to be available before the output event occurs. AND gates on the other hand require both input events to have occurred before the output event can happen. In the simplest circuits, only OR gates are required, linking alterative fault events, e.g. there may be no flow from a directional control valve due to no input flow, OR failure of the pilot signal selecting the valve open position, OR valve jammed shut. In circuits with in-built redundancy, AND gates are also required, e.g. there is no flow in a specified line when there is no flow from the main pump supply AND no flow from the auxiliary pump supply. A fault tree may be built up by piecing together small segments known as component transfer functions. Each transfer function would be obtained by failure mode analysis of an individual component, and would consist of input conditions linked by a logic gate to a single output condition. A library of such transfer functions may be built up for the components commonly used. The transfer function outputs would usually be variations in fluid flow, pressure or temperature.

iv) Primary events - Each branch of the fault tree must terminate in a primary event representing a basic component failure which requires no further analysis. This may be associated with the natural end of the component life, due to ageing, wear or fatigue, or it may represent an extreme disturbance such as a loss of control signal or power supply. All primary events should be fully independent. An analysis of these events should indicate the most likely cause of the top event. If the top event represents catastrophic failure of an important system, it may be desirable that no single primary event should be sufficient to cause the failure. Multiple redundancy may be fitted in order that failure will occur only if there are simultaneous primary events in several independent components.

v) Probability analysis - The probability of occurrence of a primary event is defined as the probability that the event occurs at least once during the defined life cycle. Such probabilities may be estimated from reliability data obtained by endurance testing or by records of the failure rates of similar components in service. The probability of occurrence of each system failure mode (top level event) is calculated from knowledge of the primary event occurrence probabilities.

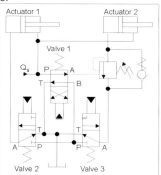

Figure 20.7 **- Hydraulic circuit.**

For events linked by OR gates only one input event has to occur. Therefore the probability of occurrence of the outcome is given by:

$$F_s = 1 - (1 - F_1)(1 - F_n)...(1 - F_n)$$

$$F_s \cup F_1 + F_2 + ... + F_n$$

For events linked by AND gates both input events must occur. Therefore:

$$F_s = F_1 \leftrightarrow F_2 \leftrightarrow F_3 \leftrightarrow .. \leftrightarrow F_n$$

Figure 20.7 shows part of a typical large hydraulic circuit. A fault tree diagram, Figure 20.8, presents the hydraulic system failures that would cause an unexpected opening of either actuator.

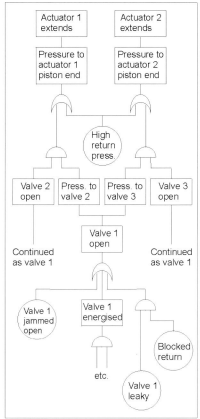

Figure 20.8: **Hydraulic circuit fault tree.**

It shouldn't take long to see that a full analysis for even this relatively simple system is going to require the drawing of a large number of state diagrams and the construction of a similarly large number of probability calculations. The probability calculations further assume the existence of credible upstream reliability data.

Failure Mode, Effects and Criticality Analysis (FMECA/FMEA)

This is a complementary form of analysis to the fault tree analysis just considered; a *bottom up* analysis rather than *top down* approach. That is, it corresponds to a question of the type "What happens if this component fails?" It is most usefully applied to non-redundant systems, concentrating on those elements which were associated with probable causes of system failure.

A functional approach may be adopted, treating the components as *black boxes* with a number of outputs and inputs. A more detailed hardware approach may be used if the components can be identified by drawings and design data.

FMEA is often tedious and time consuming work involving the following stages:

i) System definition - This is similar to the first step in fault tree analysis. It is normal practice to list all the components with a statement of their respective functions. Block diagrams are a useful technique for simplifying the circuit, illustrating the operation and the relationship between components. All system interfaces must be indicated. If a quantitative or hardware analysis is required, a check may be made that the system meets the operating specification. This requires details of component sizes and performance; the load specification and duty cycle, and the environmental conditions.

ii) Failure mode analysis (FMA) - For each component and for each operating sequence and corresponding component state, all potential failure modes should be identified. Where possible their relative frequency of occurrence may be compared. Initially this information may be provided from endurance testing, but it should be updated by service records when the equipment is in the field.

iii) Failure effects analysis (FEA) - For every defined failure mode of each component, the local effects on the function of that component, the effects on the system and on the operation should be identified and recorded. A limitation of most analyses is the practice of considering only single failures. Each failure mode should be evaluated to determine the worst possible consequences and a severity classification may be assigned. These range from catastrophic (loss of equipment or injury to staff) and critical (failure of operation) to marginal (reduced performance or availability) and minor (unscheduled maintenance required).

iv) Criticality analysis (CA) - Each potential failure mode may be ranked according to the combined influence of its severity classification and the probability of its occurrence. Often there is a lack of reliability data, and this work can only be carried out qualitatively. A criticality matrix may be drawn, points representing different failure modes being plotted on axes representing severity and frequency of occurrence. Alternatively, an arbitrary scale of numerical values may be assigned to the severity classification and to the estimated frequency of occurrence, and the criticality may be defined as the product of the two numbers for any particular failure mode.

Other factors might also be introduced into the criticality rating. Where condition monitoring techniques are used, it might be appropriate to include a factor representing the difficulty of detecting an incipient failure mode. In industrial applications one might include a factor representing the maintenance cost associated with a failure.

For the most critical items, particularly those with high severity ratings, reliability may be improved by changes in component design, changes in system design, duplication and redundancy. Condition monitoring may be used to give warning of deteriorating

performance and impending failure. Planned inspection and maintenance may be directed to the more critical components.

v) Documentation - The results of FMECA are normally presented in tabular form; separate forms being used for FMEA and for CA due to the large number of columns required. Following a definition of the component and its function, the first form should list the component failure modes, the system operating modes, the failure effects, both local and general, the severity of the effects of each failure mode, failure detection methods and general remarks. The second form would also identify the component, its failure modes and severity classification. Columns would then be provided to list the probability of each failure mode, the probability of each failure effect, failure rates and operating times, the criticality of each failure mode and each component and general remarks.

As illustrated in the schematic flow chart illustrated in Figure 20.9, the essential idea behind FMEA (and FTA for that matter) is that it is supposed to influence the design. Unfortunately, this feedback loop appears to exist more in theory than in practice in most organizations.

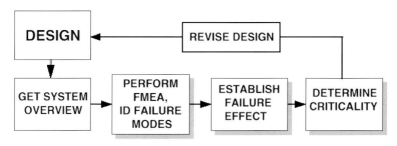

Figure 20.9: **Theoretical Link Between FMEA and Design.**

Limitations of FMEA and FTA

i) They are both tedious time consuming processes in large systems. It is usual to apply the *Pareto Principle* - concentrate on the vital few, i.e. those components whose failures have catastrophic or serious effects, or occur most frequently, and those failure events (top level events) which are perceived as being of most importance, and ignore the *trivial many.*

ii) The processes do not positively identify failure modes or effects or top level events, and some may be missed. FMEA tends to focus on the physical system structure and can miss the effects of external hazards such as operator error or adverse environmental conditions. FTA may entirely overlook the existence of a significant class of system failures by failing to consider its possibility.

iii) It is difficult to combine the reliabilities of components in series and parallel particularly for rough or irregular loading.

iv) It is difficult to allow for wear-out processes in industrial applications. In practice it is normal to use planned maintenance and condition monitoring techniques.

v) There is a lack of published life test data and service records for the original designer. Manufacturers and large users are reluctant to share such data.

Application of Artificial Intelligence

An *expert system* is a computer program which embodies the knowledge of specialists in a particular area. Running the program allows the user to have access to, and use this specialist knowledge to solve his own problems. Expert system techniques have been applied to failure mode and effects analysis, fault tree analysis, and failure diagnosis/condition monitoring.

i) *Application to fault tree analysis* - The time and effort involved and inconsistency between experts in producing fault trees attracted the interest of researchers in the area of artificial intelligence.

The results of a FMECA can be fed into an expert system, so that once a top level event is selected, the computer can automatically postulate the component failure or series of failures that could be the cause.

ii) *Failure diagnosis and condition monitoring* - This is the area which has attracted most interest, due chiefly to the increasing cost, complexity and need for safety in modern plants. The current trend is to use traditional techniques to process signals from sensors located at key points in the system. Knowledge about the system is stored in an expert system, which continuously monitors the signals from the sensors and alerts the operator when something goes amiss. The failure diagnosis knowledge within the expert system is used to pinpoint the fault within the system, and a suggested course of action is given, i.e. switch off; carry out unscheduled maintenance etc.

iii) *Application to failure modes and effects analysis* - Hydraulic and mechanical components can be modelled in a qualitative, descriptive manner, such that their behaviour is described both under normal operating circumstances and under various failed conditions. By connecting such component models together, different hydraulic circuits can be modelled in a qualitative fashion, with pressures and flows around the circuit being inferred in terms of descriptive variables such as high and low.

Insertion of particular component faults into such circuit simulations leads to a qualitative assessment of how such faults could affect the operation of the system. This information can be used as part of an FMEA for each circuit of interest.

Adding In The TRIZ Parts

There are claims in certain factions of the TRIZ community that the idea of 'subversion analysis' is something developed by TRIZ researchers. While this might be fact, it appears clear to this author that the basic underlying question upon which subversion analysis is built – and the thing that merits its inclusion in this chapter – existed in the West in a number of organisations as long ago as the 1920s. The fact that it is still not widely known results largely from competitive pressures and a failure to connect the question to other design for reliability tools.

The basic question, then, that subversion analysis adds to those offered by FTA (How could this failure event occur?) and FMEA (What happens if this component fails?) is the rather more pro-active "How can I destroy this system?"

Purportedly this strategy was devised (from its TRIZ roots) as a means of making the design for reliability task more interesting. This would certainly fit in with the relish some people feel when asked to don the black hat of the Six Thinking Hats™ concept from Chapter 3. It also has links to the 'if a customer can do something stupid with your product, they will', 'Design for Murphy' idea discussed in the fourth section.

Beyond this initial increase in pro-activity in searching for the causes of non-reliability, the other principle thing that TRIZ adds to the design fro reliability story comes from the substance-field analysis tool. In simplest terms, the S-Field tool (Chapter 12) provides a test of system viability; saying that in order for a system to exist, it must contain a minimum of two 'substances' (things) plus a field to act between them. While this test is normally used to think about the design of systems, in a reliability context it is reversed by 180° and used as a way of saying that if a 'failure' (which is after all still an example of a system delivering a function – albeit in this scenario a bad one) exists, it must come from two substances and a field.

> If a failure mode exists, it must emerge from a viable (two substances plus a field) system

A simple example should suffice to explain the concept and how it can be used as a failure finder:

Take the hydraulic coupling illustrated in Figure 20.10 as an example, and imagine that we are looking to improve the reliability of the design by reducing the likelihood of failure by leakage. Our invented failure system is thus 'coupling leaks' – we can see this also as a function description of the action-object type.

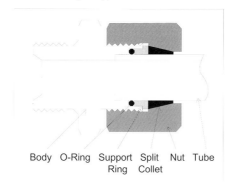

Body   O-Ring   Support   Split   Nut   Tube
                  Ring   Collet

Figure 20.10: **Exemplar Hydraulic Coupling Design.**

The test then says that if the failure system exists, it must emerge through the effects of two substances and a field. The designer thus needs to establish whether these things exist. Clearly, in this instance, if the coupling is pressurised, then there is a pressure field. Similarly, the coupling contains lots of 'substances' and so there is the potential for failure. None of the components per se, however, would give us a leak – simply because we have designed their functionality to not give us leaks. Hence we do not so far have a two-substance-plus field viable system capable of delivering the 'coupling leaks' function. Therefore something else must be present if that failure function *is* to be delivered. This might then get us to speculate that ' a channel' might be an example of a substance that might be present that would make the system (failure) viable. Examining the design, this presents us with, in this case, three possible scenarios:
   1) the o-ring has a channel
   2) the tube has a channel
   3) the body has a channel

We can present this as a cause-effect diagram as follows:

Failure Scenarios:

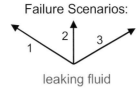

leaking fluid

If we then take one of the scenarios, say 'tube has a channel', then if that is to be possible, it too – like the 'coupling leaks' system – must emerge through a viable system. Thus the process of finding two substances and a field to deliver this failure function begins again. Again, there is a pressure field, and again there are lots of other substances in the system that may combine to produce the system 'tube has a channel' – for example 'mechanical field (e.g. vibration) on body acts on tube to produce a channel. In terms of the cause-effect diagram, we can thus extend the map for this particular 'tube with a channel' route to encompass this mechanical failure. We can also take this scenario another step further by repeating the viable system test; 'if a vibration of the body causes a channel in the tube, then that vibration must come from a viable system'. And so on for all of the other possible failure systems:

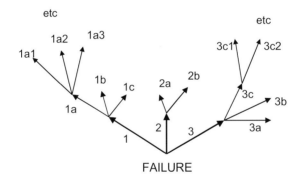

FAILURE

As with FMEA, this cause-effect map can get rather large, and, the analysis rather tedious. This is especially so if failure rates beyond, say, 10^{-6} are being identified.

Now What?

If all the preceding text in this section appears to summarise down to the facts that modelling reliability is time-consuming and tortuous work that at the end of the day will probably not help solve the problem so why bother, it would not be entirely unjustified. There are problems and times when the rigour of the above methods will be helpful. Establishing whether a particular problem will or won't be helped by this kind of analysis appears unfortunately to be primarily determined by Murphy's Law. Put simply, if you think there is any likelihood that Murphy's 'if something can go wrong, it will' dictum is present (see the last section also), all the rigour of pareto analysis, FMEA and subversion analysis is likely to count for nothing. Sad but true.

So if this is really a book about helping us to solve any kind of problem, including reliability ones, what do we do now?

The simple answer is that we revert to the 'someone, somewhere has already solved something like my problem' concept and look to industries that have demonstrated success in designing products to very high (i.e. failure rates of 10^{-12} or better). In making this examination, it is necessary to re-look at the evolutionary s-curve ideas first discussed in Chapter 7.

This is so because in exactly the same way that other aspects of system evolution hit evolutionary limits beyond which the system is unable to progress without the elimination of some form of contradiction, any given system design also has inbuilt reliability limits. In other words, a given design will only deliver a certain maximum (usually unknowable a priori) failure rate capability. To exceed this level requires some form of shift in the way the system is designed.

The key here seems to be design. The analysis conducted for this book into this concept of reliability limits clearly suggests that the key evolution driver appears to be design methodology. The underlying concept is illustrated in Figure 20.11.

While essentially qualitative rather than quantitative at this stage, the figure tries to describe how different levels of design capability will broadly determine the maximum possible level of reliability achievable for any system. Rather than getting hung up on the values – which may well demonstrate significant variation between different application sectors – it is the concept that is important in this discussion. Hence while it may be that what is described as a 'basic' design capability (i.e. one that by definition does not include the considerations detailed in the succeeding design methods detailed in the figure, or, more pragmatically, the design that might result from someone from a skilled graduate of a first degree in engineering) might result in a system failure rate of 10^{-2} or 10^{-4}, the main point is the relative improvement obtainable above and beyond this level by evolving the design capability to the next evolutionary stage.

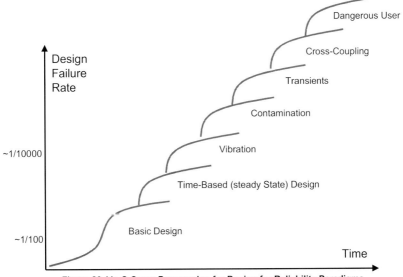

Figure 20.11: S-Curve Progression for Design for Reliability Paradigms.

A good way to think about and use this S-curve progression is like that recommended for the TRIZ trends of evolution detailed in Chapter 13. I.e. if you observe that the design strategy you are applying is not at the end of the progression, there is untapped evolutionary potential that once exploited will enable you to improve reliability. Like the trends, the progression illustrates good solution directions. A simplified version of the trend progression may also be found as a specific trend in Chapter 13.

Someone, Somewhere Already Solved Something Like Your Problem

In the knowledge/effects part of the systematic creativity toolbox (Chapter 15), the user is presented with ways and means of accessing other people's good solutions by functional classification. Such 'knowledge databases' represent a direct means of accessing distilled excellence.

The same sort of excellence distillation is available in some form for reliability issues. As previously stated, the fore-runners in this field are the space, aerospace and nuclear industries. Each of these sectors has recognized the need to not only understand what affects reliability, but also the fact that means of avoiding repeat mistakes are necessary:

"Aircraft operators often criticize manufacturers for repeating similar problems and defects from one generation of a product to another"
(Reference 20.2)

The above quote comes from a book containing a good start at a check list for designers (not just in those working in aerospace – despite the fact that this is where the design for reliability check-list originated), and as such is recommended as the beginnings of a reliability knowledge database.

A second recommendation from the 'someone, somewhere already solved something like your problem' philosophy is the extensive reliability check-list produced by NASA (Reference 20.3).

(For a very different view of designing for reliability, you might also like to check out Reference 20.4.)

4) The Future Importance of Design for Reliability

Reliability is important, and looks set to become even more critical to business success in the future. The justification for this perhaps somewhat bold statement resides within the market and economy trend of evolution described in the book 'The Experience Economy' (Reference 20.5). A version of the trend is reproduced in Figure 20.12.

Figure 20.12: Market Evolution Trend (after Reference 20.5)

The shift that has a particular influence on reliability issues is that from 'products' to 'services'. We can observe this shift in a number of industries – in jet-engines, for

example, there is a very distinct shift away from selling engines to selling the service provided (thrust) by those engines. Does the customer (the airline) want to buy an engine that they become responsible for, or would they rather have the function? The answer seems to be the latter. The same shift is happening with washing machines (called 'functional sales', in Sweden), industrial carpeting, earth-moving equipment, space technology, and so on.

The reason this 'product' to 'service' shift is so important from a design for reliability context is that the onus for the reliability issues also shifts. It shifts from the customer to the manufacturer. So, whereas in the first scenario, the design reliability target is often to achieve a product that lasts only so long as the guarantee runs out. Once the guarantee has run out, the customer is liable for any repair or replacement expenditure, and in some markets the manufacturer has set up business model that demand income from these sources. In perhaps slightly cynical terms, the sooner the product breaks-down in this product sales model, the more money the manufacturer makes (until, that is, the customer goes off in search of a more reliable product elsewhere). In the 'service' model, on the other hand, the game is shifted 180°; in this model, the manufacturer is always responsible for reliability and the customer pays every time they use the product. Hence, the longer the product lasts, the more money the manufacturer is likely to make. A 'design to breakdown the day after the guarantee expires' philosophy is no longer such a good idea. A 'design the product for maximum possible reliability' philosophy is.

Thinking about the design capability evolution trend illustrated in Figure 20.13, this means that designers look set to have to think a lot harder about Design for Murphy; if a customer can do something stupid with your product, they will. Previously they paid for their folly; in a 'service' business model, chances are you do.

What Do I Do?

'Reliability' is a very big topic. The database of tools to help do a better job of designing for reliability is still relatively immature. If you are faced with a 'reliability' problem, however, the recommendation here is:

1) Establish whether or not you can find (or will ever affordably be able to find) the root cause of the reliability problem.
2) If the answer is 'no', see if you can establish the 'root contradiction' – what is stopping you from improving reliability? Then can you apply the previously described Inventive Principles to derive solution directions? If not, can you formulate a contradiction and use the Contradiction Matrix or physical contradiction solution strategies? (See the root contradiction section
3) If not, look at the s-curve progression for design for reliability paradigms (Figure 20.11), see where you are on the trend and then see whether thinking about the next trend along will help you to solve the problem.
4) If it doesn't, or if your answer to the question in 1) was 'yes', then prepare yourself to think about fault-trees, FMEA and/or subversion analysis techniques as described in Section 3) of this chapter. Keep smiling!

References

1) Petroski, H., 'To Engineer Is Human: The Role of Failure In Successful Design', St Martin's Press, 1985.
2) Raymond, E.T., Chenoweth, C.C., 'Aircraft Flight Control System Actuation Design', Society of Automotive Engineers, Warrendale, Pa, 1993.
3) NASA/MSFC 'Preferred Reliability Practices and Guidelines for Design and Test', website, http://msfcsma3.msfc.nasa.gov/tech/practice/prctindx.html
4) MacCready, P., 'Design, Efficiency and the Peacock's Tail', Automotive Engineering, October 1992.
5) Pine, B.J., Gilmore, J.H., 'The Experience Economy', Harvard Business School Press, 1999.

21.
Solution Evaluation

"The wrong answers are the ones you go looking for when the right answer is staring you in the face"
Eeyore's Little Book of Gloom

Or

"I beseech you, in the bowels of Christ, think it possible you may be mistaken"
Oliver Cromwell

The final part of the systematic creativity process is the one associated with evaluating the solutions obtained during the previous stage. In most regards, the tools we will use to achieve this evaluation function effectively will come from outside TRIZ. There are really two tasks to be conducted at this part of the process; the first to identify a 'best' solution from within a range of pre-determined options; and the second to identify whether this solution is 'good enough' to be considered as a final solution. The chapter will examine these two activities separately. In the case of the first – 'best' selection – we will examine two forms of a technique known variously as forced decision making or multi-criteria decision analysis or simply decision analysis. The two forms represent 'simplest' and 'most accurate' capabilities. The second activity under consideration – 'good enough?' – gets us closer to TRIZ (although we will also look briefly at other tools) – firstly through the general TRIZ suggestion that we should always consider 'going around the loop' again, and secondly through a series of strategies we can use to help us focus the content of such a loop to best effect.

'Best' Selection?

Multi-Criteria Decision Analysis (MCDA) offers users a systematic method through which it becomes possible to make legitimate 'apples versus oranges' comparisons between different solution options to any complex, multi-dimensional problem. The method also enables multiple people to participate in the process and, perhaps most importantly of all, provides a means of recording the mechanics of the decision process. In its simplest form, MCDA can be conducted using pencil and paper, although for the most part, something like an Excel™ spreadsheet makes a more friendly companion. There are also a number of bespoke software tools (References 21.1, 21.2 and 21.3) to help facilitate the process.

The basic method takes two forms – a 'simple' version based on 'common-sense' calculation procedures, and a more complex form based on the fact that these 'common-sense' based procedures are actually wrong in many situations. We will also examine two extensions, consistent with both procedures, that we can use to obtain the maximum amount of useful information from the decision analysis process.

We will start by examining the simple decision analysis process. This process basically consists of the following steps:

1) The user selects the candidate solutions obtained during the previous 'generate solutions' phase of the systematic creativity process. For the sake of argument, we will label these selected solutions with a unique identifying letter , A, B, C, etc.

2) The user then selects the criteria relevant to the problem and against which each of the solution options will be judged. Typical criteria will be things like the lists provided in Table 21.1. As may be seen from the Table, the evaluation criteria fall into two basic categories; quantitative and qualitative.

Quantitative	Qualitative
Purchase cost	Aesthetics
Life-cycle cost	Stability
Weight	Durability
Volume	Maintainability
Area	Transportability
Size	Convenience
Load Capability	Adaptability
Power	Comfort
Temperature	Safety
Speed/Time	Controllability
Acceleration	Predictability
Efficiency/Inefficiency	Environmental Issues
Waste Production	
Reliability (MTBF)	
Accuracy	

Table 21.1: Typical MCDA Evaluation Criteria
(Notice commonality with Contradiction Matrix parameters)

3) The user inputs values ('scores') for each of the candidate solutions against each of the evaluation criteria. In the case of 'qualitative' criteria, it is necessary to allocate some form of numerical scoring system. This is done most readily by establishing a numerical range to represent a spectrum from 'worst possible' performance to 'best possible' performance, and then judging each solution option against the possible spectrum of scores and allocating it its own score. The main things to remember throughout the allocation of scores process are that the precise numerical value is less important than the relative values between different parameters, but that it is essential to maintain a convention across all of the evaluation criteria of either 'highest score equals best' or 'lowest score equals best'. This is easy to forget, especially when criteria like weight (where higher numerical score value is generally reflective of 'worse') and life (where higher numerical score value is reflective of 'better') are being used in the same analysis – one of the two needs to be inverted (usually using an x/value mathematical operation). If multiple participants are involved in the scoring process, it is useful to collate and average scores, discussing and agreeing any major anomalies that may emerge.

4) Next it is necessary to allocate different weighting factors to the evaluation criteria to reflect their different relative importance to the overall outcome. These weightings should again be presented numerically, following appropriate averaging if multiple participants are involved in the process.

5) Having supplied the necessary information, it is now possible to calculate a composite score for each of the candidate solutions. This calculation procedure involves a summation of (score for a given evaluation criterion X weight of that

criterion) for each of the criteria. The candidate solution with the highest (or lowest if that convention is being used) score after the end of the calculation is the 'winner'.

Figure 21.1 below illustrates a set of hypothetical decision analysis data on six candidate solutions (A-F) being ranked against nine different evaluation criteria.

	Initial Price	Running Cost	Acceleration	Top Speed	Range	Boot Space	Safety Features	Comfort	Appearance
A	12000	1200	11	98	400	40	4	4	5
B	11900	1400	10.8	100	430	20	6	6	6
C	10900	1000	9.4	112	450	20	8	8	10
D	10400	1450	11.3	110	400	20	6	6	6
E	10700	1150	10.6	115	400	22	9	8	7
F	11600	1300	9.7	106	360	18	3	6	9
Weight	50	40	10	5	15	10	30	30	40

Figure 21.1: Raw Decision Data For Hypothetical MCDA Analysis

Figure 21.2 below illustrates a sample calculation using this data. A 'highest score equals best' convention has been adopted – note how the price, running cost and acceleration scores have been inverted in order that they remain consistent with this scoring convention. Qualitative criteria like 'comfort' and 'appearance' have been allocated scores on a 1-10 scale (although any range could have been used). It is recommended that the relative scores for each evaluation criterion are normalised during the calculation procedure in order to maintain consistency. In the calculation process contained in the Figure, all of the evaluation criteria scores have been normalised to a maximum value of 10.

	Price (N)	Run Cost (N)	Acc'n (N)	Speed (N)	Range (N)	Space (N)	Safety (N)	Comfort (N)	Appearance (N)	TOTAL
A	8.67	8.33	8.55	8.52	8.89	10	4.44	5	5	1611.35
B	8.74	7.14	8.7	8.7	9.56	5	6.67	7.5	6	1711.6
C	9.54	10	10	9.74	10	5	8.89	10	10	2192.4
D	10	6.9	8.32	9.57	8.89	5	6.67	7.5	6	1755.5
E	9.72	8.7	8.87	10	8.89	5.5	10	10	7	2041.05
F	8.97	7.69	9.69	9.22	8	4.5	3.33	7.5	9	1749
Weight	50	40	10	5	15	10	30	30	40	

Figure 21.2: Sample MCDA Calculation for a Hypothetical Evaluation Activity

The second form of MCDA calculation procedure involves a technique called 'ratio scaling' (Reference 21.4). This technique was developed in response to the recognition that when faced with the above ranking methods, we all tend to numerically mis-represent the situation. This happens either because by comparing things to a fixed numerical range of score possibilities we fail to adequately measure different parameters relative to each other, or – more seriously – because we fail to capture the true significance of differences. For parameters like brightness, viscosity, 'warmth' for example, humans are generally pretty hopeless in their ability to compare one thing reliably against another. Also, when we look at some quantitative parameters we fail to capture the true significance of differences. To give an example here, using an evaluation criterion like 'efficiency' we might identify scores of 98 and 99% for two different candidates, but this does not necessarily mean that the difference between them is 1% - indeed if we shift things around to consider the criterion as 'inefficiency, then the 98% efficient solution candidate is actually 200% worse than the 99% efficient candidate. For complex analyses, it is highly likely that the errors introduced by the simplicity of the above calculation procedures will affect the outcome significantly.

The ratio-scaling method seeks to overcome these problems. Although it uses the same basic presentation format as that shown in Figure 21.1, the way in which it acquires the input data is different. The foundations of the enhanced ratio-scaling method involve scoring relative to candidates rather than against an absolute scale. The basic calculation procedure works as follows:-

For each qualitative evaluation criterion:

1) The user selects on of the solution candidates at random. This then becomes the 'datum' for the ratio-scaling analysis. This datum candidate is given a score of, say, 10.
2) The user then compares the datum solution candidate and, pairing with each other candidate in turn, the user asks the question 'how many more times better or worse than the datum is this candidate? There is no limit on the number subsequently supplied. A '1' would signify that the two are equal, a '2' that the new candidate is twice as good, a '0.5' that it is half is good, and so on.
3) After the user has compared all of the other solution candidates against the chosen datum, multiply the resulting comparative scores by the score given to the datum candidate, and then take the logarithm of all the resulting scores. These logarithm scores are the ones that are then used during the decision analysis calculation.

The process is repeated for the criterion weighting factors – a datum criterion being selected, and then the other criteria compared one by one with it.

Note that during this calculation process, some of the scores after the logarithm operation will be negative. If you are using a piece of proprietary software to assist during the analysis, it will normalise results across the different evaluation criteria scores automatically. If you are performing the calculation by hand or using a spreadsheet, you will have to normalise manually.

For each quantitative evaluation criterion:

For quantitative data where it is possible to use the absolute data (e.g. 'price', 'weight', 'efficiency', etc) to compare different solution candidates, the only important check to make is to ensure that the scores represent an accurate description of the true differences between different values. The key word here is 'significant', and the key question is 'do the scores truly represent the significance of the differences between different solution candidates?' If the answer is yes they do, then no further action (other than normalising relative to other evaluation criteria) is required. If the answer is no, then some form of mathematical manipulation should be incorporated in order that the significance of differences *is* reflected in the scores.

By way of example, the earlier description of the 98 and 99% efficiency scores may require each value to be subtracted from 100 if it is actually the size of the inefficiency that is important (in particle separator design, for example, a device achieving 99% separation efficiency would give double the level of protection of a device achieving 98% separation efficiency). The main point here is that the user needs to establish the significance metric on a case by case basis.

Figure 21.3 below provides an example ratio-scaling calculation for the analysis previously conducted for Figure 21.1.

	Price (N)	Run Cost (N)	Acc'n (N)	Speed (N)	Range (N)	Space (N)	Safety	Safety (log)(0-10)	Comfort	Comfort (log)(3-10)	Appearance	Appearance (log)(0-10)	TOTAL
A	8.67	8.33	8.55	8.52	8.89	10	5	5.37	2	2.153	8	6.939	142.3609
B	8.74	7.14	8.7	8.7	9.56	5	10	7.687	10	7.154	10	7.687	150.0861
C	9.54	10	10	9.74	10	5	15	9.039	20	9.307	20	10	175.8654
D	10	6.9	8.32	9.57	8.89	10	10	7.687	10	7.154	10	7.687	155.1836
E	9.72	8.7	8.87	10	8.89	5.5	20	10	25	10	20	10	178.1449
F	8.97	7.69	9.69	9.22	8	4.5	5	5.37	10	7.154	20	10	145.7382
Weight	30	10	4	15	2	10		40		10		2	
Corrected	3.401	2.303	1.386	2.708	0.693	2.303		3.689		2.303		0.693	

Figure 21.3: Repeat of MCDA Calculation for Using Ratio-Scaling Calculation Procedure

Points to note about this analysis:-

1) Only qualitative parameters – relative evaluation criteria weights and safety, comfort and appearance criteria were subjected to the ratio-scaling calculation as these are the only parameters subject to the previously discussed human errors.

2) In each of these cases, a datum was selected at random and the other values then compared to this value. In the case of the safety, comfort and appearance criteria, solution B was selected as the datum. In the case of the weighting factors, running cost was selected as the datum. The datum parameters were then given 10 points, and the other solutions or weights were then compared one by one relative to this 10 score. The raw data row and columns reflect the outcome of this comparison exercise.

   The basic process worked using a sequence like: -
   If solution B scores 10 for comfort, what score would you give A?
   If solution B scores 10 for comfort, what score would you give C?
   Etc.

3) The raw scores were then processed by first taking logarithms. In the case of the safety, comfort and appearance columns, these log values were then re-datumed back to a maximum value of 10 in order to maintain parity with the normalised scores for other selection criteria.

Although the case study is obviously hypothetical, it is perhaps interesting to note how the different scoring system has altered the outcome of the analysis. It is unusual for the winner to change when switching from simple to ratio-scaled calculation methods like this, but very common for some order change to take place.

Sensitivity Analysis

Occasions when it is possible to supply a single, accurate value for each of the scores and for each of the evaluation criteria weighting factors are rare. This is particularly evident during the scoring of qualitative criteria and the weighting of criteria relative to one when multiple participants are involved in the process. It is often the case in these situations that different opinions will result in potentially considerable differences in scores obtained. In other cases, it may simply not be possible to ascertain or agree any form of 'score' – thus leaving holes in the data.

Sensitivity analyses can help to establish whether these differences and holes are significant or not. Sensitivity analyses are usually only practical using some kind of automated calculation procedure – either Excel or one of the previously mentioned pieces of proprietary software. A typical sensitivity analysis will take pairs of elements within the calculation grid (i.e. either individual scores or weighting factors) and systematically vary them over a pre-determined range based on the level of uncertainty associated with them. Generally speaking the elements analysed during this activity ill be the ones where the level of uncertainty concerning their score is highest. A typical output of this type of paired parameter sensitivity analysis is reproduced in Figure 21.4.

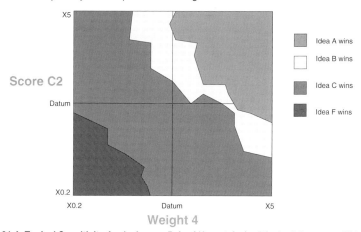

Figure 21.4: Typical Sensitivity Analysis on a Pair of Uncertain (or Missing) Scores or Weights

The figure illustrates how changes in the scores of the uncertain elements of the analysis impact on the ranking of the candidate solutions. In the plot above, only the impact on the winning idea is included, but other forms of presentation may be used to illustrate different phenomena depending on the flexibility of the presentation media.

The main purpose, then, of the sort of picture shown in the figure is to identify how sensitive the 'answer' produced by the analysis is to variation in different elements. In the hypothetical example presented in the plot, the presence of several possible 'best' solutions over the range of the two varied elements suggests that the decision is highly sensitive to variation. On the other hand, a plot that exhibits little or no change in outcome as the two elements are varied is indicative that the sensitivity of the solution to variation is low.

In situations where the sensitivity is shown to be high a useful strategy is to go around the systematic creativity loop again, looking to establish possible ways of integrating the best features of some or all of the solutions the sensitivity analysis is suggesting are potential winners.

Robustness Analysis

The general idea behind robustness analysis is to identify which of the evaluation criteria scores and weighting factors have the greatest impact on the outcome of the analysis. The analysis is, like the above sensitivity analysis, quite intensive from a calculation intensity perspective, and as such is most practically achieved through a software implementation.

The basic calculation procedure used in this kind of analysis is for each score and each weighting factor to be gradually increased in turn until a change in the candidate solution with the highest score occurs. The calculation sequence is repeated until all scores and weights have been analysed. The changes can be recorded in various ways. Figure 21.5 illustrates a technique using colour change.

The basic idea behind this kind of robustness assessment is to gain a general view across the complete range of variables as to how much of a change needs to occur before the 'answer' produced by the analysis changes. If the analysis indicates that large changes (say 40% or greater) have to take place before any change in outcome occurs, the solution produced is a robust one. If, on the other hand, even small perturbations produce changes in result, it is prudent to consider going around the systematic creativity loop again, combining the best features from relevant candidate solutions.

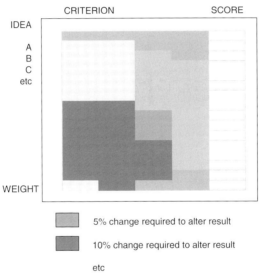

Figure 21.5: Typical Robustness Analysis Output Plotting Format

Good Enough?

Whatever the outcome of the evaluation procedure used to identify the 'best' solution from a range of candidates, TRIZ will recommend that we consider going around the define-select-solve-evaluate loop at least two times. This is to overcome the psychological inertia problem of our brains entering 'satisfied' mode (Chapter 4) once we have what we think is a good solution. In TRIZ terms, we can always do better. In practical terms, countless examples – including some described throughout the book – suggest the prudence of going around the loop at least twice.

So, how do we decide if our winning solution is 'good enough'?

The simplest way, of course, is to compare the solution to the benefits and 'how will we know when we have got there?' questions we should have answered right at the beginning of the problem/opportunity explorer (Chapter 5) part of the problem definition activity. If the solution meets all of the requirements stated here then we theoretically have good cause to believe we have 'finished'. On the other hand, we would always recommend that you at least briefly explore some of the 'good enough?' tests described below.

We will briefly discuss a number of techniques and tools – some more formal in their approach than others. In all, we will examine four:-
1) Axiomatic Design
2) 'The Next Contradiction'
3) Resource Assessment
4) Combinations

Axiomatic Design
Nam Suh's Axiomatic Design (Reference 21.5) has already been mentioned in the context of the Trimming tool (Chapter 17). The method provides a useful test of whether a given solution meets Suh's criteria of what makes a good design. In particular, this means establishing independence between functional requirements and the design parameters chosen to achieve those requirements. In Suh's terms, the method demands a working knowledge of matrix algebra. In more practical terms, it means establishing whether if we vary one element of our chosen solution, does it impact on more than one of the functions being delivered. If the answer to that question is yes, then, the method suggests, we should think about re-designing the solution so that there is no coupling effect.

'The Next Contradiction'
Finding a 'good' unresolved contradiction is an excellent lead into finding a better way of solving a problem. Using the solution that has just emerged as the best from the evaluate part of the systematic creativity process, see if you can spot what the next contradiction is going to be. Imagine the solution in use, the useful functions it delivers and how those functions might be expected to evolve in the future (more? less?). Then try to imagine what in the system will prevent this evolution from taking place. This will then give you a good indication of what the 'next contradiction' will be. Use Chapter 10 or 11 to identify possible means of resolving this contradiction.

Resource Assessment
If looking for the next contradiction is the best way of 'going around the loop again', then identifying resources that you haven't taken advantage of in your chosen solution is not far behind. The key question to be asking here is, did you find a resource (something not being used to its maximum potential) that still is not working as hard as it could? If the answer is 'yes', then explore ways of integrating something from this under-utilised resource into the solution.

Combinations
If you see features you like from different solution options, see if there is any way of distilling some of those features into the chosen solution. See Reference 21.6 for more details of formal methods for achieving such integration. If you can see such opportunities, take whichever ideas you are looking to combine and feed them into the start of a new iteration of the systematic creativity process.

What Do I Do?

If you are looking to find the 'best' out of a group of solution alternatives, use one of the variations on the multi-criteria decision analysis theme discussed at the beginning of this chapter. If the solution you are looking at represents a relatively simple system and the criteria you are using to evaluate one option against another are few in number (say 5 or less), then a simple ranking or absolute score based evaluation system should be accurate enough. If the solution is complex, and the evaluation criteria many, then you should use the ratio-scaling technique to ensure accurate identification of the winning solution option.

If you have access to a software-based evaluation tool, you would be well advised to conduct sensitivity and robustness analyses in order to satisfy yourself that the solution you have picked is genuinely the best one for the greatest possible range of circumstances.

In terms of is your solution 'good enough', you are always encouraged to go around the systematic creativity process at least twice. Use one or more of the techniques identified in the previous section to help clarify the form and direction of that next iteration.

References

1) CreaTRIZ v2.2, Multi-Criteria Decision Analysis tool option, www.creax.com.
2) Decision Lab, www.visualdecision.com
3) Analytica, www.lumina.com.
4) Lodge, M., 'Magnitude Scaling – Quantitative Measurement of Opinions', Sage University Papers, Quantitative Applications in the Social Sciences, 1981.
5) Suh, N., 'The Principles of Design', Oxford University Press, 1990.
6) Pugh, S. 'Total Design', Prentice Hall, 1991.

22.
Into The Future

"Reality is made up of circles, but we see straight lines."
Peter Senge

or

"First things first, but not necessarily in that order."
Doctor Who.

The future of TRIZ has been the subject of significant discussion in recent times (Reference 22.1, 22.2). Opinion differs as to whether it is still at the beginning or has reached the limits of its evolutionary potential. The conflict can be both understood and resolved if TRIZ is recognised as a just a part (albeit a very important one) in a much bigger system. For the sake of providing this bigger system with a label, we will propose the term 'systematic creativity'.

TRIZ places great importance on the existence of evolutionary S-curves. In these terms, the difference between the s-curve for TRIZ (actually, bearing in mind the different TRIZ proponents and variations, such a TRIZ s-curve should be seen as the average of a cluster of subtly different s-curves) and an average curve that might be constructed for 'systematic creativity' is illustrated in Figure 22.1. The conflict between 'is TRIZ a mature system or an immature one?' is thus explained by the point marked on the figure illustrating the current evolutionary state. The point suggests that TRIZ is at the mature end of its evolutionary potential (thus concurring with Vertkin's comment (22.2) that 'there hasn't been a single new concept introduced into TRIZ in the last 12 years'), but that TRIZ and the current position are still at the relative beginnings of the over-riding 'systematic creativity' curve. In terms of 'systematic creativity' it is evident that there have been many new concepts emerging in the same period. This paper discusses the emergence and integration of some of these concepts. The basis for the discussion is that as TRIZ – being both toolkit, method, strategy and philosophy (Reference 22.3) - is by far and away the most comprehensive of any of the available models, it is also the most appropriate foundation for a coherent 'systematic creativity' model.

The idea that TRIZ is one s-curve (system) inside a bigger system for now called 'systematic creativity' emerges from the concept of recursiveness in systems. Recursiveness as discussed in the Viable System Model, NLP and other emerging texts on, not just creativity, but all system evolution is an example of a concept which has not previously existed in classical TRIZ. The current prevailing view is that recursion will be an important element in the successful realisation of a 'systematic creativity' o ourve.

The idea of TRIZ representing one s-curve inside a higher order s-curve explains the s-curve figure constructed by Savransky in reference 22.1, which suggests that the next stage of 'TRIZ' (but actually to give some credit to the mass of other creativity research outside the current scope of TRIZ, 'systematic creativity') evolution is the integration of different methods.

This chapter is divided into two unequal parts. The first part describes ongoing work on the development of TRIZ in which we hope to show that, although the system is relatively mature, there is still scope for significant improvement and extension. The second, longer, part of the paper examines some of the main 'other' creativity tools, methods and philosophies and the role they may be expected to play in the bigger 'systematic creativity' picture. To varying degrees all of these other tools, methods and philosophies may be represented as systems with their own series of s-curves. Rather than attempt to position such s-curve approximations relative to TRIZ, the paper focuses only on their role in serving the higher order systematic creativity s-curve development.

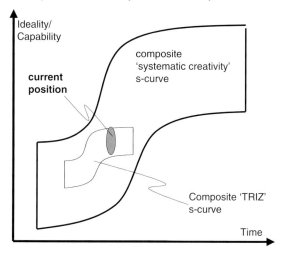

Figure 22.1: Systematic Creativity Evolutionary S-Curve

EVOLVING TRIZ

If Igor Vertkin's statement about the absence of new concepts in TRIZ in the last 12 years is correct, it should not be taken to also mean that there has been no new work in TRIZ over the same period. The success of TRIZ Journal, for example, should provide ample evidence of the spread and expansion of TRIZ in recent times.

Much of this 'new' work on the other hand may be seen as refinement and re-arrangement of knowledge that is largely the same as that extracted through early TRIZ analysis of scientific and patent databases. One of the consequences of this is that TRIZ tools like the Contradiction Matrix and Inventive Standards are often inadequate (see Reference 22.2 for example) and in some cases fail to handle certain types of problem. One of the underlying problems here is that the world has moved on significantly since the original analysis was conducted. One manifestation of this progress is that the Matrix, for example, often sends users looking to solve software or electrical problems in directions that are significantly different to those being used by the most successful inventors of the last 15 years. The world was a much more 'mechanical' place when the initial analysis was happening.

An extensive programme of work was instigated at the beginning of 2000 by CREAX to begin to rectify this situation. A team of researchers is now undertaking a patent-by-patent analysis of invention disclosures over the period 1985 to 2000. The aims of this research are to:-

- update the Contradiction Matrix in terms of both its form (updating the list of 39 parameters for example) and content. Initial results suggest that in several key contradictions, inventors are now using significantly different strategies to those of their pre-1985 predecessors.
- identify the emergence of new Inventive Principles
- identify the emergence of new trends of evolution. In this regard, we believe that we have already uncovered at least ten trend patterns not previously found in TRIZ.
- identify the emergence of new Inventive Standards (we have already identified and incorporated two to add to the original list of 76).
- identify and incorporate new tools.

In line with an increasing tendency for individuals and organisations to not patent their good solutions, and in order to extract strong solutions from fields not involved in patents (e.g. architecture, business/management, industrial design), we have also introduced a programme of systematic search of other knowledge sources. The overall idea is to ensure that we can offer users access to the most effective solutions – benefits not features again! – from wherever they occur.

EVOLVING 'SYSTEMATIC CREATIVITY'

A systematic programme of research to compare and contrast different creativity tools, methods and philosophies in terms of their relevance to primarily scientific, engineering and business applications (Reference 22.5) has concluded that TRIZ currently offers the most useful foundation for a higher order systematic creativity model and that given this foundation, the other available methods that are best able to complement and help deliver the higher order model are those shown in Figure 22.2.

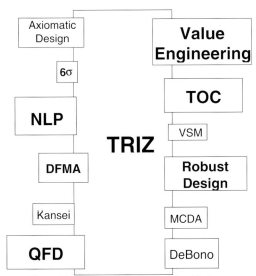

Figure 22.2: Integration of Innovation Tools

To varying degrees, all of these additional methods have already been the subject of some form of work to explore the benefits of integration with TRIZ. The paper briefly reviews such work and projects how and why such integration should progress in the future

TRIZ and Function Analysis/Value Engineering

The function analysis/value engineering methodology initially developed by Larry Miles (Reference 22.6) is probably the method most closely linked with and integrated into TRIZ. Reference 22.7 is probably the first text to talk about both function analysis and TRIZ in the same place (albeit the understanding of TRIZ is woefully inaccurate). It does not make any mention, for example, of the simple but profound conceptual addition to function analysis made by TRIZ – that of using the function analysis to describe the harmful, ineffective and excessive functional relationships in a system as well as the useful ones drawn in classical function analysis. This simple shift in thinking transforms a method that is useful into one that offers an extremely effective means of both modelling complexity and defining problems. Reference 22.8 describes how the current TRIZ addition to function analysis is being further evolved by incorporation of new concepts such as modelling of system attributes, time-variant problems and transition between problem definition and the selection of the most relevant tools to help solve the problem.

The definition of 'value' in value engineering is close enough to the TRIZ concept of ideality as to interpret them as similar. The more complete vision of ideality – and particularly the Ideal Final Result concept – in TRIZ means that value engineering appears to offer little else to enrich a 'systematic creativity' model.

Of all the methods considered, the integration of function analysis/value engineering into TRIZ is to date the most comprehensive and complete. Future evolution thus looks set to occur at the detailed implementation rather than conceptual level.

TRIZ and QFD and Robust Design

The integration of the 'holy trinity' of TRIZ, QFD and Taguchi methods was the subject of Reference 22.9. Theoretically, the three complement each other very well; QFD is about capturing the voice of the customer and translating it into design specification; TRIZ is about generating solutions that fit the specification; and Taguchi/Robust Design tools are about optimising the implementation details of the solutions offered by TRIZ. The practice is currently seen to be some considerable distance away from the theory for the large majority of users.

The biggest problem encountered by these authors involves the usual failure of QFD to accurately capture that customer voice. Customers are frequently unable to describe what it is that they want other than in terms of 'better' than the thing they already have. Few if any customers would ask for a digital camera given a conventional film camera and a request for ideas on creating a better solution. This is an area where TRIZ – and particularly the technology trend prediction elements – is emerging as a more effective start point than QFD.

Integration of QFD and Robust Design techniques into TRIZ looks set to continue. At least one significant conceptual level integrative step remains unexploited at this point in time. That step sees its roots in the inadequate ability of TRIZ to handle problem non-linearities. The strengths of Robust Design in this area and their integration into TRIZ is the subject of Reference 22.10.

TRIZ and Design for Manufacture and Assembly (DFMA)

DFMA shares the same problem as a good number of the other tools and methods described here, in that it contains what can be seen from a TRIZ perspective as the 'insert miracle here' moment. DFMA is very good at defining problems and even better at quantifiably evaluating solutions, but between the two, it offers users little more than the suggestion 'now generate some ideas'. That being said, the method does have something to add to TRIZ. The already mentioned solution evaluation capabilities – basically providing a framework allowing users to benchmark manufacture and assembly times for an object and thus provide quantified improvements between 'before' and 'after' situations – are a useful addition, as are the questions developed within DFMA for identifying whether parts are actually needed in a system. This part of DFMA is closely linked to the 'trimming' ideas contained in TRIZ. Combined together, a problem solver is offered a more comprehensive list of questions to ask when considering the simplification of technical (or indeed business) situations. Figure 22.3 reproduces the combined DFMA/trimming question list used in Chapter 17.

- Do I need the function offered by the part?
- Can something else in or around the system perform the function?
- Can an existing resource perform the function?
- Can a low cost alternative perform the function?
- Must the part move relative to other parts
- Must the part be of a different material or isolated from
  its mating parts?
- Must the part be separate from mating parts to facilitate
  assembly or dis-assembly

Figure 22.3: Combined TRIZ/DFMA Trimming Questions

There appears little scope for additional high level conceptual integration between TRIZ and DFMA. The creation of combined DFMA plus function analysis plus trimming tools appears to offer benefits in terms of use-ability.

TRIZ and Axiomatic Design (AD)
The integration of AD and TRIZ has already been discussed in Reference 22.11. TRIZ can be used to show that the AD 'axioms' have some very useful exceptions, and that they are thus not axioms, but nevertheless, axiomatic design still offers designers a series of useful rules to help define and achieve 'good design'. The likely future complementarity between AD and TRIZ currently appears to be restricted to the incorporation of these 'useful rules' into the solution evaluation part of TRIZ, although the AD scheme for correlating the functional requirements of a system to the selected design parameters to the subsequent method of manufacture may offer some additional benefits to TRIZ.

TRIZ and Viable System Model (VSM)
Stafford Beer's Viable System Model emerged from the study of organisation structures and resulted in two very important conceptual findings. The first involved the identification of five essential elements that a system had to contain if it were to be 'viable'. The second involved the idea of recursiveness – and the discovery that the five element viability test still applied at different hierarchical levels of consideration of a system organisation structure. Reference 22.12 describes how this first finding contradicts the TRIZ definition of 'system completeness' and how it ultimately therefore provides a stronger definition of completeness than TRIZ (interested readers might also like to check out Reference 22.13 – which provides an alternative perspective on the Law of System Completeness). The second concept of recursion is still only just being introduced into TRIZ (and the higher order 'systematic creativity' system hypothesised in this paper), and is believed to offer significant scope for fundamental conceptual evolution of systematic creativity.

TRIZ and Multi-Criteria Decision Analysis (MCDA)

There are a growing number of available methods for enabling problem solvers to make legitimate, recordable and reproducible 'apples versus oranges' comparisons between different systems. Several such techniques – most notably the logarithmic scaling techniques of Lodge (Reference 22.14) – are described in Chapter 21. These methods offer the potential to enhance the solution evaluation aspects of TRIZ.

TRIZ and Six Sigma

As described by Domb (Reference 22.15), Six-Sigma is more a decision than a method. Perhaps the greatest thing it can teach TRIZ is the highly effective manner in which it has marketed and spread itself. At a more detailed level, there are a number of potentially useful tools and techniques contained in (but not necessarily created by) Six Sigma. These tools centre mainly around the process of problem measurement, and specifically variants of Shewhart/Deming based statistical process control techniques. They offer the potential for some small beneficial advance once incorporated into the problem definition elements of TRIZ.

TRIZ on the other hand, has much to offer Six Sigma. Not least of the things it can do is the provision of systematic strategies for overcoming the fundamental limitations of systems. Figure 22.4 illustrates the mechanisms of this in action. Say an organisation decides that a certain production-line is going to become a six-sigma production line. While this might make an excellent target, it is one that can never be met if the fundamental limitations dictated by the production line s-curve are less than six-sigma. In this situation, the only way to improve beyond the fundamental limits of a system is to change the system. In TRIZ terms, this means solving a contradiction (the principle reason why systems hit fundamental limits) or using knowledge/effects or the trends of evolution to find a new way of doing things.

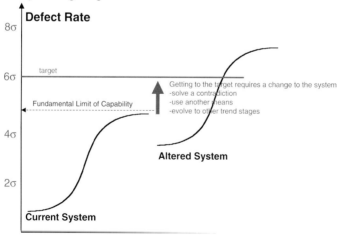

Figure 22.4: Using TRIZ to Overcome Fundamental Defect Rate Limitations

TRIZ and Theory of Constraints (TOC)

The process of integration of Eli Goldratt's Theory of Constraints into TRIZ has also begun (Reference 22.16). The Theory of Constraints matches TRIZ in its recognition of the importance of defining and eliminating contradictions and while it offers less in terms of strategies to overcome contradictions, it does offer the Evaporating Cloud tool which does offer increased richness in terms of increasing problem understanding and entry points for breaking the contradictions. Related to this, but also a much more important area where TOC can be expected to enhance TRIZ comes with its emphasis on modelling causes and effects inside systems. This area looks set to be the main conceptual enhancement to TRIZ, but several other important TOC ideas (identification of bottlenecks, strategies for overcoming bottlenecks for example) can be expected to find their way into future TRIZ/'systematic creativity' models.

TRIZ and De Bono

The work of Edward De Bono is both extensive and widespread in its use. Many of the strategies identified or uncovered by DeBono have direct equivalents in TRIZ – for example the idea of working back from an ideal rather than working forward from the known solution (albeit DeBono has nothing as extreme as the Ideal Final Result strategy in TRIZ), the importance of function, the need to shift from either/or to win/win thinking, the trend for systems to evolve in a manner which sees complexity increase before it can decrease, and the concept of psychological inertia and tools to overcome all exist in some form in both pieces of work.

Elements of Dr DeBono's work that have no direct equivalent in classical TRIZ include the Six Thinking Hats™ idea, water logic versus rock logic and the 'flowscape' tool, the 'po' operator, and 'sur/petition' concepts. The thinking hats concept – and specifically the idea that different modes of thinking are treated very differently in the human brain and so should be segmented – is particularly useful in the context of being able to use the bigger, more complete TRIZ processes like ARIZ to more potent effect (Reference 22.17).

In several senses, the psychological and physiological elements of DeBono methods offer more to help direct and influence the evolution of 'systematic creativity' than TRIZ, and consequently it would be inappropriate to ignore the opportunities presented by further integration of the two.

TRIZ and NLP

Although instigated more recently than TRIZ, Neuro-Linguistic Programming has evolved from a very similar philosophical startpoint. Both TRIZ and NLP have been built on the study and abstraction of 'excellence'. In the case of TRIZ, the global scientific and patent databases provided the basis of method development; in the case of NLP it was cognitive science research into linguistics, psychology, cybernetics and anthropology. Both have sought to study 'creativity' from the perspective of modelling known successful creative personalities. Latterly, NLP has drawn additional knowledge from psychotherapy – including Gestalt and Hypnotherapy. Perhaps these latter two extensions have tended to draw NLP away from the mainstream somewhat, and certainly exploitation of NLP in business or scientific practices for example is practically non-existent in most fields of endeavour. This is undoubtedly a pity as NLP offers significantly greater richness than TRIZ in many areas. Initial research to understand the areas of common ground and opportunities for mutual benefit (Reference 22.18) between TRIZ and NLP have highlighted a significant number of high level concepts that exist in one or the other but not both.

By way of a simple example, Reference 22.19 discusses the 9-window or 'system operator' scheme in TRIZ and how NLP can be used to extend its essentially two-dimensional space and time perspective into a third dimension which might be called 'interface' or relationship. Figure 22.5 illustrates this new three-dimensional operator as an example of a concept that exists in neither TRIZ or NLP, but emerges purely from the integration of the two.

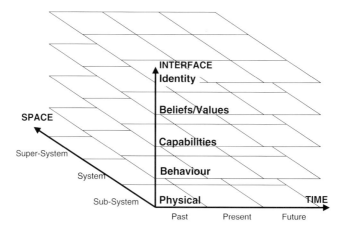

Figure 22.5: Extension of TRIZ System Operator into 3-Dimensions Using NLP

The integration of TRIZ and NLP tools, methods and philosophies (both rightly claim to feature such hierarchies of application) is very much at the beginning of what may be expected to be a long and fruitful road. Several important conceptual advances can be expected to emerge. Some of the ones already identified include:-

- strategies emerging from NLP research into application of combinations of inventive principles
- explanations of why 'asymmetry' provides such an important inventive strategy
- identification of how the meta-programmes underlying the way the human brain work and how they in turn determine our behaviours both individually and in groups.

TRIZ and Kansei

As TRIZ extends further towards industrial design, architecture and the arts it becomes apparent that issues like aesthetics are not well handled by current models. The idea that it is possible to systematise those elements of design that relate to the things we describe as 'x-factors', 'the mysterious wow', and other labels implying that we don't understand what makes one design better than another one, is positively offensive to some. Kansei engineering on the other hand represents an attempt to achieve exactly this kind of understanding of why people prefer one artifact over another one. Kansei is undoubtedly also at the beginning of its evolutionary potential. It is already possible to embody a number of Kansei principles and strategies into a tool integrated into the TRIZ/'systematic creativity' framework, but too soon to speculate on whether the integration of the two will create new high level conceptual benefits. All we can say with certainty, is that TRIZ is weak on aesthetic issues and that Kansei is currently the best available tool to explore as a suitable foundation for integration.

FURTHER AHEAD

We have speculated here that TRIZ is but one component of a higher level creativity capability we have chosen to label 'systematic creativity'. We believe that it is fundamental to the evolution of such a 'systematic creativity' model is that it will emerge – initially at least (as detailed by Savransky (Reference 22.1)) – from the integration of the different tools, methods and philosophies that currently exist.

There are several emerging creativity models that have not so far been explored in the context of their place in a bigger 'systematic creativity' picture. These include game theory, chaos theory, spiral dynamics and general periodicity. Work to explore the relevance and potential benefits of integrating these models into the TRIZ-based model described here (or, indeed, the other way around) has barely begun at this point in time.

In the meantime we all have problems to solve, and opportunities we wish to explore in inventive ways. Some people may want just a few tools or strategies to help them, others may be looking for a higher level start-to-finish process, and still others are looking for a higher level creativity philosophy from which they hope everything else might emerge. In other words, we are all different, work in different ways and want different things. There is currently no single 'creativity' entity that will satisfy every individual desire. If there ever is, one thing it will have to encompass is due recognition of individual difference, and (to introduce a TRIZ concept) be self-adapting to accommodate those differences. At a practical level, this might simply mean that person A likes DeBono, TRIZ and QFD, while person B uses NLP and TOC and doesn't like TRIZ and that both can still work effectively together. The aim of the CreaTRIZ creativity framework (Reference 22.20) is to achieve this kind of flexibility. As with a 'systematic creativity' s-curve, it is still early days. Our hope is that we've at least realised a framework that offers users the prospect of tangible benefit now.

What Do I Do?

TRIZ specifically and 'systematic creativity' in general are both evolving at a steadily increasing rate. If the overall goal of TRIZ and other philosophies/methods is to encapsulate excellence from 'all that is known', then it is difficult to ignore. Some people will decide that they are happy with just a small element of the enormity of TRIZ, others will find themselves wanting not only to expand their knowledge, but also to contribute towards the task of evolving things.

Those intending to do either should subscribe to TRIZ Journal, the CREAX Newsletter and some of the emerging hard-copy academic journals featuring TRIZ and related articles. The next volume in this hands-on systematic innovation series will also hopefully offer a useful progression.

REFERENCES

1) Savransky, C., 'Engineering of Creativity', CRC Press, 2000
2) Vertkin, I., 'TRIZ Development From The Past Into The Future', keynote address at TRIZ Future 2001 conference, Bath, November 2001.
3) Mann, D.L., 'TRIZ For Everyone (Even Those That Don't Want To Spend A Year Learning It)', TRIZ Journal, January 2002.
4) Mann, D.L., 'Assessing The Accuracy Of The Contradiction Matrix For Recent Mechanical Inventions', TRIZ Journal, February 2002.

5) Mann, D.L., 'Towards A Generic, Systematic Problem-Solving and Innovative Design Methodology', paper presented at 12th ASME DETC Conference, Maryland, September 2000.
6) Miles, L.D., 'Techniques of Value Analysis and Engineering', McGraw-Hill Book Company, New York, NY, 1961.
7) Park, R., 'Value Engineering – A Plan For Invention', St Lucie Press, 1999.
8) Dewulf, S., Mann, D.L., 'Improved Function and Attribute Modelling Techniques and their Role in the Problem Management Process', paper presented at TRIZ Future 2001 conference, Bath, November 2001.
9) Terninko, J., Zusman, A., Zlotin, B., 'Systematic Innovation – An Introduction to TRIZ', St Lucie Press, 1998.
10) Apte, P., Mann, D.L., 'Extending TRIZ to Help Solve Non-Linear Problems', paper to be presented at TRIZCON2002, St Louis, April 2002.
11) Mann, D.L., 'TRIZ and Axiomatic Design: Compatibilities and Contradictions', Parts 1 and 2, TRIZ Journal, June and August 1999.
12) Mann, D.L., 'Laws of System Completeness', TRIZ Journal, May 2001.
13) CREAX Newsletter, 'System Completeness versus System Viability', "http://www.creax.com", January 2002.
14) Domb, E., 'Using TRIZ in a Six Sigma Environment', paper presented at TRIZCON2001, Woodland Hills, CA, March 2001.
15) Lodge, M., 'Magnitude Scaling – Quantitative Measurement of Opinions', Quantitative Applications in the Social Sciences Series, Sage Publications, London, 1981.
16) Mann, D.L., Stratton, R., 'Physical Contradictions and Evaporating Clouds', TRIZ Journal, April 1999.
17) Mann, D.L., 'TRIZ Thinking Hats', TRIZ Journal, February 2001.
18) Bridoux, D., Mann, D.L., 'Evolving TRIZ Using TRIZ and NLP', paper to be presented at TRIZCON2002, St Louis, April 2002.
19) Mann, D.L., 'System Operator Tutorial: 3) Another Dimension', TRIZ Journal, December 2001.
20) CreaTRIZ v2.2, www.creax.com

'DEFINE' PACK

This pack offers a series of questions you should be asking
during the DEFINE stage of a problem or opportunity.
The main aim is to get you to think about your situation in terms of how it is affected by TIME and SPACE
You may not be able to answer all of the questions.
The important thing is that you ask them.

Print the sheets out, or fill them in electronically.
If you need more space, make copies or use blank pieces of paper.

Although the pack gives you a structured way of communicating your situation to others
it is up to you to use the sheets in a way that best suits the way you work.

Project Title

Project Sponsor

Project Customer

Project Team

Date

Benefits

Where are we trying to get to (what are the goals)?

How will we know when we've got there (measures of success)?

Sponsor

Customer

Team

What Is The Problem?

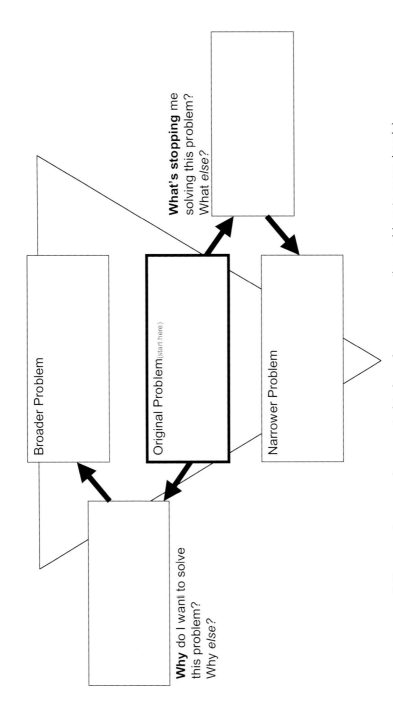

Broader Problem

Original Problem(start here)

What's stopping me solving this problem? What *else*?

Narrower Problem

Why do I want to solve this problem? Why *else*?

(NB: procedure may be repeated to broaden or narrow the problem to more levels)
The aim of this sheet is to get you to think about what your problem is, and at which level you are going to try and solve it

What Is The Current System? (based on the level of problem you decided from the previous sheet)

TYPES OF INTERACTION

Effective

Missing

Insufficient

Excessive

Harmful

(Plot the current components in the system, then identify the positive functional relationships between the components, then identify the negative relationships)

How does TIME affect the system? (If there is a time either in the past or in the future (or both) where the functionality of the system is different, record those differences here)
(The 'past' or the 'future' may mean less than a second or it might mean more than a decade)

Past (meaning?)

Future (meaning?)

Resources - Technical (Function, Substance, Field) (Pay particular attention to the things that are not being used to their maximum effect, and negative things)

	Past	Present	Future
Around the system			
System			
Within the system			

Resources - Knowledge

	Past	Present	Future
Around the system (SPONSOR)			
System (including CUSTOMER)			
Within the system (TEAM)			

Constraints - Technical (Function, Specification, Process, Tools)

	Past	Present	Future
Around the system			
System			
Within the system			

Constraints - Business (Time, Cost, Risk, Skills)

	Past	Present	Future
Around the system (SPONSOR)			
System (including CUSTOMER)			
Within the system (TEAM)			

457

Sore Point

What are we trying to improve?

What are the things that are stopping us?

Physical parameters - weight, linear dimensions, areas, volumes, shape

Performance parameters - speed, forces/loads, stresses, pressures, strength, use of energy, stability, duration of action, temperature, brightness, use of energy, power,

Efficiency Parameters - waste of energy, waste of substance, loss of information, waste of time, amount of substance

Manufacture Parameters - accuracy of measurement, accuracy of manufacture, manufacturability, device complexity, productivity, level of automation

'lity Parameters - reliability, convenience of use, repairability, adaptability, harmful effects, control complexity

Sore Point

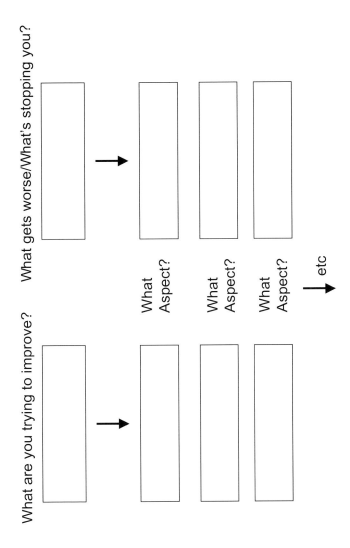

What are you trying to improve?

What gets worse/What's stopping you?

What Aspect?

What Aspect?

What Aspect?

etc

Sore Point - Where/When are the potential or known bottlenecks and contradictions?

	Past	Present	Future
Around the system			
System			
Within the system			

(It may be that the sore point exists in only one of these boxes)

IDEALITY (You should only use this sheet if your constraints allow you the freedom to think of clean-sheet of paper solutions to your problem)

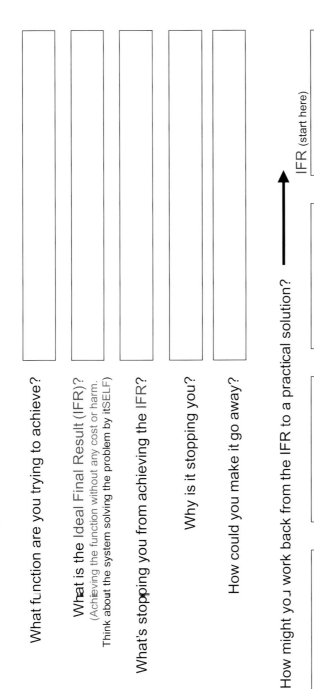

What function are you trying to achieve?

What is the Ideal Final Result (IFR)?
(Achieving the function without any cost or harm.
Think about the system solving the problem by itSELF)

What's stopping you from achieving the IFR?

Why is it stopping you?

How could you make it go away?

How might you work back from the IFR to a practical solution?

IFR (start here)

(As you work back from the IFR solution, apply minimum compromise at each stage, and concentrate on conceptual solutions rather than specific ideas. The further back from the IFR you go, the more possible concepts there may be.)

How Mature Is The Current System?

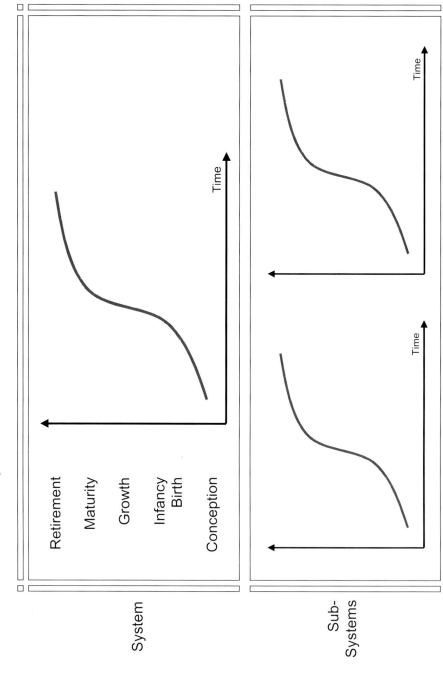